ROTTING HILL

ROTTING HILL

By

Wyndham Lewis

Henry Regnery Company

Chicago, 1952

Foreword

I_F I write about a hill that it rotting, it is because I deplore rot. For the decay of which I write is not romantic decay. But specific persons or Parties are in no way accountable for the rot. It is either the fault of everybody or of nobody. If we exist, shabby, ill-fed, loaded with debt (taxed more than any men at any time have ever been), let us recognize that the sole explanation of this is our collective stupidity. If it soothes us to pin the blame upon our masters, past or present, by all means let us do so. The fact remains that this is only a subjective judgment. But who is responsible for ten years of war in a generation? All human groups, whether French, German, Italian, Polish, Korean, Japanese, Chinese, Czecho-Slovak, or any other are like our own a raw material, and are not responsible for the shape they take. I should add that our ostensible masters are raw material too. War is what is immediately responsible for the chaos which afflicts us at the present time. No cause can be assigned for these fearfully destructive disturbances (though of course we account for them in this or that conventional way, in our history books and in our conversation). The most *recent* wars have entirely altered our lives, that is all we can say.

In 1945 we ended a second, a six-year spell of war. We came out of this a ruined society, our economy destroyed, our riches vanished, our empire reduced to a shadow of itself, but our island-population (optimistically built-up to the absurd total of fifty millions) undiminished and requiring just as much food as when we had the money to pay for it. Naturally everybody was dazed. But into this situation burst a handful of jubilant socialists, voted into power, with an overwhelming majority, on the Labour ticket. They were in no way dismayed by the national situation; they proceeded to extract by huge taxation, direct and indirect, the colossal capital needed to stage a honeymoon for the liberated manual-working mass. This of course gave no one any time to despair at the disappearance of national prosperity. The majority of the nation was highly stimulated: and if the landed society was taxed out of existence, the middle class in rapid dissolution, on the whole England became a brighter rather than a darker place. To symbolize this extraordinary paradox the capital city burst into festivities all along the south bank of the Thames; there was whoopee at Battersea, there was the thunder of orchestras in a new national concert-hall, a thousand peep-shows, culminating in a Dome of Discovery lower down the river. This was staged in the ward sanctified by Shakespeare. In the Parliament the lamb lay down with the lion; the Tory bleated softly and snoozed beside the rampant socialist lion: all England seemed to have decided to forget that it had lost everything, and to live philosophically from day to day upon the Dole provided by the United States.

Such is the situation at the moment of writing. In spite of this extremely brilliant, if exceedingly artificial situation, nevertheless decay is everywhere, as might be expected. If an aristocratic society suddenly drops to pieces, after many centuries, and if a mercantile class of enormous power and wealth drops to pieces at the same time, there is inevitably a scene of universal wreckage and decay, as when demolition work is in progress. In a great city like London large areas, until ten years ago expensive and "select," become shabby or even slummish overnight; the food and other shortages make an end of good restaurants, the shortage of power dims the streets, the high cost of everything turns a well-heeled citizenry into a shoddy, shabby herd, which shuffles round the shops from morning till night in a dense tide.

For the seamy side of socialist splendour the socialists are blamed. Mr. Patricks, the socialist shop-man whose toy-shop you are invited to visit in the ensuing pages, says that his customers even blame the heat and the cold, the rain and the snow and the sleet on the Government. And then, of course, the very bounty of the socialists, their lavish honeymoon spending, militated against the austerity of life and dedication to work which was required to build the New Jerusalem. Decades of ca' canny and the ingrained habit of go-slow, producing a population of the laziest workmen in Europe, has proved the arch-enemy of socialism. So there is a big cancer, a deep rot in the heart of the industry now controlled by the new masters, which it may require a very harsh dictator to eradicate.

I have now supplied you with the credentials of the Rot which is the subject matter of this book of stories. Among the persons gathered between the covers of *Rotting Hill* those who are more or less adult talk a good deal about the situation created by the rapid conversion of England into a Welfare State; the toiling majority naturally do not discuss "Welfare States," merely respond vocally to the pleasant or unpleasant stimuli for which the "high-ups" of whatever political philosophy are responsible. But most of my personnel belong to the disintegrating middle-class, and they naturally discuss the Welfare State since it has a good deal of bearing upon their destinies.

At this point I should perhaps meet the question, to be anticipated after the above delivery of the credentials of the Rot, "Is this a political book?" Not more, it can truthfully be answered than some of Charles Dickens' books, and all by Mr. Shaw, to go no further afield. If my characters are obsessed by politics, it is because today our lives are saturated with them. It is impossible for a work of narrative fiction worth reading to contain less politics than *Rotting Hill*. And those who would contradict me and assert that contemporary fiction can be otherwise than steeped in politics are those who would prefer that you would not have anything to do with books that cause you to use your rational faculty. Best to confine your reading to Detective Stories and to Western Yarns! Nay why read at all, they would argue? Why not save paper so that the Government may have more for its multifarious bureaucratic activities—more than it *already* takes? Just turn on Dick Barton, then take the dog for a nice long tree-crawl and go to bed and dream of next summer's Butlin Camp holiday!

"Socialism" is a word to which we need not pay very much attention. Socialism is merely the name of something which is happening to us, something which could not otherwise than happen, in view of all historical factors present, above all the proliferation of mechanical techniques. If we refrain from looking upon it as a purely *political* phenomenon we shall understand it better. In the present work there is, however, one factor which is especially stressed; namely, socialism seen as a final product of bible-religion.

Conscience is at the root of the principle of Social Justice—without it what would be there? That ethical impulse is of a potency to which no "law of nature" could attain. It is all that remains of Protestant Christianity excepting Christmas Carols, the sacraments of baptism and of marriage, especially in villages where the church is the only public building: and except for burial, of course, since there is nowhere you can dispose of a corpse except the churchyard. But the conscience is almost entire still with some people, though they regard God as quite as Victorian a phenomenon as The Lady of the Lamp and would couple the Bible with Euclid as part of the quaint furniture of childhood.

They would be very surprised indeed to hear they had a conscience. Let me try and show in a few words, how absolutely impossible socialism would have been without the Christian religion. Mr. Attlee and Sir Stafford Cripps as much as Mr. Gladstone are good church-going Christians: and their "socialism" is Mr. Gladstone's "liberalism" taken to its ultimate conclusion. In other words, liberalism was an early stage of socialism. And the nineteenth century of liberalism was demonstrably a product of Christianity: it was at long last the Christian seriously trying to put the New Testament into practice. The culmination of this movement, still using the word "liberal" to describe itself, was Lloyd George's National Insurance Act. That was a most revolutionary measure, far more "advanced" than any adopted in any other country at that time. Finally, the logical conclusion of Gladstone and Morley, and Lloyd George and all their fellow preachers of social fair play, of social justice, was for the classes possessed of money and power to surrender them, and, of course, for England itself as a nation owning a quarter of the globe to surrender everything—as has recently been done in the case of England's greatest possession, India—except this island; and even that must in the end not be looked upon with too possessive an eye.

Now, without the teaching of the New Testament—and we must not forget the Old, and that the Jews were the most moral nation the world has ever seen—or some similar teaching such as Stoicism (and there are exceedingly few teachings of this type), no man gives up anything he has acquired whether it be wealth or land or goods. Why should he? He will fight to defend them with desperation. If you informed him that "Property is a theft" he would laugh at you. Such a saying, in the first instance, to be successful, had to appear with a supernatural sanction. To test the accuracy of what I am saying, you only have to consider whether you would give up anything but a small fraction of your property in order to share it with your less fortunate fellows. There are very few of us who could willingly do so. But a long process of religious conditioning (latterly operating through such words as "decency," "fair play," etc. etc.) has led us to a point at which we empower the State to deprive us of practically everything. This is the work of Jesus.

As I have suggested, it would be absurd to take to task contemporary socialists for carrying to its ultimate conclusions nineteenth-century liberalism. It would be slightly more sensible to criticize the earliest liberals (for, as you would assert, their sentimental and unreal policies), as undoubtedly you would do, were you a catholic or felt no longer, even in "hangover" form, the spell of the Sermon on the Mount. Above I have advocated the discarding of the political approach to contemporary happenings. And I cannot do better than to end this foreword upon a reminder of this earlier counsel. Let me couple with this the advice that you look upon the politician as it is best to look upon a war, as a visitation of the Fiend.

Contents

ROTTING HILL

CHAPTER 1: The Bishop's Fool

——— 1.

Rᴇᴛᴜʀɴɪɴɢ from Sweden a short while ago, in the M.S. *Volsung*, a sumptuous ship, I experienced the utter peace which only sea-travel can provide. A few passengers, I among them, had made their way to the sun-lounge beyond the American bar. We wallowed in deep cushioned receptacles, rocked upon the gently heaving sea; a music programme of the Swedish radio crooned away at a suitable distance. Like all peace it was artificial, and no doubt a little sugary, but all of us were conditioned to appreciate any kind of peace. It was one of the appropriate amenities of a neutral vessel: we were going back to blood, sweat, and tears No. 3. Even the boastful growl of the alcoholic American which could be heard from within, nearer the bar where he crouched over a table, vainglorious but confidential, even this was soothing, like the rumbling of a volcano not in eruption. And upstairs three young Englishmen, innocent of vulgar emulation, hurled deck quoits or whatever they were called, and when their quoit was expelled from its transitory nest complimented the other fellow and obviously preferred to be the loser. Success is always a little beastly. It is less glorious to sit upon another fellow's chest than to be sat on by another fellow—if he is a decent fellow. For this voyage at least we were all to be out of reach of human passions. Even the unseemly effort involved in the propulsion of this luxurious monster from one side of the North Sea to the other was only felt as a muffled throb, an agreeable subterranean tom-tom.

For some reason I began to think just then of Rymer. Were

Rymer on board, I said to myself, what a different ship this would be. He would be arguing with the American within, or with one of these peace-loving inmates of the all-glass sun-lounge, arguing that Soviet Russia was maligned by Press-magnates, and that the North Koreans were as a matter of fact in no way connected with the Kremlin: that the South Koreans (very corrupt and scheming puppets) had been the first to attack, and were of course the actual aggressors, though the Press unanimously asserted the opposite. Then on the upper deck, where the quoit players were, Rymer would have taken a quoit from one of the young Englishmen and proceeded to demonstrate how the game ought really to be played. There is little doubt that before we had reached Tilbury the captain would have received some valuable tips as to how to navigate his ship, and had Rymer got into the engine-room the chief engineer would soon have acquired a good deal more knowledge about the handling of marine engines than he had possessed twenty-four hours before. Finally, should this energetic friend of mine have happened to be crossing at a week-end with Sunday supervening, he would have insisted upon holding divine service anglo-catholicly for English passengers, with a parade of Roman formularies, which (few English tourists today belonging to classes susceptible to ritual) would not have been well received. But whatever the special circumstances, with Rymer on board the ship would have ceased to be at peace. Such pacific bliss as I have dwelt upon would have been out of the question: politics, religion, and the itch-to-teach would have combined, a trinity of irritants, to sow disquiet in the ship from one end to the other.

Whether this is the best way to approach the subject of Rymer I hardly know, but there is this: you are introduced not to the man-in-the-flesh, with all his physical irrelevancies, but to disembodied action. You see only ideally what he *does*, what only *he* would do, like the action of a Poltergeist: an invisible something, with the famous Yorkshire name of Rymer. So, anyway we start with the functional essence of Rymer. Having begun with the effect I will turn to the cause; give an account of this unusual creature, whom you may judge to be a Christian pest, a dangerous busybody, or a saint in motley.

We met in the following manner. It was not in fact a *meeting* but he had the next place to me in the Reading Room of the British Museum. This accident has no more significance than sitting next to somebody in a bus—it does not, happily, constitute a "meeting": and if it is converted into a meeting by one of the parties, is properly resented. Not a Webb addict, I had on this occasion, by the purest chance, put in a slip for some Fabian tracts and this was the uppermost of a half-dozen books awaiting me on my return from lunch. I should perhaps add, for the benefit of those unacquainted with the B. M. Reading Room, that the official ticket protruding from each book brought by the attendant displays the name as well as the seat number of the reader for whom it is destined. This may be a relevant fact.

I was preparing to begin work when a shadowy figure existing only in the corner of my eye, occupying the chair and desk-space to my right, unexpectedly thrust out a hand and gave the Fabian tracts an emphatic slap.

"Splendid stuff, Mr. Wyndham Lewis!" was the unwelcome oral accompaniment of the pawing of my book. Then there was another vigorous pat. I looked fixedly and coldly at the intrusive hand, ignoring the shadow in the corner of my right eye to which it belonged and from which it had strayed uninvited into my reading territory. I turned to the left, presenting my back to so unduly extrovert an organism. This is all I remember, beyond the fact that when I had finished my reading and stood up to go, I noticed that the chair to my right was vacant.

It was ten days later that a letter arrived, with a Midland postmark, at the foot of which I read Samuel Hartley Rymer (Rev). This was fairly carefully written: for these were the only words in the whole letter that I felt absolutely certain about. However, I thought I gathered that my correspondent—"if not," as he feared, "quite beyond my means"—desired to purchase a work of mine: "a small painting? or a drawing which is probably all I could afford." I disentangled these sentences from the shapeless jumble of his script. Finally, he was reminding me, it came to light, of the impertinent stranger who had spoken to me in the Reading Room of the Museum. "I am afraid that was me." So! My neighbour who had smacked my pile of books was a parson? I saw at once how that might be.

The Museum episode was not calculated to recommend me to Mr. Rymer but I thought I would see him. It was two hundred years since the Enlightenment and six centuries since the Age of Faith. And of course I knew that in its "dry" form the Rot was in the wood roof of the churches, in reredos, in pulpit, and in pew. It was my idea that this might be a good opportunity to learn whether the Rot has entered into the Cloth. Did it rage beneath the surplice and eat away the roots of faith, in the impalpable centre of belief. For though faith began to die in the flock half a millennium ago, I have always supposed that a priest must secrete a little of it.

When I went to the door in answer to Rymer's knock, a large passionate and weary and frustrated face was thrust up towards mine—a not unhandsome one I thought. (We are of the same height, but it was thrust up because of the clerical crouch, and there was the prayerful angle of the supplicant's eyes.)

To a Frenchman, in my place, *a slovenly overgrown school-boy* would have been standing there on the doorstep: which would have been to overlook or ignore the English tradition of expressing superiority by means of shabby garments: and then the fact that it is not the Englishman's idea to get *mature*. Maturity pertains to another ethos, continental and not insular. Let me add in this context, that irresponsible boyish "mischief" is a favourite alibi with the Anglo-Saxon.

But to return from the general to the particular, my visitor was a hulking forty-something, hatless, spectacled. Not come as the well-heeled patron, surely. Just dropped up from a by-no-means fashionable watering-place to get a glass of milk, trying to look at once commanding and appealing as the farmer's wife comes to the door.

My first impressions I was obliged later very radically to scrap, to Rymer's advantage, I mean. I am the possessor of a tough eye. It does not soften what it sees: it hands me everything like a photographer's untouched photograph. In this case, it noted with a relentless acuity what had narrowly escaped being a lantern jaw, which it was only prevented from degenerating into by his masterful vitality. It registered the eloquent feminine mouth which pursed itself almost primly and then shot out its lips at right angles, the rest of the mouth not moving, to be a spout for speech to rabble-rouse or to exhort—as urchins do in their word-battles. He reads verse better than anyone I have ever heard: he was the quietest crooner, he was soft like a man talking to himself about something he had seen, at once matter-of-fact and un-earthly. And he knew the weight in Heaven of every word in the dictionary.

As I saw him for the first time I observed of course the eyes of a somewhat worried but stubbornly amused, big dog. I saw that the nose was shapely, the brow large. Those first impres-sions did not have to be modified: but in the end one would forget the ecclesiastical chin-line; one would assess at their proper value the disfigurements associated with eloquent verbal discharges—such as the spout-like propensities of the shooting-lips, the wildly wrinkled brow.

There was no clerical collar on his large weather-beaten neck. It was framed instead with the gaping collar of a soft blue shirt. "Where is your collar?" I demanded. Minus his master's name upon a brass-plate, collarless and unidentifiable, this big dog was at large in London. But, "Got it in my pocket!" came popping out the brisk rejoinder: "Do you want me to put it on?" He had pro-duced it and held it in his hand. "Not before coming in," I said. "Not at once," he echoed, putting the collar back in the pocket.

The collar had looked authentic. "Please come this way," said I, leading my incognito man-of-god upstairs, into my work room. I looked narrowly at him of course. We were there under the vast sculptor's window: he exposed his rugged worried countenance to the glare of the sky without an unbecoming diffidence, but quite simply as if to say, "Well here I am. Since you seem inclined to scrutinize my person, this is what I look like." I was searching for signs of the Rot, of course.

What he actually said was: "You must have thought it great cheek for me to write to you. I feel I am here under false pretences." "You must not feel that," I said. "Why should you?"

"It is very good of you to say so."

"Please sit down," I told him as I sat down myself. He followed suit, silently. Rather stiffly expectant he sat there as if awaiting my next move. I sat studying him, however, and he did not look at me.

It was not that he really felt in a false position, I'm sure of that: and there is nothing shy about Rymer. At this first meeting, for a little while, I had a sense of a youthful manner: of an attempt rather curious in view of his massive maturity—to suggest the early years of manhood. This did not survive our first meeting. It was perhaps a manner he adopted, under certain circumstances, with strangers. I think he produces (however battered it may be) the undergraduate he once was. In any case, it was a very different approach to the aggressive book-slapping of the Museum.

"You like pictures?" I enquired, as I saw him looking at a Rowlandson which hung near him.

"I do very much. I have some. Two or three, perhaps you might like."

"I understand you wish to add to your collection?" I then said, for *this* patron would have to be brought to the point, if he was a patron. And if he was not, it was best to find out what his errand was. His response was satisfactorily prompt and clear.

"Yes. I should like to acquire a work of yours, unless it is altogether beyond my means."

After I had produced two small canvases, and perhaps a dozen drawings, he stuck one of the drawings up against the back of a chair, returned to where he had been sitting and proceeded to examine it (from much too far off, as a matter of fact). It was a large, strongly coloured, gouache of a number of nude horsemen. Rigidly stylized, certainly; but with the black arcs of the horses' legs against a shining lagoon, and so on, possessing enough romantic literary appeal to recommend it to an intelligent clergyman. I knew it would look far better on his walls than he could foresee.

I left him in front of the drawing, and went downstairs to answer the telephone. When I returned he was standing up. He asked me whether I would sell the drawing—he liked it very much. I told him I was glad and the price of it was thirty pounds.

He began making out a cheque, saying as he did so, "May I take it away with me?" There was no objection of course, and shortly he handed me that cheque and received the drawing wrapped in brown paper, with an arrow to show where it should be held. I pushed cigarettes over; he took a horrific pipe from his pocket and asked if he might be allowed to smoke. We neither of us wished to terminate the interview with the production of the cheque (I was quite prepared to find that it bounced). We talked for a short while about pictures—my hours of work, my training in Paris—the disadvantages of the naked overhead sky as a source of light. Then he had pipe-trouble, and when we were able to converse again I asked him about himself. What manner of life did he live at Bagwick Rectory and if he came up to London?

No, he did not come to London often. He could not afford to: and very quickly I found we had passed into astonishingly uninhibited intercourse. Yielding to my discreet invitations he opened up, and I looked in, as if into a woman's handbag. I must confess that what I saw there in the matter of hard cash embarrassed me for a moment. The thirty pounds in my pocket (in the form of a cheque) had left about tuppence three farthings; all mixed up with the bus-tickets and hair-pins and little girlish secrets. And far from being averse, I found, from laying bare economic secrets, he relished exposing them. Somewhat abashed, as I have said, by his unexpected exhibitions, I steered off on to more general subjects. I attempted to distract him with *racontars* and perhaps a few caustic indiscretions. In these early hours of our friendship, I recall, Rymer played the parson a little. For instance, in response to one of my exposures of a colleague's vanity he exclaimed "You wicked man!" as parsons had in England in the heyday of the Cloth, over muffins and seed cake—the parsons the inimitable du Maurier, and Trollope, too, of course, were acquainted with.

While these pleasantries were occurring I had time to think. My new patron's annual income as Rector of Bagwick was, he disclosed, theoretically six pounds a week, but naturally it was not tax-free and neither he nor his wife had any means of their own. The pound sterling slides downhill all the time, but there is one thing that is stationary as a rock in England, namely the clergyman's stipend. That does not rise correspondingly. Clergymen cannot strike so their wages are not adjustable to meet rises in the cost of living. Had I unaware got a dustman for a patron I should have been amused: as it was I said a little crossly, "So you are paying me a month's salary?" "Yes," with firm relish he assented—it amused him as much as if he had been a ragpicker: "Yes—about."

I privately examined the likelihood of his being a phoney. Of course I could have given him the thing. If he was really so poor a clergyman I would do that. I decided to be cautious. Then I enquired, "Why are you indulging, Mr. Rymer, in this absurd extravagance?" and something like the following dialogue ensued:

Myself. "You have about five shillings a week pocket money?"

Rev. Rymer. "Sometimes!"

Myself. "Is not this drawing an absurd extravagance?"

Rev. Hymer. "That's what my daughter says!" (In a classy rhetorical whine—apt to terminate in a comic wail—to which he was sometimes addicted.)

Myself. "You're a wicked man!"

Rev. Rymer. "Yes," with unabated promptitude, "I'm a miserable sinner!"

Myself (*kindly*). "Does not your conscience prick you?"

Rev. Rymer. "Ought it to?" (Parsonically quizzical.)

Myself. "I know mine ought to, if I accept money for that drawing, now I know your circumstances."

Rev. Rymer. "That is absurd. It was generous of you to let me have it so cheaply. I make a little money on the side."

Myself. "How?"

Rev. Rymer. "Oh, by coaching. Not very much, but it is a little. I only spend *that,* on my London trips—and this, of course."

Myself. "I have a special cheap rate for poor men of religion, 'rich of holy thought and work.' You could have availed yourself of that. Had I known. . . ."

Rev. Rymer. "Have you a special fee?" (He gurgled merrily.) "Have you many of us as clients?"

Myself. "Quite a few. But you can't even afford . . . You would be straining your resources if you bought a picture-postcard *Sunflower* of Van Gogh!"

Rev. Rymer. "Oh well, provided we can laugh at such embarrassments."

Myself. "Poverty is not a laughing matter—for an artist. For a priest it is the preordained condition and affluence is disgraceful. You can go on laughing."

Rev. Rymer. "But I am not really poor. I live in the country. You do not realize how inexpensive life is at Bagwick."

Myself. "You six-quid-a-week capitalist!"

Rymer is an individual not without dignity. He is large and serious and worried. And he is quite exceptionally arrogant. If he heard this he would not like it, but he is the most aggressive dogmatist I know, as was indicated in my preamble. If your electric oven is a serious problem, or your studio painfully hot in summer, he will, with his invariable promptitude and patness, and with an affectation of salesmanship technique, propose a gadget to regulate the first, and install (in theory) a novel ventilation system to correct the second. There is no handicap he will not convert in the twinkling of an eye into a triumphant asset. Should you suffer from asthma he will be your doctor: if you are a philosopher assailed with doubt he will overhaul your system—

or if you do not fancy a system, he will show you the best way to get on without one, as a light-hearted empiricist.

It is easy to see how a village-priest is apt to develop into a wiseacre, and where this technique might be highly appropriate. Of course with me he has to behave himself up to a point, but he would be a bad man to have around if one were in a wordly position defenceless against this amateur lawgiver. Though a kind man, he could not resist the opportunity. He literally boils with the heat of his private absolute. Sometimes I have had to wrestle jovially for hours with this didactic dragon.

If this is a fault which takes up a good deal of room here, out of proportion to its importance, his virtues are unusual. He is one of those men with whom one finds oneself conversing at once with the freedom of two tramps meeting at a dusty cross-road, open to one another in the freemasonry of the propertyless. He is touched with the heroism of the destitute, even if it is *malgré lui* that he is of that caste. He is not a throw-back to the religious mendicant, he is an advance copy (imperfect but authentic) of the hobo-holiness of Tomorrow. So actually we get on because both are poor, and a fastidious absence of dignity (the intelligent hall-mark of English education) neutralizes, in its operation, such faults as the relic of class-bossiness, in its parsonic form, which I have described. Oxford has cooked Rymer so successfully that whatever else he may be he is not raw. At times I have felt he is over-cooked, or perhaps it would be better to say *overoxfordized*.

A clerical playboy he emphatically is not. But at times *il en a l'air*. Much is, as I have suggested, mannerism induced by *métier*. I hope the man of parts I write of is not disappearing beneath such elaboration: not this poor clergyman who forgets he has no money, who yearns for honour—who certainly has dreamt of fame, but who dreams incessantly now of social justice and a new, bright, bossy, fraternal world—a new Jerusalem. He comes from a part of England that has bred rebels like rabbits. His verse is of a wizard elegance, the song of a rather mechanically cheerful bird, on the highest and frostiest bough in a frost like the last frost of all, celebrating the winter of our discontent as though it were the morning of the world.

With a brave curl of the chapped lip Rymer is ready to take on his cavernous jaw whatever buffet, in spite of his prayers, cruel Providence swings at him. This, if not mute, inglorious Rymer, eating his heart out in a remote rectory, risks going short of fuel or food every time he buys a ticket for King's Cross for no strictly clerical purpose—just to come up for air: to spend a few days in London, go to hear Grosser preach, go to see a high-brow film at the Academy, or stare at paintings in the small Galleries.

It took quite some time to digest Rymer. It was like overcoming the flamboyance of French prose in an author who by chance has something to say. His verse is the reverse of the personality however. If he conversationally bludgeons his way through the world, if that is the outer animal, within he is attentive and quiet. On top of all is social splashings, but beneath there abides in the Rymerian deeps something which is only seen in his verse, which has at times a submerged quality of great intensity. It might be the noiseless canticle of a cephalopod. I shall have to take back the wintry mechanical bird, this is a better image.

How it was we came, at our first meeting, to be communicating with such rugged readiness immediately will be a little plainer presently perhaps. Rymer did not come in as a stranger you see —almost with a "hallo!" He refuses to be a stranger to anybody. He has the secret I think of his divine Master, he is no mere official of the Church. Within five minutes, with someone he had never seen before in his life, he would be telling him how to fix his lighter, the best way to get to sleep at night, or in what to invest his money.

The talk about his status as a patron, to go back to that, died down. Further personal revelations however followed. His situation looked to me a very ugly one. At this point the actual field-work began. What he was telling me, now, concerned his position as Rector, and it was related to the new standing of all the rural clergy in England. The final ruin of the landed society was factor number one, though Heaven knows no traditional Squire would have tolerated Rymer—he himself representing a new brand of parson. However, before I proceed I ought to say that the information I am about to impart was not all acquired on the first day we met. Nor, of course, was Rymer the Rymer I now know yet. The process of progressive understanding by means of which density is acquired by the phantom stranger, even with such an extrovert as Rymer demands some little time. Again, the facts he divulged concerning his life at Bagwick I only fully grasped the meaning of when a little later I passed some time in the different parts of the post-war English countryside. I went where he lived and functioned too, and checked at first-hand. So what is the narrative proper will now begin, ending with the last news I have had of him—most disagreeable events which I fear will change his life for the worse.

English village life until quite recently was, of course, dominated by the Squire: the old order, which had long ceased to have any meaning in the towns, clung on in the English villages. It was with the Squire that the Rector, or Vicar, had to deal. Often he owed his appointment to the local big landowner, and in any case he was apt to have the most say in questions relating to the Church. That is still the position in many places, certainly, though it is manifest that this last faint shadow of the feudal situation is about to disappear completely. From the fifteenth to the twentieth century has been an interminable fade-out. In what an American magazine described as "the Crippsean Ice Age" there is no room for the "country gentleman"; even a clergyman in the old sense must be an outrageous exotic.

Those of the landowning class who have disposed of their "seats," parks and estates, may even now not be the majority. Comedy to which they are not averse, lightens the lot of those who will not be frozen out of their seats, or who retain a toe-hold in some cumbersome seventeenth-century Renaissance palace. Some convert their country seats into apartment houses for local business-men (I know of such cases in Wales for instance), them-

selves occupying a modest suite in one of the flanking towers—
from which vantage-point they can keep an eye on their lodgers.
One, I know, lived alone with a man-servant and his now decrepit nannie, in a house about the size of Wellington Barracks.
The Park is now a golf-links, the Club-house a hundred yards or
so from the Hall: tradesmen from the neighbouring city put and
stibble all around the main entrance. Then I remember being
told of a well-known Marquess and his Marchioness who dig and
hoe side by side in the vegetable garden adjacent to their palace
(which they would describe of course as a "country-house"), in-
habiting the few rooms that can be kept clean with a vacuum
cleaner wielded by an elderly domestic or by the not very robust
Marchioness. Finally, there are those who live in a gardener's
house upon the estate and act as cicerone to sightseers come to
visit the huge and ostentatious shell where one of the greatest
lords of England used to live in state. There is one case of this
sort in which a handsome young Countess, a former "school
teacher," married to the earl during the blitz, escorts parties
around. It is reported that she levels some very caustic cracks at
her husband's ancestors, whose portraits snootily placard the
towering walls of the rooms of state.

Seeing how long ago the feudal age ended, it is remarkable
how intense a sentiment of pleasurable inferiority still subsisted
in the English countryside as late as the first years of the present
century, from which the Church derived advantage, and which
sentiment it encouraged. Anyone familiar with the countryside
before the radio and the automobile, would be inclined to feel
that the end of the Manor must mean the end of the Church. But
Rymer has a quite different destiny for the Church. What he
would really like, I believe, is that it should replace the Manor.

However, a new power has come on the scene, most unexpectedly, in many parts of the country, and automatically has
occupied the place left vacant by the Squire. I refer to the new-
rich Farmer (rich partly owing to Government subsidies). The
men who have the big farms, of a thousand acres up, are the new
variety of big bug, once you get outside the town, for they are

in fact the biggest thing in sight. Wherever a Squire, or other aristocratic authority, has dropped out, the force of circumstances, if not their own volition, pushes these other agricultural bosses in. The Farmer's tenure of power will be brief: but there he is. He will remain until such time as this Government, or the next, as it must be, much more radical, collectivises his property. Who can say, without unwarrantable optimism, that he will not be shot as a Kulak?

In the rural parish of which Rymer is the agent of salvation such a transference of power as I have indicated has taken place —much to his disgust. A farmer possessed of fifteen hundred acres, himself coming of a long line of yeomen farmers, but (odious complication) grammar-schooled at the school once attended as a day-boy by Rymer himself, and hovering between yeoman and gentleman, is the big man in the eyes of the village now. Most of his labourers in fact live there.

The Squire is a highly intelligent man, not cut out to play that part at all. He has sold his farms and other property, is seldom down at Bagwick—which is a perfectly hideous place, though the Manor is a fine specimen of the Dutch Gable period proper in the manorial architecture of England. So he has little say in village affairs, and the fact that he is well-disposed to my friend does not alter the situation. It is Jack Cox, the young farmer, with whom Rymer for his sins is confronted. This little rustic capitalist is Samuel Hartley Rymer's cross. For Jack Cox neither likes Rymer's politics, nor his brand of religion (Anglo-Catholic), nor his big sweet worried argumentative face.

For ten years Farmer and Rector have not spoken to one another: or if the latter has proffered a Christian greeting, the former—the farmer—had disdainfully declined to return it. Rather, this *was* the position until only the other day, to which I will come later on. The farmer's aggressiveness has become much more marked since the war: he has addressed complaints personally to the Bishop; then he drew up a petition, for which he obtained a number of signatures in the neighbourhood, for Rymer's removal. Several times my friend has been visited by the

Archdeacon who acts as a one-man Gestapo, the Bishop's emissary detailed to investigate any case of this kind and report. If a few vague and desultory enquiries can be called a cross-examination, Rymer underwent that at the hands of the Archdeacon. The Rural Dean has bent a puzzled eye upon him. So poor Rymer has been the object of too much attention to be comfortable. But the last time the meek envoy of the Cathedral showed up, with elaborate casualness he observed: "Let us see, Rymer, did I not hear it said that you wrote—er—articles? It seems to me I did." When Rymer agreed that he had indeed done that, the Archdeacon added, smiling a little slyly and shyly, "And *verse*—or am I wrong?" Rymer made no difficulty about admitting that he was married to immortal verse. But the interpretation he put upon this interrogatory surprised me at first. He regarded it as a very favourable omen. His literary habits, he felt, would excuse a good deal, especially the writing of verse. The farmer's indictment would melt away confronted with that fact, or at least would be blunted.

The charges brought by the farmer, it seems, are multiple. First, there is the usual one with which all clergymen have to contend, namely that he is lazy, lies down on the job, keeps the church in a dirty condition, never visits the sick for fear of infection: that he just draws his pay and lazes around, except for an hour or two of very hot air on Sunday—which does not however warm the church and the children come home sneezing their heads off, and old people who were fond of going there had stopped doing so because it was too dangerous after October the first.

Next come his papist habits: the stink of incense that one can smell half the way down the road, the flexing of the knees and other ungodliness. All farmers like a "broad churchman" and dislike and suspect a "high churchman," and Jack Cox was no exception to the rule. But there was another charge that may have carried far more weight, if only because it is not often heard. Jack Cox accused the Rector of being a "red"—the farmer's bane

—of stirring up his labourers, of contaminating the parish with radical doctrine, of being a disturbing and immoral influence.

When first Rymer disclosed this latter charge I stared at him. I said "A Red, too!" He gave his little short breathless laugh, his eyes never participating. "Yes. It is true," he told me, "that I am in favour of telling the United States to keep its beastly dollars, and to trade with Russia instead." He stirred about vigorously in his chair, I noticed. Any mention of the United States inflamed him, but because of his sacred calling he was obliged to smother the flames within, or to bottle them up. This engendered a physical uneasiness.

"Is that being *a red*?" he asked, "If so I am one."

"But you advertise a desire for more social justice?"

"Certainly!" he protested. "Don't you?"

"Well, you are a socialist."

"Call it that, if you like."

"Which of course would make Mr. Attlee 'a red'."

"Exactly."

That was as far as I got upon that occasion. He did tell me a little later that he had "sat on the same platform" as the Red Dean (of Canterbury). I, of course, do not know everything. The farmer had a case, I suppose. He could be described as a "political priest," no doubt, which is all, under certain circumstances, the farmer would need. But those circumstances did not exist as it happened.

The Archdeacon, dispatched by the Cathedral the first time, unseen by Rymer, poked around the neighbourhood in his shabby clerical automobile, discussed with some the weather, with others the crops, learned that Rymer was a total abstainer, that he affected to smoke a pipe—but there was rarely any tobacco in it: that he had never been known to make passes at the maid at the rectory (there had never been any there). The Archdeacon had had some practice in mollifying parishioners on the score of the "redness" (or "liberalism," as he had learned to call it) of their vicars. He had got rather to enjoy doing this, as peo-

ple who play a game well welcome opportunities of displaying
their skill.

As for Anglo-Catholicism, that was apple-pie to the Archdeacon. One might almost say that he had been specially trained in
the art of turning people's minds away from the swinging of the
censers in the churches of the diocese—and he had had reason
to observe that a certain "redness" or "pinkness" was frequently
associated with these liturgical eccentricities. The Bishop no one
could accuse of a tendency to totalitarianism; on the other hand
he was one of the "highest" bishops in the country. So of course
this conjunction of the "pink" and the "high" was not invariable.

As an ecclesiastical administrator the Bishop was no man of
iron. A rather picturesque-looking aristocrat, he would listen, his
eyes half-closed, the graceful silver-curling head bowed far more
in sorrow than in anger, to the reports of his clerical watchdog
—who was not a very fierce dog either. "Ah!" the Bishop would
intone despondently as the Archdeacon uttered the dreadful word
drink. "Mum!" the Bishop would softly ejaculate as the Archdeacon muttered *young girls of fifteen* (or *choirboys in the Vestry*) as he reported his findings in connection with some poison
pen letter, or on some accusation levelled at a curate who was
said to use scent.

But it is probable that were Rymer discovered (to make use of
an extreme illustration), when the teller's back was turned, with
his hand in the till of the local branch bank in the nearby market-
town, the Bishop would only murmur, "Rymer is an extremely
impetuous clergyman, defective in judgment, I think. He is apt,
don't you agree, to forget that he is now a weighty and responsible incumbent and acts as wild curates sometimes do. In
the present case he would undoubtedly have returned the bundle
of five-pound notes later: for I assume he was testing the vig-
ilance of the bank clerk. It is most like him to interfere in what
does not concern him. Poor Rymer! Always his actions rather
resemble those of the practical joker." And were it further alleged
that Rymer, when discovered, had produced a gun, which he
pointed at the teller, the Bishop would have observed: "A re-

volver? Rymer would be more likely to blow *himself* up with such a weapon than to harm anyone else. It was clearly some prank—everything points to that, I think. Poor Rymer! I have often thought Rymer missed his vocation, he should have been an actor. However, I regard him as the right man for Bagwick, quite the right man. The people like him. And . . . as a living Bagwick is not a very attractive proposition." Were Rymer on the other hand to murder the gamekeeper of a neighbouring Coal Board executive, it would not be because the famished Rymer had been caught poaching—no. It would be because Rymer had mistaken the gamekeeper for a poacher. There was no imaginable crime of which a clergyman stood accused, which would not have received this treatment—been melted away in the mellow mildness of the Bishop's mind.

It was the Bishop of Storby's invariable belief that clergymen in his diocese were *popular*. Then the anglican priesthood is the worst-paid calling in Great Britain today. This is a major fact that must be ever present to the mind of a high functionary of the Church. Indeed, should any man be so eccentric as to express a desire to join the greatly depleted ranks of the clergy, a warm welcome would be given to a ticket-of-leave man, an ex-Borstal boy, or a tubercular hunchback who could with difficulty sign his name. It is as bad as that: and in this particular diocese the position was exceptionally acute, because of the county's marked absence of amenities. As it was, nearly half the clergy made themselves responsible for two churches. Should the pound sterling continue to lose its value, many churches would have to be closed down, clergymen seeking other work. Rural populations would have in their midst a large empty building, standing in a graveyard, symbolising the vacuum where once there was Faith. The ex-Anglican parishes would become the missionary field for the witch-doctors of a variety of cults.

Accordingly anyone prepared to face the rigours involved in entering holy orders, is eligible—rigours which might make a holy calling of this again. In the rural diocese of which Rymer's parish formed a part, one of the vicars was an ex-hairdresser. He made a first-rate clergyman and on Saturdays cut his parishioners' hair free of charge. Though he lacked the equipment to give them a "perm," he interviewed the local belles at the vicarage and advised them as to the style of dressing most suited to their hair and personality. So you can see that it really was not much use signing petitions to have a clergyman removed. And were Rymer removed the See would be obliged to find him another living—such, it seems, is the law of the Church. The rectory he vacated might quite well remain untenanted, its church padlocked, its bell unrung, a bad advertisement for Jesus. In view of all this Rymer (as he put it in his letters) "sat back." Why should he worry? It was tails I win, heads you lose. He felt completely master of the situation—up to June 28. But he was a fretful, discontented man, his bubbling masterful surface-self, his big arrogant poker-face the bluff, as he recklessly played his hand, of a very pessimistic player.

_____ 2.

ON my first visit to Bagwick I decided I would go unannounced. First I would spend a night at the cathedral city, then drive over to Bagwick, have a drink at the village pub, see what sort of flock Rymer's was, and afterwards walk up to the Rectory. The eastering Midlands are the dullest part of England from the window of a train. Storby, my destination, does not impress: it has never been very important, has no charter, it is a county town no more. The county, I have always found, has not much identity, it has to be hunted for on the map: being on the small side; being a county that fits in, not that stands out; not upon the sea (and having a coastline always helps one to remember the position of a county): lastly, with a name which is too long, and one not written in large letters upon our palates, like Devonshire Cream, or Worcester Sauce, or Yorkshire Pudding, or Dundee Cake. Upon its eastern side, for half its length, it melts into a bleak-fen county, on the other side it is blackened by a forest of chimneys, where the furnaces of its big industrial neighbours are producing mechanical legs, taxi-cabs and toy-locomotives. Storby is on its eastern border, which is why it stands in so flat a landscape. Bagwick lies directly west of the city. Once you have crossed six miles or so of plain as flat as a billiard table the land begins to rise, but of course not very much. It is a county that never rises into the air more than the height of Box Hill.

The spire of Storby's Cathedral stuck up like a spike out of the perfectly flat collection of roofs. As there are no other steeples or buildings of any size, it causes on arrival one to feel that the Cathedral possessed of this unusually tapering horn is all that is outstanding in this cold and lonely community. In fact, once you are part of the flatness yourself, that is inside the city, it is found to be swarming with people on bicycles and others selling barrowsful of flowers, and a goodly amount of ribaldry can be heard passing between bicycle and flower-laden barrow. There is much vitality in the large market-place upon a river bank, and entire streets that are still mediæval. The inhabitants get more out of them that way than if they demolished the open-timber houses bulging over the ancient cobbles, and erected prosaic contemporary abodes, touristically unprofitable. The aura of antiquity extends to the hotels, no *good* hotel being of later date than Queen Anne.

Storby's Cathedral dominated the market, as a Cathedral should. Fans of Perpendicular became delirious as they approached it, sticking up propped and buttressed as in the stone-age of building it must be. It is entirely deserted by the clergy—you would expect to see one *corbeau* from time to time. But like Rymer I suppose they all wear sports jackets and sports shirts. There seemed to be a lot of people about, it is true, obviously not enthusiasts of the Perpendicular: they may have been some of the staff off-duty. I saw no one anywhere in the city who showed any sign of being a clergyman. What might be described as *the flight from the Cloth* certainly makes the churches and cathedrals seem more derelict even than they are.

When on the way to my hotel from the railway station, the taxi crossed a river. "What is the name of the river?" I enquired of the young taximan as we were moving over the bridge. He drove on in silence. "Is it perhaps the Stor?" I suggested. He muttered, and it appeared he actually did not know. He was a native of Storby. I suppose the war had come before he had got around to asking the name of anything, and once he got back (at about the age of twenty-three at a guess) he had other things to think about. However when I laughed understandingly he began speaking again, saying that for *his* part he could not see why people came to Storby (he thought English Perpendicular was my weakness of course), he could see nothing very exciting about Storby and in fact took every opportunity of getting out of it. Having got this off his chest, in Storby idiom and half-said to himself, he resumed his eloquent silence. I gave him a handsome tip, he was the sort of citizen I like.

Next day, as I had planned to do, I was driven out to Bagwick in a hired car. If anyone is interested in fields, hundreds and hundreds of them, tilted up and all running the same way, with telegraph poles to give variety to the scene, it must be a lovely drive. After fourteen or fifteen miles of implacable farmland but no sign of man or beast we entered Bagwick. There was no one there either. It was a sizeable village, with a pub and a few shops. Its street was not straight, it kept bearing round to the left. As we moved forward we came in sight of a solitary figure, coming in our direction, followed by a barking dog. Towards this infuriated animal the solitary figure turned, appeasement visibly his policy, but it was the wrong dog, to judge from the disappointing results. Suddenly, as we drew nearer, I realized that it was none other than my reverend friend himself. I asked the driver to stop.

Rymer in the metropolis is a dude compared with Rymer at Bagwick. As I walked towards him he was saluting me with raised arm and sending up a welcoming wail of astonishment, tinctured with embarrassment—the raised arm having a bad effect on the dog, at the same time exposing a gaping armpit, the tattered tweed suggestive of the coarsely hirsute.

The Rector of Bagwick was the village "bum" it seemed. In

sweet Auburn ugliest village of the Plain they had a scarecrow to preach to them! His attire was terrific. No mendicant friar ever hobbled down a street in a more tatterdemalion advertisement of poverty.

A brownish tweed that was so obsolete that it necessitated a vertical patch the size of a folded newspaper in one place, the sleeves of which had to terminate in cuffs of leather three inches deep, and demanded to be reinforced with leather at the collar line and to have two pocket-tops bound with pigskin, was already qualified to serve the tramp-comedian in his act. Particoloured patches practically everywhere had plainly been selected for their effect. Only that could explain the mighty patch placarding his left side: for did it have to be *black*? It was a piece of "the Cloth" called into service—perhaps cut off what was left of the trousers he wore as a curate. Oh, Rymer—*cabotin*!—almighty clown! That was my *first* reaction to the Rector *chez lui*.

The flabby and sagging droop dawdled nearer, with his high-pitched cry: "Why didn't you telephone, you should have telephoned: I'd have fetched you." Then his big smiling face, ruggedly handsome and anxiously sweet, came up. I took him by a small corduroy patch upon his sleeve and said "Greetings your reverence!" And he said "I *am* glad to see you!" But the reverend gentleman moved away to pick up a stone. He bent down and oh what a vast expanse he had for sitting purposes! which now presented itself—lingeringly while he picked his stone. A small fluffy hole half-way up the left posterior for which a darning needle would soon be imperative—was this a declaration of independence on the part of a proud parson, or had he not noticed when a nail had torn his trouser-seat? He stood up, and with placatory absence of passion he cast the stone (discovering a ragged elbow). The stone however struck the dog. "Oh, did I hit you, Jacko?" he called with patronizing contrition. "I am sorry, I'll bring you a bone, honest injun. Tomorrow!" But the dog as was evident held strongish views on the throwing of stones. He had retired out of range to denounce Rymer with a deeper note of warning to whom it might concern.

Reactions on my side continued to be uncomplimentary to such playing at the down-and-out as I regarded it in my short-sightedness. How would this big fat baby like to be homeless, his stipend what he could pick up on the street? He read my thoughts and flapped deliberately the black patch of obvious clerical origin, which seemed to be coming unstuck at the bottom. The dog interpreting this as an insult rushed towards us his teeth bared like a Hollywood glamour girl. Rymer flapped it again, and I expected to see one of his patches ripped off and with luck a bit of the flesh behind it. I thought Jacko would try for the big black one—or failing that go off with the blue strip on one of the knees. But the dog was petrified by a piercing cry as a gaunt villager flew out of a lane. "Jacko!" the woman shrieked, and the voice had the effect of the radar wave said to stop ducks in mid-flight. "Come here, do you hear me, Jacko!" She yapped as she flew and the dog fell to the ground as if he had been shot, his ears glued against his head and his belly scraping the street.

The woman's eyes as she ran darted at Rymer; where to her mind the blame lay was plain enough and she would have told him so I thought if I had not been there.

"Ah, Mrs. Rossiter, thank you for saving my life!" In a high-pitched yell he musically greeted his saviour. "Very kind of you, Jacko is unusually naughty this morning. I must bring him another bone—a nice big *bone!*"

Driving Jacko before her, his tail stuck tight between his legs, Mrs. Rossiter retired swiftly into the lane out of which she had come, with a rather dangerous growl followed by a spit.

We looked at one another.

"Exit Jacko. Quite a dog!" said I. Rymer, ruffled more by Mrs. Rossiter than by Jacko, agreed that the latter was *just all dog.*

"Mrs. Rossiter's a nice woman really," he observed.

"I thought she was nice," I told him.

"It's very sad, she lost her husband a year ago, he was killed by one of Jack Cox's bulls."

"Oh dear."

"Yes, it's very sad. Jacko's all she's got." He looked at me.

"I *see!*" I said. "Of course. . . ."

"He does that every time I come this way. He never seems to get used to me."

"It must be difficult for you to come into Bagwick," I observed. "Why don't you carry a stick?"

"I can't do that," he answered shortly.

Then he gazed at me with polite enthusiasm, welcoming me to Bagwick.

"Well, I *am* glad to see you," he exclaimed, "but why didn't you *telephone?* Shall we go up to the house? You must be hungry aren't you? My wife will be delighted to see you—come along."

Pointing to the "Lord Salisbury" I enquired: "Can't I get something at that pub?" I had to say something. "Will you come with me? A nice mousetrap sandwich and a glass of ale." But he of course said "Nonsense," so we drove to the Rectory, a few rat-like heads poking out of doors, watching us depart.

"What a jolly little village," I said.

"Yes, it is rather nice," he responded modestly.

As we drove along I took back the terms *cabotin* and *clown* which naturally at first I had hurled at him *sotto voce*—at the tatterdemalion Rector of Bagwick doubtless on his morning tour of duty, showing himself to his parishioners. Then I recognized I had been quite wrong. First of all, at Oxford he had enough money no doubt to dress the part of a young gentleman, but, of course, bar the patches, he must have looked much as he does at present. For a fashion of stylistic shabbiness (which he would seek to outstrip if I know my Rymer) would have turned him away from what "a young gentleman ought to look like" to "what in practice he *does* look like."

Today, however, he really had not the means to buy new clothes. A good suit costs forty pounds odd, a bad one twenty. The Oxford training would lead him to make a great big comic virtue of necessity. That was the first, and negative, side of it.

Next, what could he wear? In his circumstances, and with his beliefs, should he have adopted the overalls of the labourer? The Cathedral would have disapproved. To the petty, brushed-up-till-it-shone, shabby-genteel he objected. He preferred to satirize his poverty, to clown, rather than to conceal. Indeed there was protest in his get-up. He preferred to parade the streets of his parish in rags—to go up to London and buy a drawing costing as much as a new suit—I looked at the bobbling black patch with appreciation. I actually had his cheque in my pocket. Noticing my glance, he wobbled his patch at me. He had once said he would like to be the Bishop's Fool, I remembered.

We entered the Rectory drive, the car poked at by the wild overplus of vegetation which was certainly not that of a normal garden. Such coarse-tongued plants as put in their appearance where there is no finer life or competitive human culture, were visible out of the window of the car. The car described an arc around an island that was a miniature wilderness, a dusty jungle growing to a considerable height above the gravel, upon which it dropped unidentifiable vegetable matter. When I left the car, I found that the Rectory was hemmed in by the same nameless growths, swarming up its walls with an ugly vigour.

"Polygonum," said Rymer, giving a name to what I was looking at. "It's rather nice stuff unless it gets out of hand." He paused. "It has got out of hand."

"It does look slightly like a riot. Why don't you grow roses?"

"Why don't I grow roses?" Rymer looked at the savage scene facing his front door. "Oh, I don't know: snake-weed is just as good. This stuff is rather nice: when it doesn't get out of hand."

The Rectory was unexpectedly tall, this was even apparent above the eruption of polygonum threatening it on all sides. A roomy house, it had been built to contain the bulging families which the Victorian clergy regularly produced between evening and morning prayers.

The place had a big parched lonely look. Nothing grew upon its pale brick face. But since it is an Ark which obviously for a long time has ridden the wastes, no emblem of stability, like ivy, would be likely to attach itself to this mansion meant for the Deluge. So it is as bare as when it was built, except for dust, droppings, or the kind of warts that neglected houses have.

Although, without, the scene was so savage, the Rectory within, excepting the hall which was a little wild, was otherwise like the popular idea of a rectory. Rymer had acquired a few other small pictures besides mine, the radio put the Rymers in touch with the intellectual giants of Britain on the Third Programme, and of course all programmes supplied buckets full of music. A piano enabled them to perform themselves. His wife is charming: he is for her a big wilful schoolboy. Thus he was peremptorily dispatched as soon as we arrived to put on his London suit. For his son, too, whom I met on another occasion, Rymer is a bit of a youthful terror. That very grave and severe young man is at Oxford, though how he got there Heaven knows. A scholarship I suppose from the local grammar school. Both Eleanor and son Robert love him, but are strangers to his exuberances. Therefore even in his home he is alone with his excess of imagination, his poet's passion. All that is most serious to him seems like play to his family: his pastel, his politics, his pride in his poverty. This is not to say that his family are wanting in taste or vitality, only that he has *too much*—for a life passed on the poverty-line. Indeed he is like a domesticated troll who having fallen in love with Eleanor had consented to live as humans do —and I have seen Eleanor stare at him with puzzled affection and he waggle his black patch at her and give a merry clerical whinny. For of course he is *not* a goblin but a born clergyman.

The living quarters are in the back of the house. Out of the drawing-room windows however it is the same as out of the front-door. Nature coarsely proliferates, and man does nothing to check her: she throws up her low-grade creations. No one in the house has the energy to go out and cut the stuff down and burn it up. Let it grow all over the building, let it do what it likes, so long as we can get in and out, so long as it is not inside!

Such is the response I think of the inmates, exhausted by petty hardships, harassed with taxation, worn out with wars, threatened with expulsion—it was their answer to an existence to which they had not been born or bred, in the golden aftermath of the Victorian era. But gazing out of one of the windows, I dismally re-

sponded to the scene of squalid vegetable fecundity, the solid
sea of snake-weed, polygonum, or whatever it was, nettles and
dock leaves of course adding themselves to this chaos. An inglorious duck-pond appeared in the near distance—it is forced
upon one whenever one looks out of one of the vicarage windows, how this man exists upon the frontiers of a vacuum of a
new sort. The well-furnished room, with its gouache horsemen
and its piano, is an advance-post: there is the no-man's-land between our age and the darkness to come. He is the last of a
species (to which we all belong) and in him in travail—and there
are none of us do not experience the travail too—is another
species.

Dressed in garments literally dropping to pieces he moves
around his parish, among people who dread and loathe poverty
and want. And he stands in spite of himself for poverty and for
want. He is one of the first English clergymen to stand for poverty and want. And as he moves around, from house to house, the
doors quickly shut at his approach as if he were infected with
some complaint which no one was particularly anxious to have;
and out of rags tacked together his "Oxford accent" issues with
incongruous patronage; his encyclopædic affectations exasperate,
his great-heartedness abashes—for there is no *cash* only credit in
Heaven, the currency of religion, no longer legal tender. The majority of the shopkeepers and labourers' wives of Bagwick have
given up "the opiate of the People," they are no longer addicts.
Does Rymer at times wish he had another drug to peddle? I have
often wondered. And as to Sundays, in patched surplice (it can
hardly be whole, to judge from the remainder of his wardrobe)
he goes through a majestic liturgy accompanied on a small har-
monium, before a congregation usually of the odd villager plus
the family.

On this occasion it was that he took me over to see his church,
situated a couple of hundred yards down the road. The building
was not large but it was absurdly lofty, like a thin slice of a
cathedral. The vault near the entrance, for it grew to its greatest
height at the farthest point from the altar, would not have been

out of place at Canterbury. The font was so high it was not possible to use it without placing blocks of wood against it. I had no
difficulty in understanding, as soon as I saw it, what had happened when first Rymer took up his duties at Bagwick. He saw
the towering arches; his imagination, to his undoing, got to work.
He made the great original mistake out of which all his subsequent miseries issued.

I had heard, almost in the first half-hour of our earliest in-
timacies, about the beautiful reredos purchased by him for Bagwick. The protests and intrigues it had brought down on his head
were things, one saw, of obsessional dimensions, looming up behind his unemotional narrative, when he spoke of the days when
he first went to Bagwick. The extravagance had revealed to the
village, it was easy to understand, the order of man that had
come among them. They glimpsed the big troll I have spoken of.
Promptly they started to gang up. No ordinary sensible man
would be so lacking in judgement as to import the side of a house
into a small village church! Some distant cousin of Don Quixote
was in their midst—soon he might mistake them for the Saracens
and begin cutting them down. Their faces hardened, not soft
at the best of times north of The Wash, their tongues wagged.
There was a village cabal at "The Marquess of Salisbury." Finally
after years of bickering, the reredos had to be disposed of, sold
at a crushing loss, and it was he who incurred it, not the village.

Our luncheon, I am ashamed to say, was excellent. There was,
I am sure, the week's meat-ration, also the week's bones in the
nourishing well-peppered soup. More than half the week's rations
were accounted for in this chivalrous hospitality. From a small
farmer Rymer received certain favours. But this big arrogant
man in rags, who always knew everybody's business better than
they did themselves, would be a protégé that not everyone would
choose. I can see some farmer giving him a half-dozen intact eggs
and a few cracked ones *once*, but not making a habit of it. Much
food for nothing, or at its market value, he would not get, and

he has not the money to pay the black-market price for things, nor would it be wise to do so if he had.

Soon all clergymen in this country will have vows of poverty thrust upon them as I have already suggested, and a new type of ministry will come into being. Quite probably it is the *only* way to secure a truly Christian Church. It may after all be God's will. In His great wisdom it would not be likely to escape Him that a penniless clergyman is better than one who rides to hounds. Then the country people will have to bring gifts of food —a fowl, bread, pickles, a tin of sardines, pig's-trotters, apricots and greengages in season, as the moujiks once would do to their holy men. Otherwise the clergy quite literally will die out. An unpleasant transition is at present in progress. But people have so little sense of the future. The majority are completely defective in this sense. They fail to realize the significance of a process until life is suddenly quite different to what it was. They then adjust themselves at a disadvantage. The clergy should prepare themselves for penury; else quite unprepared they will find themselves the poorest class of men. Fasts would not be amiss. And they should accustom their parishioners to the idea that their sacred calling must reduce them to great poverty.

In the meantime we find Rymer, for a start, without clothes to his back, or only a travesty of clothes; and there is no other class of man that must go in rags, except the vagabond. I told him that I should come down in a year or so and discover him walking through Bagwick in a loin-cloth: what would Jacko say to that? How would Mrs. Rossiter react? It is one of those cracks that have an uncomfortably prophetic ring. Heaven avert the omen. Rymer still feels too much "the gentleman," of course, as his forebears were fine parsons in plump livings. He is a *master* type, of his own accord he will never go *the whole way* to the new model, to the country-clergyman-in-the-loin-cloth: soliciting alms in the name of God, or sitting near the altar of his church as people lay their gifts on the steps—sleeping on a camp-bed in the vestry—I am not saying that will happen tomorrow: and Rymer was heroic, in the way a prophet is, as clothed in tatters he went poker-faced to meet his fate and that of all his kind. For the village dogs will not care much for the New Model man-of-God and the villagers not improbably may stone them.

That Rymer has the seeds of heroism I hope by now is plain. If need be he would sit naked at the foot of the Cross (though it might be with the superior glint of the *Have-not* in his glazing eye) and die if he was not fed.

————— 3.

DURING lunch food—or its absence—was not discussed as invariably it is at any mealtime in England today. One felt that something vaguely was the matter. Then one realized what it was: a *certain topic* was conspicuously absent.

One soon discovered, however, that the difficulty of getting enough to eat was only one of a large class of topics under an interdict. Eleanor Rymer happened to refer to the difficulty of obtaining a proper supply of reading-matter—of books. But at the word *difficulty* Rymer blustered into action, with that inimitable imitation of automatism of his, which his large wooden poker-face facilitated.

"Difficulty? Nonsense. There is no more difficulty today than five, ten, or fifteen, years ago."

"How about the petrol, in the first place?" Eleanor retorted with a show of fight, which of course was indispensable. "I cannot get books at Bagwick."

He pounced on *petrol* like a cat on an unwary tom-tit.

"Petrol? There is all the petrol that *I* can see." (He might have added *can afford.*) "There's plenty of petrol."

"Excuse me . . ." his wife began, laughing.

But he swiftly intervened.

"I know what you are going to say," he told her, "that you haven't got all the petrol that *you* can use. Before the war you took out the car once a fortnight at the outside. Now you feel you want it every day. You never went to Cockridge unless you could help it. *Now* you are always thinking of things in Cock-

ridge or in Storby that you must have this minute." He turned to
me. "Because there is a *ration*, a limit, people imagine they are
short of something they never had so much of before, or perhaps
never *heard* of before. To hear them talk you would think that
formerly they covered hundreds of miles every day in their car,
ate enormous porterhouse steaks daily, chain-smoked from the
time they got out of bed to the time they got into it again, bought
a box of chocolates every morning after breakfast and another
just before tea."

"I know a number of people just like that," Eleanor agreed.
But I felt Rymer must not be allowed to get away with everything.

"There are shortages," I remarked.

"Shortages," he retorted, "yes, if you want the earth. People
today have as much food as is good for them—some, more than
is good for them. People are putting on fat. I am. They have as
many cigarettes or as much tobacco, as much beer as is necessary."

"As many clothes?" I enquired.

He stopped and eyed me blankly for a few seconds, as if holding a conference behind his poker-face.

"Clothes," he said slowly, "are not rationed."

Had he been dressed in the less formal of his two suits he
would, I felt, at this point have stroked his black patch.

His wife was intelligent as well as beautiful, and addressed
herself to the consumption of her piece of offal. (Why should the
butcher, or, rather, the Food Office, employ this ghastly word?)
She was accustomed, it was obvious, to being halted, turned
back, and admonished upon the threshold of certain topics.
Rymer would allow no one to grumble. No criticism of conditions
under socialism passed unchallenged. He did not demand the
quality of the bacon to be extolled (just eat it, would be the
idea, and think of something else, such as how happy our grand-
children would be in a world from which *all* capital—small as
well as great, had been banished): he did not require ecstasies
at the mention of the Purchase Tax (some day there won't be

much left to purchase, so there won't be any *tax*)—no, all Rymer exacted was *silence* about conditions under socialism. The Government are at war with Capital, it is total war: war conditions naturally prevail. Therefore, silence! Shut that great gap! Enemy ears are listening! All criticism aids capitalism.

Even Rymer would deny the existence of any obstacles in the path of socialism-in-our-time: his view of the socialist government's prospects are blindingly sunny. When he is foretelling an unprecedented export-boom, if (in the interests of sanity) one should mention the fact that the United States can supply itself with everything it requires, which it manufactures far more efficiently than any other country is capable of doing (*vide* Mr. Lippmann), Rymer pooh-poohs such a statement. He describes it as ridiculous. American goods, he will assert, are of very poor quality: the Americans would be jolly glad to get ours if they had a chance. We market our stuff badly over there to begin with. "But believe me once our industry is on its feet again our exports will soar, you see if they don't." Rymer has never been to the United States and has not the remotist idea what American goods are like, so he is not cramped in these patriotic flights by first-hand knowledge. His boundless optimism is firmly based in the most blissful ignorance. Should you speak anxiously of Great Britain's situation, living as she does upon a massive dole from the United States, he will say that *that* is our fault for having anything to do with the U.S., with Wall Street. Were we to arrange to receive a dole from Russia instead—say a billion or two, marrying the pound sterling to the rouble—we should soon be out of the wood! If we had the guts to cut ourselves loose from the Yankee capitalists, stopped spending money on an army which we didn't need, and had a pact with Russia, we should be as right as rain.

Eleanor now brusquely changed the subject. She selected one quite free of political entanglements. The unprecedented, the sumptuous summer weather—that had nothing to do with a planned economy or the redistribution of wealth. No one was to blame if the weather was bad, no one had to be thanked except

God if it was fine. And then she went on to say how perfect the
weather had been up in London, where she had been on a visit
to relatives. She thought nostalgically of London, and I asked
her if she had been to any shows. No, she said, no: *just shops.*
But she continued—with great inadvertence—to complain how
difficult it had been to shop. There were such dense herds of
people. Where on earth did they all come from!

Rymer waited until she had finished, and then he struck:

"Where do *you* come from, my dear, there is always that."
The slightly Johnsonian answer to her conundrum his wife re-
ceived with a wry smile, having detected her *faux pas* too late.
"Those people are the masses of women. . . ."

"They weren't all women!" she laughed.

"Women," he said firmly. "They come in their millions from
the suburbs and the slums and the slums and suburbs of other
cities. The pavements are impassable. It is like cutting one's way
through a dense and rubbery undergrowth."

"What an excellent description!" his wife exclaimed.

"I agree they are *dense,*" he went on. "Of course they are. For
the first time in their lives they have sufficient time and money to
go shopping in the most luxurious stores—where they could not
go before."

Here I joined in with alacrity.

"Could not go," I said, "because of their *class*—without being
followed around by store-detectives, stared out of countenance
by shopgirls from behind counters, asked every minute by a shop-
walker what articles they required. Any charlady now can go in,
try on a mink coat or two, then fling them down and say she
thinks she'll wait till next season when they may have a better
assortment. Harrods is jammed with charladies. The working-
class throng Selfridges like Woolworths at Christmastime. That
really *is* socialism. Observe that in Moscow the slums are barred
from any but the slum shops."

We returned to the drawing-room after we had eaten and sat
talking for a long time; it is a very peaceful spot, but in Rymer
there is no peace. My hostess was washing up the dishes. She

was absent at least and there was no one else in the house. The knuckly proliferation of the polygonum waved beyond the window-sill, the yellow leaves tumbled past from a tree, a wasp appeared on his way from the larder where he had been able to find no jam, no honey—nothing sweet, because the English had won the war and consequently are not allowed to grow sugar in their West Indian islands, and there is not enough beet sugar to go round. Also I noticed a sick-looking bird. The crumbs put out for it were, of course, full of bran and chalk. I suppose it was constipated. It should have pecked off as much corn as it wanted before it was cut, making a rule to touch no human food. The corn gone, why not fly off to some more sensible country? What are wings for?

I think that politics and poetry are what interest Rymer almost exclusively. At that moment politics were uppermost in his mind because the question of communism (at his instigation) was coming up the following week at the diocesan conference, and he was of course to speak, or hoped he would be able to. Communism is with him something quite unreal, for he certainly is not a communist. He is of the generation of the great fellow-travellers of the 'twenties, who painted the universities pink. But it was a solemn rag, a generational badge, and meant no more than a painter's stunt, painting for a little *all red* or *all blue*, to make a "period" with. Rymer like scores of thousands of others, had had his "pink period." It shocked all the aunts of the time terribly, and scandalized his clergyman-father. It was revolt—it symbolized *Youth*—his most glamorous moments had been pink.

Youth past, these *redmen* of the Oxford and Cambridge Colleges forgot all about it—real life began, dressing-up was at an end, the minarets of Moscow faded on the horizon. And in any case Soviet Russia had proved a somewhat tough and embarrassing comrade to "travel" with. On the other hand, because Rymer had been buried in the depths of the country ever since Oxford he lived in the past a lot, and continued to potter around with Karl Marx, like a mascot of his youth rather, and he still got a kick out of it. That was *part* of the story of Rymer and the Krem-

lin. The rest of it was traceable to professional religion: the
frivolous sizar and the fakir must be mixed.

When I asked him what he was going to say next week to the
crowd of clergymen he said he would point out that in the contemporary world communism, or marxism, was, because of the
huge development of Soviet Russia, too great a factor in world-
affairs for the Church to ignore, as it had been disposed to do
up to now. "Let us put aside our prejudices," he would invite
them, "let us examine this controversial theory of the state, and
let us ask ourselves if there is anything in it which we as Christians should endorse." He and Herbert Stoner the "red" Storby
parson, had succeeded in "winning over" several of their col-
leagues. He named others who would have nothing to do with it
—who asserted that the Church should set its face against "this
atheistic creed" and all its works. These were he told me the
"place-seekers," clergymen on the climb, who dreamed of dean-
eries and bishoprics. The only imaginable consideration which
would impel clergymen to feel other than sympathetic towards
communism was self-interest. Such was his extraordinary view.
As this was absurd I thought I would help him to dispel from his
mind so foolish an error.

"Ordinary people," I explained to him, "find it difficult to reconcile with their conscience anything short of censure of the methods employed by the Russian leaders. I do for instance. I see
what is good in the theory, but I cannot swallow the practice."

To this he made no reply. He could have argued, for instance
(for even the worst cause is polemically defensible) that bar-
barity had marked the regimes which the revolutionary governments had supplanted, in Russia and elsewhere. He even could
have instanced the cruelties still inflicted upon people daily by
the operation of the capitalist economy, or any existing economy,
or spoken of "poverty in the midst of plenty": to which of course
there are answers, too, for a good debater. There are plenty of
answers to the criticism of *any* policy. He is not interested in
being an *advocate* however. He just enjoys pushing under people's noses something they detest. He does not want to find

himself in the role of *selling* it to them, of being too serious about it. And, as I have said, he is genuinely no Red.

Where politics are concerned Rymer is not, as I have also said, merely what-is-left of a 'twenties undergraduate fellow-traveller. What *does* conspicuously remain, it must be confessed, is the juvenile impulse to *épater le bourgeois*. But behind the exhibitionism is an authentic issue, that of the priest inheriting a rotted religion from his laodicean fox-hunting ancestors which he would naturally desire to reinvigorate. That he should borrow a little reality from politics and pump it into the decayed tissues of the Church is an obvious proceeding, more especially as his instinct must inform him that what he would be borrowing had, in the first instance, been stolen from his religion. That that *instinct*, alone, is involved was proved by Rymer's reception of my subsequent identification of socialism with Christianity.

Whatever is at work behind the mask has the character of a religious experience: i.e., *he knows*. With any cause that he embraced, it would not be a civil marriage. Meanwhile he is as tightly sealed-up as a clam. In his secretiveness (that of the priest, resembling the woman's) he sees no point in exposing what he *knows*, or intuits, to the crude processes of the human reason. So he remains very reticent and his manner is aloof and also casual. "Here it is. What do you think of it?" That kind of thing. Then he will turn his back and saunter away: *never* get into a serious argument if he can help it, though he is willing enough to argue provided you do not show signs of pressing matters too far.

If socialism, instead of Christianity, were an official cult, and he it's bonze, he would teach from the absolutist angle—carelessly, almost disdainfully, without "proofs." He would deal in mystical fiats, allowing of no argument. But socialism is *not* his religion. He probably regards it as a reflection, upon an inferior (a political) plane, of Christianity. Or he would so regard it if he were going to be rational and orderly about it, and come out of his muscular mist.

Of course Rymer is quite explicit about a number of things.

He asserted for instance on this occasion that "whenever Christianity and communism have been confronted, Christianity has won the day." But his reason for making this assertion was not in order to arrive at some objective certainty, but in order to sway opinion. From this it would follow, if I interpret him correctly, that Christians need not fear to hobnob with communists, for the communists would all succumb to the superior medicine and become Christians—or, the only alternative, take to their heels. If communism, like any other form of socialism, were in fact only Christianity on a lower and mundane level, then (1) in close contact and association with Christianity it would naturally be elevated and in the end rise to the Christian level: and, further (2) there is an obligation to protect socialism against the wicked world. He did not push on into all these implications of what he said, though I have done so. His policy was to lead the mind in that direction—though I was never quite certain what he explicitly proposed.

Russia, he observed, must be regarded as "a great missionary field." "Ah, you mean to effect conversions, do you, among the reds?" I asked. "You propose to convert Stalin to Christianity?"

He looked down, then said shortly and cheekily: "Yes—p'raps."

He knew he was talking nonsense, but he didn't care.

After this absurd conversation I felt discouraged. Sitting a little while in front of Rymer's poker-face makes one feel that way as a matter of course. That socialism was something that needed defending against the wicked world was a proposition with which I was in agreement—provided it was the Western variety. But these were propositions existing in isolation from reality. For socialism could be taken over by the worldly, and then who or what was it required protecting? The worldly are never so dangerous as when they masquerade as idealists.

I have been building up an inductive Rymer which has some coherence: but that is not at all what transpires on the outside. He was dishing out to me the kind of rigmarole he had prepared for the conference. The diocesan conference was going to be a grisly affair.

But I then decided to see if I could break into this absurd re-serve, by enlarging upon the whole question of Christianity and communism. I thought I would explain something about it, and see if I could tempt this cleric out of his shell. It was a passing *énervement,* no doubt, but at that moment the large, blank, harassed, formality of the mask in front of me was a challenge. The reserve struck me as insolent and stupid. Why is this silly fellow playing a part with *me!* is what I was disposed to ask. It is the way one is bound to react in the end, before a shut door. This is particularly the case, if from behind the shut door comes a constant stream of words, all vetted for public consumption. Anyhow—verbally—I charged at the shut door.

"It has always been obvious to me," I began, "that the Chris-tianity of the Sermon on the Mount plays a major role in the history of socialism."

"Not the Sermon on the Mount," Rymer, a little sullenly, but lazily, objected.

"Oh, I see: not the Sermon on the Mount," I said.

"Well, why that?" he asked.

"I understand perfectly, as a matter of fact, your objection to that. Contemporary socialism is so phenomenally tough that you would rather not have the Sermon on the Mount mentioned in connection with "purges,' faked trials, and labour camps."

Rymer said nothing.

"The idea that socialism is unthinkable without Christianity does not appeal to you. Yet was it not fundamentally a Christian impulse that moved the Western intellectuals (even though no longer Christians) to champion the cause of the oppressed and 'underprivileged,' the underdog?"

He neglected the second member of this compound question, answering the first. "Socialism," he said, "is not unthinkable with-out Christianity."

"In that case you differ entirely from the present socialist ad-ministration."

"Do I?" he sang, amusedly musical.

"So it appears. One of their brain trusts is my authority." And

I produced a cutting from among some papers in my pocket. "Here is a cutting from the Paris *Herald Tribune*."

It would be impossible for Samuel Rymer to scowl, he is really too gentle in spite of his brutal dimensions but he made an effort to do so. At the mention of anything to do with the United States he reacted violently. The United States, in spite of its weaknesses, I like, so this is of his idiosyncrasies the one that appeals to me least. He drawled, in a bored and withering voice:

"Do you read the *Herald Tribune*?"

"Sometimes. But listen. The headline reads 'Ex-Adviser of Attlee Attacks U.S. Capitalism as Immoral.'"

"I'm glad Americans are being told what their capitalists are like," he breathed guardedly. "That's good."

"So you are prepared to accept *a moral* basis for the indictment?"

He blinked and let that pass.

"Well, listen now." (*I read.*)

"American capitalism was attacked as immoral and producing a neurosis with 'the stature of a national disease,' in a long article in *Fortune* magazine by Francis Williams . . . former public relations adviser to Prime Minister Clement R. Attlee.

"Mr. Williams called his article 'The Moral Case for Socialism'. . . .

"'I am a socialist,' wrote Mr. Williams, 'because I believe that only within a socialist society can human rights be assured. . . .'

". . . Mr. Williams said it is no accident that many early leaders of British socialism were drawn from the churches and non-conformist chapels. 'It was not personal economic interest but ethical compulsion that drove men like Attlee, Cripps and others to try to build a more moral society,' he wrote . . ."

(*I stop reading.*)

"Finally we are told that Mr. Williams speaks of the 'great American tradition of *freedom* and *democracy*'."

Rymer's response was instantaneous. "Which is utter nonsense, the Americans have never known what freedom is. It is funny to hear freedom spoken of in the same breath with the lynchers and witch-hunters."

"You are interested in *freedom* now?"

"Of course I am." He was aggressively bland and blank.

I sighed. "Freedom, reverend sir, is what socialism takes even less interest in than does monopoly-capital. A socialist sympathizer must learn to be very guarded where *freedom* is concerned. Alas, there are far more political prisoners and concentration-camps—far less freedom of movement, less freedom of speech, in the Soviet Union than in the United States. Socialist England is far more regimented already than is the United States."

Rymer muttered something about the "third degree" and "prohibition." We were now approaching that invisible line, dividing the terms on which he was prepared to discuss something, from the terms on which he was not prepared to do so.

"But once we begin to discuss *freedom* . . . ! *Cela n'en finirait plus.* Let us say that Christianity and socialism is our subject. Would you object if, instead of leaving this question of the religious origins of socialism floating about in the clouds, I brought it down to earth and attached it to a few hard facts from which it could not escape?"

"Why should I mind," he smiled, "if you regard it as important?"

"Our conscience must be *clear*. A muddy conscience is a bad conscience. But how can the conscience be clear unless we *see* clearly? Our conscience has no rest, nor has for years, it is being appealed to all the time by the contemporary politician. But before the conscience can function properly, or be of any service at all, we must *see clearly*. The politicians have a policy to sell us: let us get the clearest view of it we can—and of the politician! It may be a genuine moral article: or of course it may only be baited with a big moral appeal. No moral judgement is possible without a sharp image of the thing at issue."

"An almost cartesian desire for clarity!" Rymer smiled tolerantly.

"Appeals to the conscience seldom fail especially with the English. The fact that it is the *conscience* to which appeal has been made is so reassuring, too! A political party so appealing must be a peculiarly *moral* party! One takes for granted that a man appealing to one's good feeling, to one's humanity, must surely himself be a good humane man—the majority at least are apt to draw this conclusion."

"You are saying I suppose that socialists are attempting to secure power disguised as men engaged in a moral mission?"

"I am saying nothing of the sort. Nothing should be taken for granted. It is advisable to gain a *clear* idea of what is actually proposed, lest the conscience, working in the dark, mislead one. That is all."

"Are you saying," Rymer enquired, "that a stupid person cannot possess a conscience?"

"Obviously not so good a one as a wise man."

"Oh!" howled Rymer.

"When a matter is beyond their understanding people cannot judge it morally any more than in any other way. But that is what I wanted to discuss. I am not as clear as I would like to be myself upon a number of points. But this is really a side-issue."

"No it isn't," he interrupted. "Your case stands or falls upon that."

"My own conscience feels clear, as I am quite sure yours does. I would like to check up on its functioning however. The way to do that is to test the validity of one or more of the main beliefs responsible for the clear feeling. I always suspect a clear conscience, don't you?"

"Yes."

"In giving my own conscience this overhaul I may assist you to discover whether *your* conscience is as sound and as clear as you think."

"Speak for your own conscience. Mine is all right."

"You *think* so. You may be mistaken. People often buy things in a shop and when they get them home find they do not like them at all."

"Short-sighted people usually."

"Why, exactly. What they *thought* they saw in the shop has changed into something else: into its real self. They have bought something they did not bargain for. Now the kind of socialism which people, in their woolly and hazy way, have fastened on their back, may be one of those things that look very different later on to what at first it seemed. As an indication of what I have in mind, there have been many things to cause misgivings in socialist behaviour (especially in the official class) since the Welfare State took over from free enterprise. In a word, those who have come to rescue us from Power have themselves displayed too patent an appetite for power. The old bosses are being economically liquidated. Too often it seems that Bossiness has come in their place. As this state-power grows more absolute, will not these disquieting symptoms develop? English socialism as we know it today is complex: in it what is desirable and what is undesirable do battle."

"Because a few officials misbehave . . ." Rymer waved his hand to dismiss such insignificant blemishes.

"There should be an extremely searching debate upon the type of new society—'collective,' as it is called—being thrust upon everyone in England with practically no debate—such as a parliamentary Opposition is supposed to provide. I am not against that new society: I am against the way it is being adopted. To confer such unheard-of powers (such as no feudal king in England has ever possessed) upon a group of politicians just because they say they are 'socialist,' is absurd. In the mind of the majority 'socialist' signifies a selfless person dedicated to the welfare of mankind. Somebody may not *like* socialists, because he thinks they are too good and moral to suit him. But the *moral* status is taken for granted."

"Are you disputing the bonafides of socialism?" he asked me.

"No," I answered. "It is frightfully important that that moral essence of socialism should be a reality, that is all, and even more that it should *stop* a reality. I believe that some machinery should be invented to make certain that it does so stop. Finally there should be no blank cheque."

"You are too distrustful."

"You are too authoritarian. Are we for Authority, however corrupt or callous it may become? My conscience cries out for checks."

"That conscience of yours is dreadfully over-developed, isn't it. I don't remember ever hearing of one like it." His face was furrowed in mock-concern.

"I think it is yours that is under-developed," I told him. "If it is as modest in size as I suspect, mine must, of course, seem enormous."

"An enlarged conscience is pathologic," was how that bout ended, he nodding his head admonitorily as he spoke. "It is nothing to be proud of; I should keep it quiet if I were you."

We laughed humourlessly.

—————— 4.

IN this talk we were having it was my idea to say just enough to oblige him to forsake some of his romantic conventions and to adopt a more realistic attitude: *or* come out and defend his obscurantist absolute. "I have been speaking," I went on, "*of socialism by consent*. It is an odd phenomenon to occur in a country like England. But the English voted themselves into 'Labour' (which promptly transformed itself into 'socialism,' of the toughest, the 'total,' type). They would have voted themselves into anything that promised speedy demobilization. Six years of Churchillean Tory heroics had been too much. They knew Labour would turn them back into civilians much quicker than Churchill would. That was Aneurin Bevan's explanation of the Labour landslide. It was, I think, the right one, in the main."

"You think that is all—an over-long war?" Rymer breathed a little crossly and sleepily.

"Something the long war precipitated. The background was a hundred years of Liberalism. A hundred years rushed down in the 1945 landslide. The history of the nineteenth century in Great Britain recalls the thousand small steps of a Mayan pyramid, each step a liberation for some depressed class. So Britain mounted to the present pinacle, a real live working-class Government, with teeth in it like an alligator. From Chartism to the Steel Bill is a long purposeful *moral* ascent. It is the moral foundation, deriving directly from the teaching of the Gospels, of this monumental progress culminating, in 1945, in the mass acceptance of ethical politics—it is this which is to be my theme."

"You will be preaching to the converted," Rymer threw in.

"The nature of the dynamism is obvious. That the working class played a part is a political fairy tale of course."

"Oh!"

"The British working class is the reverse of socially ambitious. Always it has been the despair of the agitator, a mass as difficult to ignite as a rain-soaked mackintosh. It has been content to be an animal, fond of beer and of football, not envious of the well-to-do because it could only be envious in terms of beer and football and Château-Yquem and golf fails to stir its pulse. It has been terribly easy to exploit and to 'keep in its place.' It is unnecessary to add that ethics is not its strong point. The *moral ascent* in question was a middle-class phenomenon. The progressive levitation of the mass of manual workers is one of the miracles of Christ. It is on a spectacular scale the Raising of Lazarus."

Rymer was tying up his shoe. "Rot" was all he said.

"The mere mass, the numbers, of the working class could have produced no such result. To argue that it could is like saying that a mountain must merely, because it is so large, submerge a village at its foot. And so it might if someone placed so tremendous an atomic charge within it as to blow it up."

"The working class is not inanimate," Rymer growled.

"You must have something more than mass, than numbers. The way workers have extricated themselves from underneath the middle-class is often likened to the manner in which the latter supplanted the aristocracy. There is in fact no analogy whatever. The vast colonial expansion of Great Britain and temporary industrial monopoly enriched and expanded so much the class of bankers, merchants, industrialists, that that class wrested the leadership from the landed society. What was responsible for this revolution was something with an action equivalent to atomic fission, namely money."

"The aristocracy were only business men. Money was nothing to do with it," Rymer heckled automatically.

"Now strangely enough the rise to power of the working class was only made possible by money too: not its own money, for it has none, nor for its thirst for power, for it was not interested in power. It was a purely middle-class money which has caused the artificial elevation of the working class at the expense of the middle class."

"How on earth do you make that out!" Rymer expostulated, lazily.

"You see, even all the agitators, from the creator of Marxian socialism onwards, belong to the middle class. Lenin, for instance. Our Fabians, the Webbs, Shaw, or Cripps, have been typically of the middle class. H. G. Wells, who came from the working class, protested at the revolutionary zeal of his 'betters'."

"Where does the *money* come in?"

"Have you ever thought of the immense sum involved, in this century alone, on socialist propaganda? Money has always been forthcoming—millions and millions of it—to advertise the beauties of the Left Wing. It all came out of bourgeois bank accounts, where it was not straight political subsidy."

"Why should the middle class or any section of it spend so much money in order to have the middle class supplanted by the working class. Was it economic suicide?" Rymer was wearily withering.

"Various explanations of this curious fact have been advanced. There may, of course, be several secondary interests involved. I am concerned exclusively with the major and essential impulse."

"Good! *Gooood!*" sang Rymer with bantering patronage.

"The *complete* emergence of the working class from underneath the possessing class (which it abolishes—or which is abolished for it) is perhaps meaningless. Fifty, or a hundred million people cannot rule. What would they rule? They can only be *told* that they are ruling, which is another matter: and meanwhile of course they go on labouring just the same as before. The people who *tell* them they are ruling, those people are in fact the rulers. As we see in Russia, the majority must always toil. It is an age in which paper takes the place of bullion, and the verbal of the physical."

"It is a different thing working for yourself and being exploited by some boss," Rymer interjected. "That is solid enough."

"There is always a boss. They have a different line of talk, that is all. And the abolition of the middle class is a disservice to the working class, it seems to me. The classless society has been proved a myth. If *class* we must have, then a trinity of classes is preferable to two classes. The natural class-arrangement is to have a middle class, involving the perpetual *individual* emergence and ascent of manual workers, passing into the middle sphere, the reverse constantly occurring too, duds dropping out of the middle class into the working class. This *individual* emergence should be facilitated. Complete 'emancipation' would signify everybody being relieved of the necessity to work, when they could divide their time between the football-field, the dog-track, and the cinema: which is absurd. In the last analysis, for one man to be slaving down in a coal-mine, and another man to be passing his time between august Downing Street and luxurious Checquers, is unjust: which is emotionally true but otherwise absurd.

"The present theoretic eminence of the working class is a piece of illusionism. It is pure Maskelyne and Devant. The situation today speaks for itself. Workers' wages, after spectacular rises, are frozen in order to enable the devalued pound to push up the cost of living, so that the workers will be economically where they started, before the honeymoon. In the end all they will have gained is millions of free dental plates and pairs of spectacles. Even these retrospectively they will be made to pay for."

Rymer cleared his throat, and the new National Health Service dental plate stirred indignantly about. "The working class is no better off than it ever was then?" said he with mild derision.

"I did not say that. The Socialists have not improved upon the Liberal achievement, that is the point."

"Give them time. And besides the advance has in fact been enormous. Ask them!"

"A bogus inflationary advance, and a supply of ideologic stimulants. But the idea of a Glorious Working Class World has to be paid for and it costs billions of pounds. The *actual* workman has to pay for the advertisement of his imaginary self."

"The view of most people of course," said Rymer, "is that the working man is over-privileged, is spoilt."

"Everybody, not only the manual worker, is taken in by the advertising, that is all. His prestige but not his pocket has benefited. It is the same as with Culture and the Arts. So much money is spent in advertising how artistic and cultivated we are that there is no money left for artists or for *real* culture. All the money goes in the salaries of officials, public relations men, promoters, and in official publications, large buildings, educational activities, entertainment, and so on. There are now millions of political administrative parasites on the back of the working class, and their numbers multiply hourly. Every working man has a *petit bourgeois* appointee on his back."

"How about the parasites that were there before?" came from Rymer in a sardonic shout.

"The Liberal dream of 'the just' and the 'fair' and the right to liberty and the pursuit of happiness, people will live to regret in the rigours of the 'total' society."

"I thought utilitarian thinking had been sufficiently discredited," Rymer broke in again. "Men are great idealists. That is what you forget. The negative satisfactions of 'peace and plenty' do not appeal to them."

"Etcetera!" I answered him a little sharply. "Every power-thirsty Führer endorses those arguments and is clamorously in favour of 'heroism', 'living dangerously', plain living (a little 'mouse-trap' cheese and a glass of watery bitter beer). That shows a splendid spirit, they think. That people should be prepared to endure hardships makes them ever so enthusiastic—those who aspire to be their tyrants."

Rymer began tearing up a piece of paper into smaller and smaller fragments.

"Then think—war after war: what could be more utterly unutilitarian than that—and the consequent debt that is heaped upon the unprotesting nations—more crushing debts at each fresh massacre. No greatest happiness of the greatest number there! England is finished, tomorrow America will be finished, riddled with war debts, rotted with inflation. All this accepted without a murmur! What *heroes* we are! What idealists! The wars of our time are the means by which men are being pushed towards total servitude."

"Or towards a free world."

"Certainly not that. Such freedom as man may enjoy is perhaps all in the past."

"Freedom to exploit!" heckled Rymer.

"In any event, historians—unless such irresponsible snoopers into the past have to shut up shop—will marvel at the twelve decades in which the 'liberal' ferment was at work in English life. From such early steps up as the Cotton Factory Regulation Act they will see it at work, through thousands of measures of Christian legislation, up to such a climax as Lloyd George's National Insurance Act. The present socialist government is, then, the most spectacular achievement of a truly idealizing cult—and it will be its last. The moralist politics of Protestant Christianity was violently anti-authoritarian, in contrast with the Catholic philosophy. This is its last Protest, as it were."

"Why its last?" asked Rymer dully.

"Because it has given birth, now, to its opposite: to something tough and authoritarian. It must mean it is exhausted. Or perhaps, after all, it has achieved its end. Jesus said, you may recall, 'The first shall be last, and the last shall be first'."

"I remember that."

"Nietzsche who described Christianity as a 'slave religion' . . ."

"That I remember too!"

". . . could have opened his argument by quoting those words. Today the first are becoming the last and the last are loudly advertised as being the First. Liberalism has done its work? What do you say?"

"What are your politics?" he enquired.

"Liberal, really," I laughed. "Liberal, yes."

"Oh. I never would have thought of you as a liberal."

"No? I experience some anxiety as to whither my idealism may lead us. It is my conscience. My liberal conscience."

He sighed. "That conscience again! How long have you suffered from conscience? However, it does not obtrude in everyday life; in fact, no one would know you had one."

"You are less fortunate," I told him. "Its absence is all too apparent with you."

A cat at this point appeared from somewhere and rubbed itself against my leg. It was a thin cat, I could feel its ribs as it pressed its body against my trousers.

"Fond of cats?" I asked.

Rymer shook his head.

"Not very. Pussy is anti-social."

I am not fond of cats, either, but I scratched its bony, independent head.

"Having," I said, "put my hand to the plough, I will just finish the furrow. The evidence is abundant and conclusive. That the *sentimental conditioning* of the English public by constant injections of a Christian ethical-political preparation is responsible for *all* we see. Without having soaked themselves (or been soaked, which shall we say?) as no other nation has, in burning sympathy for the oppressed, no surrender of India or Egypt—no sentimental enthusiasm for the 'great Russian experiment' (we should have noticed long ago it was an ugly despotism)—no conservative Opposition so full of trimmers as to make it appear merely a socialist right-wing. No mythical British 'kindliness,' therefore, but Reformation Christianity in its Victorian and Edwardian swan-song laid the foundations of the Welfare State.

"The tough institutionalism of Rome has naturally seen to it that the Latin countries are provided with a class that has *some* resistance to set a limit to professional indiscipline or red excesses. In France or in Italy communism is more open, not 'crypto' as with the English. The declared communist is easy to check. It is instructive to speculate what a purely Catholic Europe would be like at this time. In all likelihood a practical and orderly society would be there, instead of a feverish ideological patchwork, the rabid indiscipline of parties. With the fearful deterrents to revolt, or even to criticism, at the disposal of a twentieth century ruler, where there was any real authority the agitator would not exist. In Russia today he would be instantly *liquidated,* as we know in any non-Christian society that is what would happen."

"You believe in bumping off everyone who disagrees with you?" was my listener's comment: comments usually made in the form of a question, but hardly anticipating an answer, though on this occasion receiving one.

"No. I am in fact conducting a polemic, among other things, against absolutist methods."

"Stupid of me. Sorry."

"In my last remarks, for I have been indecently long and must finish, there is the evidence I must not omit, of how the rich have taken their squeezing to death by the State."

"They had no choice. They had no option."

"The average coarse illiterate tycoon, banker, or manufacturer one might expect to defend his property with savage desperation. But he does not do that, in these islands at least. He hands it over like an apologetic sheep, who has taken more than his share and knows it."

"Not in this county!"

"No, they are as if spellbound, 'like somnabulic cattle.' This is the result of the long *conditioning.* It is, otherwise, undeniably our nature as men to put up a fight to protect our property. I should myself defend, with gun if necessary, my typewriter, let us say, against a nocturnal intruder. I have no right to such a possession, except for that nine-tenths of the law possession takes with it. I just *have* it, have worked for it, and should defend it. If a man entered my flat, laid his hand upon my typewriter crying, 'Property is a theft,' I should answer, 'Get out, you thief!' If he did not leave, I should take steps (however violent) to prevent my typewriter from being removed and passing into his hands."

"Oh, wouldn't you let him have it? I should." Rymer pretended to look astonished at my possessiveness.

"But you haven't got anything!" I indignantly pointed out. "It's easy for you to talk. You haven't got a typewriter. I am speaking of normal property-owning people, who perhaps have a nice overcoat they do not want to lose: and of course the normal possessing class in a free enterprise society, with whom it would be, only greatly magnified, the case of my typewriter."

"Yes, I see the sort of people you are talking about—whose mobile police would machine-gun strikers and jail their leaders."

"That, more or less, is the normal behaviour. Our life is animal. What I mean is that we have the most house-trained set of magnates here on record."

"They had no choice," said Rymer dully.

"The Russian communists, to return to that, deal with dissent as a Bengal tiger would. This—once more—is because they have rooted Christianity out of their system. They are 'sincere': they are an ideologic tiger. They are dangerous, unless you feel like joining them."

"But what are you driving at?" There was a new note. Rymer, my Chorus, was showing signs of returning to personal life, and ceasing to be a mere heckler. "I see what you want to prove. But what then? Supposing I say, 'Very well. Socialism is a product of Christianity.' What happens next? Why should you wish to convince me of that?"

"I can clear that up for you at once," I told him. "The way things have gone has involved for us a terrible dilemma—for us ex-Christian liberals. The Third War approaches. That deepens the dilemma; since it will be a war between a liberal principle, and an anti-liberal principle."

"What war is this? What war are you talking about?"

"Soviet Russia has never been socialist according to Western ideas (and *Western* connotes Liberal). In the same way the communists misuse the term democracy, as we understand it. But the twentieth century Left Wingers repudiated the Western norm: totalitarian socialism they regarded as just an up-to-date model —extreme perhaps but authentic. The Left Wing, of course, shades off into Liberalism where Mr. Attlee stands. And much muddy thinking develops: terms originating in the West, implicit in them the backgrounds of the Western mind with its roots in Aristotle or in Plato, come to be used to describe their opposite. Terms like Democracy and Liberty are stood on their head, or turned inside out. Verhovenski, and William Morris or Mr. Herbert Morrison, are supposed to stand for the same thing. Meanwhile the old men at present in control in England are good if confused men. All are hospital cases, however. Bevin's doctor accompanied him everywhere: Bevin has dropped out. Cripps, the strongest of the Christian-socialist leaders, has dropped out too, though still alive. Attlee was in hospital for some time and it was believed he would have to lay down the premiership. Morrison was many months in hospital, his complaint phlebitis. None of them can survive the wear and tear of office for more than a few years. Who will it be then? How long will our rulers go to Church? How long will they understand, like Mr. Attlee, that socialism was born out of Christianity? The natural twentieth century drift must be towards the eventual repudiation of Christianity, or its sentimental political puritan hang-over. We see that occurring everywhere, do we not? In a word, the danger is that in its hour of triumph socialism will forget, ignore, or violently discard, the ethics by means of which it was able to gain acceptance and to mount to power: indeed that it may strip away all our civilized Christian freedoms and thrust us back into a system of villeinage and worse. Socialism without ethics is a terrible thing."

Stopping as if it were a book I had finished reading and was now closing with a snap, I looked over at Rymer. I saw that he was deeply upset. It might take him a half-hour to recover. I have explained how his is the religious approach: what he enjoys teaching he wishes to see treated as a sacred text. A hint that this fabric of salvation *could* have a fatal flaw was highly distasteful to him: the view that the very basis of socialism in Christian ethics might be its weak spot must have distressed him deeply. For when Christianity vanished, all socialism's angelic credentials, as being so obviously unselfish that the power of Ghenghis Khan might be entrusted to it with absolute safety, would vanish too.

That all such credentials would become worthless, was an odious suggestion to a man who would not even allow his wife to discuss the No-Food Minister's Monkey Nut Scheme. So poor Rymer was miserable, had been sealing himself up with sealing-wax for fear he might burst, and I should have to break the wax.

But I thought I would round off my discourse; so bending a stern eye upon him, I said:

"As a priest yours is a great responsibility."

"Oh, really?"

"Yes. To advocate socialism, as you do, is perhaps natural for a Protestant clergyman. It is good Christianity. But surely it is your duty to be critical and if necessary to denounce tendencies on the part of political extremists, to transform a basically Western theory into its illiberal opposite, substituting a violent caricature of the Hegelian State for the City of God."

"Well, no one can say," said Rymer, with his brashest smile, "if I neglect to do my duty, that I did not know what it was."

Unexpectedly the tension relaxed. He shook himself and smiled sweetly. "Very interesting," he told me in a most affable way, "although supposing you decided that socialism is too dangerous to go on with I do not see what you would do about it."

I shook my head and shrugged my shoulders.

"That was not the point. I neither wish, nor should I be able, of course, to take any action. We were talking about *you*—about official Christianity. Your natural enthusiasm for the triumph of the Christian ethic in the triumph of socialism should be tempered by the thought that the political expression of the Christian ethic is administered by ambitious men who might betray it. The Church, a rejuvenated Church, should be on the bandwaggon and seek to function as the conscience of the politician. It is surely the Church's privilege to do this: it is after all its ethic that has been used."

"The Church consists largely of ambitious men also," Rymer pointed out sedately.

"You must get a new Church for the new socialist society," was my answer to that.

"Are you a socialist, would you say?" he asked, sitting up.

This was the counter-attack.

"I belong to no party, seeing that, if you do, the only truth you are allowed is a partisan truth. Your judgement then must function only pragmatically. I prefer to concern myself with a non-pragmatical truth. A literature at the service of propaganda ceases to be an art: it becomes an agent of intoxication and of deception."

"Not a socialist," he summed up laconically. "He says he's *not* a socialist," as it were to himself.

"That's not quite true, either," I objected. "You have assured me, Rymer, that it is not necessary for your parishioners to come to church on Sunday. They can be equally good Christians by stopping at home: is that correct?"

"Yes," he answered with a shade of defiance.

"Well, as a good non-church-going Christian man I cannot help being, to some degree, a socialist. Socialism is lay-Christianity. I am what a good socialist ought to be."

Getting up, I went over and looked out at the waving jungle. "My conscience compels me—unofficially and not as a party-man —to approve of the idea of socialism, which I understand as an attempt to realize the brotherhood of man."

The savage vegetation waved hysterically as a gust from the sky blew on it. " 'Socialism' is a term that covers very different state-forms. Some are like primitive communism, some like highly-organized capitalism. 'If there were dreams to sell, which would you buy'?"

I returned from the window. Rymer is physically a slothful man. He was still huddled in his chair.

"Please show me," I said, "those new poems of yours. Those epigrams and things you spoke about in your letter. Let us forget the Sermon on the Mount and turn to the Song of Solomon."

"Would you really like to see them?"

He had them wedged in a book at his side. So we passed over into the other compartment of his mind. I took one after the other verses of half a dozen lines perhaps, each emptied of anything possessing weight. Most feelings had to be excluded, ideas were his enemies.

His lines drifted across the mind like a shadow of a bird. Some were deliberately concrete: say a feather out of a white cloud. But it was visibly dissolving as you held the paper. What he set out to fashion were words that melted as the eye rested on them. His heaviest words had come to rest on the page like the whispering leaf of a canary bush falling like a shadow upon the emerald lawn of a Persian miniature. He did not always succeed. Several were far heavier than air, and one contained an idea: it had slipped in somehow. Then he had written quite different verses, but now they were apparently always like this. As he drifted heavily through Bagwick in the costume of the Bishop's Fool, he was, I expect, lightening a line, or looking for a word that would fall like a snowflake, a silent self-effacing word.

I picked up the last of these pieces; even the paper on which he got the schoolmistress in Cockridge to type his verses, was the flimsiest available. He sat in shapeless huddle in his chair, as though there were no bones inside his clothes, but a great jellyfish. His face was as careworn as that of a Chinese sage, umberfaced, umber-eyed, every furrow at its sharpest and with the expression of a miserable malefactor—one who knew that he had murdered a violet or been guilty of weighting with too ponderous a dew the rose upon the grave of his friend.

As I lifted the sheet of paper there was a thumping in the hall and a ringing: immediately Eleanor came in to announce the Storby car. It was a little windy outside. As Rymer drooped like a dejected porpoise over the sash of the car-window I warmly shook the poet's hand. He cheered up as I shook him and as I drove off he was singing his goodbyes. I head Eleanor's firmer note and agitated my hat out of the window.

_____ 5.

I NEVER had such a good visit again to Bagwick. Either there were young people there or Rymer was preoccupied by the worries of his *cure*, connected mainly with the hostile activities of the young farmer. But when he came up to London he was in better spirits. He returned to the excitements of his youth: he would have been to see a new Italian film which reminded him of the early Russian ones when he was an undergraduate. Another time he would have been to see a socialist curate in an East End parish who reported packed churches of slum-dwellers, to listen to a sensational mixture of inflammatory social doctrine and tawdry mysticism.

Two months or more after my visit I sent him a post-card message as follows:

"Recalling my discourse socialism and Christianity. Have just seen something written or said by David Low, the famous Cartoonist. Here it is.

" 'If any man come to you from the Right or the Left and promise you economic security on condition that you first surrender your personal and political liberty, kick him downstairs. You won't get the security and what is more having surrendered your liberty, you will then be in no position whatever to argue about it.'

"I fear that Low will have lost an admirer in Bagwick."

Whenever I saw Rymer I made a point of enquiring if any new moves had been made, by his enemies in the parish, to have his living taken away from him. I got the impression that they had given it up as a bad job. He did not say so, but that is what I gathered was his view.

Then one day in January, while a young Italian workman was "hacking out and reglazing" one of our hall windows, the icy wind from Siberia still blowing in, there was a knock at the front door. The young Italian went on hacking. Mr. Rushbottom, my old man of errands, my washer-up and guardian of the street-door key was standing hat in hand, counting with difficulty his silver. "Shall I see who it is, sir?" he enquired. I asked him to do so, and he went out into the hall. A moment later he returned, practically walking backwards with his customary exaggerated deference. He was followed by the massive form of Rymer, limping, and with a large black patch over his left eye. The Rymer that looked at me out of the other eye was a stranger.

"Rymer, of all unexpected visitors!"

"I'm sorry," the stranger said.

"Aren't you cold? Come over here and sit by the fire."

"I'm not cold," said the stranger.

"Sit down," I repeated. "Have you hurt yourself?"

"No. I have not hurt myself."

"No? And you are limping, too. Bad luck. One moment, I will settle with Mr. Rushbottom."

I accelerated Mr. Rushbottom's ritual of the-change-out-of-a-pound, dismissed him with old-world courtesy on both sides—a bow from Mr. Rushbottom at the door towards the ominous vault of Rymer's back. That finished, I returned to the fire, facing my visitor.

"You look as if you had been fighting," I observed.

"I have," said the stranger.

Gradually I grew accustomed to the lonely eye, staring at me with a new expression. It was not the eye of the Bishop's Fool. Samuel Hartley Rymer was there, as he had begun: the parson that was underneath the rags and patches—which he was not wearing today: the man who played the Bishop's Fool for my entertainment. Even the poet had deserted this forlorn figure.

All those attributes removed, the personality was as it were undressed. However, this sort of psychological nudity was presented to me with dramatic satisfaction, so the old Rymer was there after all, peering at me dully out of his one eye.

There was a long silence. Rymer looked down at the floor. The "hacking and glazing" the other side of the door filled the room with violent sound. Rymer turned towards the door.

"Who is that?" he enquired.

"Why, that is an Italian workman," I told him, "putting in a new pane of glass. He cannot speak, nor can he understand, the English language."

A silence ensued.

"See this?" He pointed to the black patch obscuring his left eye.

"I do," I nodded.

"The farmer did that," he told me, panting a little.

"I am sorry, Rymer. How disgusting."

"Yes, I've come up to see a lawyer. And a doctor."

There was a short deep silence.

Several deep groans broke from him like successive belches. He took out his handkerchief and wiped his uninjured eye.

"Will this lead to anything tiresome?" I asked him.

"Lead to anything! I have been told to pack. I am to move into rooms in Storby. The Archdeacon came over last night. I was still in bed, he came into the room and told me no other course was open to them, I must go *at once*. I asked him what I had done. I have done nothing, people have done things *to me*. It is not I who should move away from the neighbourhood, it is Jack Cox. But they are such liars, a lot of people have come forward to testify that I . . . *was drunk*."

"You *drunk*!"

"*Drunk*. They say that I *stank* of whisky. I never drink anything at all; even if I have people to lunch or to dinner and buy a bottle of wine for them at the grocer's in Cockridge I never have any myself."

This I was able to confirm.

"I noticed," I said, "when you brought a bottle of claret back for lunch one day, that you drank nothing yourself. Here, I have offered you everything from beer to burgundy—certainly you do not *drink*. You're the driest man I ever met."

"No, I don't drink. But they say I do and that's all that matters."

"A beastly situation! How did it all come to pass? You seem to have a lovely black eye."

He told me then how he had been trapped. Knowing him as I do it was not difficult to reconstruct the scene. I could see him as clearly as if I had been there, attempting to extricate himself. But a clergyman is a very easy prey, and this one perhaps especially so. He was a most unpractical man and at the same time over-confident in himself. His was so subjective a temperament that he was disposed to feel he could subdue to his will the most resistant fact. He behaved often as though the objective world were clay to be fashioned—not rock to negotiate. If a solid fact came into collision with him, as in this case for instance with his eye, he would be nonplussed.

How things began was as follows. A married woman in the village in whom his wife and he had taken an interest (I suppose because she was a bad hat) had got herself in a fix. She had stolen something in a shop in Storby, and the presence of the stolen article in the house had led to difficulties—the details are immaterial. He wanted to ask his wife to come down and see this woman, and he went into "The Marquess of Salisbury" to telephone to the Rectory.

The public telephone was situated at the far end of a passage, and in order to reach it one passed the two doors leading into, first, the public bar, and, next, the saloon bar. It was Saturday afternoon about two o'clock and there were people in both bars. As he passed the second door, which was open, he saw Jack Cox at the bar with two other farmers. He telephoned, and, having done so, as he turned around he found Jack Cox was standing there in the narrow passage looking at him.

"Ah, hallo, Jack. I thought I saw you inside with Joliffe."

But Cox did not speak. What was more, he did not move and there was no room to pass him.

Rymer is the most pacific and friendly of men, for all his arrogance, and I honour him for it, I cannot imagine him speaking roughly to anybody. Cox was plainly barring his way out and it might be assumed that he had been drinking enough for his ego to have swollen. There was probably nothing to be done but to push him out of the way. But English clergymen are not supposed to push human obstacles out of the way.

"Well, Jack," said Rymer, as if addressing an awkward child. He rested his shoulder against the wall and crossed one leg over the other, as though settling down for a chat. "How is the farm? I must run up there and pay you a visit. I've been intending to for some time."

"I shouldn't," said Cox.

"Oh, why not, Jack?" he sang musically, with a teasing note, as if Jack was being a little silly.

"Because I'll kick you out of it on your bloody neck. That's why."

"But *why*? That's nonsense, Jack. Aren't we friends?"

At this point the most pacific clergyman should have taken steps to bring this colloquy to an end. Not so Rymer. No, he would charm this enraged animal into docility.

"Jack," he coaxed, "you've got this all wrong you know. You are not pleased with me, of course I know that, but you've got the wrong idea about me. Let's talk it over, Jack! Shall I come up and see you tomorrow?"

"Yes, come and convert me to communism. You've tried it on all the men who work for me. Come up and try it on me. But first of all take *that*."

With which he hit Rymer, the blow breaking two of the new set of Health teeth. Rymer straightened himself in a bound, putting his arms up in front of him—not pugilistically but to create an obstacle, and advancing at the same time: but Cox sprang to one side and shot in a second blow which brought the blood out of his nose.

Jack Cox, whom I have seen, is half Rymer's size, a little legginged English yeoman with a reddish bullet head. Although much older, I should suppose the larger could have annihilated the smaller had he wanted to. In this case the annihilation took a different form. With a great roar of "Jaaack!" which echoed all over "The Marquess of Salisbury," the Man of God, as if in an access of love, flung himself upon Jack Cox and folded him in an ardent maternal embrace. Dropping blood all over Jack's face and shoulders—when they caught sight of them people got the impression that Cox had been half murdered—Rymer practically carried him out of the public house.

"Now, Jack Cox! Will you behave yourself," he croaked huskily and breathlessly in Jack's ear, as he hugged him under the inn sign of a bearded man, ostentatiously plastered with stars and medals.

Those in the bars had come out into the street and people had come out of their houses, men, women and children, so that by now most of Bagwick was watching him. They did not watch in silence. The greater part of the men were Cox's labourers. Rymer was surprised at the hostility towards himself. He had always believed himself popular and several of the hostile faces he could see as he struggled with his foully cursing prisoner belonged to men with whom only recently he had had most friendly conversations about labour conditions. But apparently they hated him! He thought inevitably of Christ and the Jewish populace.

His tattered suit, under the strain of this violent encounter, was showing signs of disintegrating. Several patches had been torn off by Cox and he could hear a man derisively shouting: "Hi, sir, ye 'comin' onstuck! Why don't ee get t'misses to sew ee together!" But voices on all sides gave him very little comfort—the great tattered bleeding clergyman, hugging and heaving this way and that the little farmer, who was spitting insults up into his face like a little geyser of wrath, was not the sort of man to appeal to Hodge. He heard them cry: "Let him go! You coward, stand up to him!" "Trip him up, Jack! Kick him, Jack, he'll drop yer then!" "Murder! Parson's murdering Jack Cox!" There were no counter-cries to these. All were against him.

Then Bill Crockett, the village "red," arrived on the scene.

Rymer could hear him coming and his heart sank. It only needed Bill Crockett to consummate the scandal. It would become a political issue, that man could be guaranteed to make political capital out of a dogfight. The "red's" voice could be heard in raucous argument not far away, though there was so much noise he could not hear what he was saying. Rymer for the first time began to despair—this was just what Cox wanted. "Go away, Bill Crockett!" he called. But he had loosened his hold a little in order to expand his chest to shout, and Cox managed to jab him under the rib. Suddenly Crockett was shouting in his ear, "Squeeze the life out of the dirty little exploiter, Mr. Rymer. Teach him to soak the poor!" "Go away, Bill, for Heaven's sake!" Rymer panted. But Crockett was kicking Cox on the shin-bone in his ideological enthusiasm. There was an indignant roar from Cox's chorus, and out of the corner of his eye Rymer could see Bill Crockett exchanging blows with one of Cox's men.

Rymer became more depressed, confused and obsessed with the dread of the consequences every minute. "This is a bad dream. It cannot be *happening!*" was the semi-comforting idea that helped to sustain him.

Releasing Jack Cox, and stepping back, he said:

"Jack, let us put a stop to this disgraceful scene. You see what is going on. It does credit to neither of us. Do be sensible, Jack, and stop striking me. I am a clergyman, you know I cannot strike you back. It is cowardly to attack me."

Cox's little eyes shone with malice as he stood listening and his little fists were tightly clenched. One of his little fists flew up into Rymer's face. That is how he got his "shiner." This nearly sent him to the ground; it also made him angry. He sprang at his enemy before the little fists could be used again and this time pinned him to the wall of the inn—holding him as before in his arms but up against the brick wall. That way it was less hard work, the wall assisting. Not of course that Cox remained just a bundle in his arms; he kicked, jerked this way and that, and stamped on Rymer's toes. Nor, of course, did the people round them give him any peace and they might suddenly intervene in favour of their boss. Bleeding, perspiring, panting, he rode his little nightmare in a chaos of shouts, oaths, kicks, and chatter. The shrill voices of women pierced the murky fever of his mind. Mrs. Rossiter's voice was the nearest and shrillest. His left eye was closing up now, so what happened to the right of him (the brick wall being in front) was less in his field of vision and less distinct.

He could see no issue to this but, as a final absurdity, a stand-up fight with the farmer—for as he struggled in a hot blur his mind darted about seeking a means of escape. He saw the headlines in the Storby papers, "Fighting Parson. Riot in Bagwick. Farmer Cox's story." For more than a decade this man had been his enemy and it was most unlikely that he would let him off with anything short of the extremity of humiliation and scandal. His appeals to "Jack" he saw had been absurd. There was always Providence—it even passed through his mind that the Archdeacon might pass that way. He ran through all the most unlikely visitants before reaching his wife. But Eleanor had said on the telephone that she would run down in the car almost at once, so it was after all in her that the best hope of intervention lay. He would hold this little rat pinioned to the wall until Eleanor stopped the car a few yards away, jumped out and hurried over to "The Marquess of Salisbury." She would of course be horrified. "My poor darling!" she would cry when she saw his face, which was in a bit of a mess. And when she noticed Jack Cox was unmarked wouldn't she just give Jack a piece of her mind which he richly deserved—and these brutes too, standing around here and allowing their Rector . . . well, he *was* their Rector!

So in a sense he became numbed to outer sensations, he no longer heard the invective directed at him by his captive, he prosecuted the locking up of the little fists of Cox as an automaton. His mind supplied a feverish daydream to distract him as he rocked about on top of Cox. It ran on like a clockwork producing consoling images.

But Jack Cox began to wriggle and to sink—he was slipping down all the time. Rymer tried to pull him up, but he had got down almost on his knees. Rymer at last was obliged to slip after him until *he* was on his knees too. It was impossible to hold him like that. He had to throw him over on his back, an operation he found none too easy. He did at last get him over, receiving a nasty punch or two in the process, and he then lay on top of him. Perhaps the earth would help him to hold Jack Cox better than the wall had.

Meanwhile this was psychologically a less satisfactory position. He would have looked, to anyone suddenly arriving on the scene, more like an *aggressor*—lying there on top of a man as if he were a victorious wrestler, than he would have while they were both on their feet, and he obviously pinioning Cox's arms, in the way a quite gentle police constable might. That, Heaven knows, was not a pretty picture: but this was a *worse* picture—should the Bishop happen at that moment to drive through Bagwick. He shuddered as he thought of the Bishop's reaction on finding one of his clergymen lying on top of a man in the street, surrounded by a jeering crowd.

He panted on top of Cox and it was much more difficult in this position to immobilize him. Their bodies lay parallel to the houses so he looked up at the road before him, the direction of the Rectory. Eleanor was taking her time!—or had something made it difficult for her to get away? (He refused to say *impossible*: difficult, perhaps.) Then, with a howl of pain, he leapt off Cox as if suddenly a bar of redhot iron was there in place of Farmer Cox. He rushed away doubled up, in a crouching run. There was no longer any question of *holding* Cox. Without thinking, a wounded animal scuttling blindly for safety, he bolted from Cox as if that harmless-looking little countryman were possessed of some malignant property, fatal to life. He did not look back; he looked nowhere, heard nothing. Crouching and scuttling up the road he made for the Rectory.

Jeering laughter followed him. Everyone was laughing and chattering, great hilarity prevailed in Bagwick as their Rector ran away from it screaming with pain. "Take it to y'missus, parson, she 'ull fix it for ee," one of them called after him, a gust of fresh laughter beginning before the jeer ended. But the malice of Bagwick took a more tangible form. Mrs. Rossiter's Jacko, from the start at his heels, now ran level with him, and, to round off the whole performance, plunged his teeth into Rymer's calf. "First Jack—then Jacko!" as I said when he told me of the payment of that long-outstanding debt—pulling up his trousers and pants and showing me the relevant bandage.

Eleanor appeared almost at once, he saw her red tam-o'-shanter. As she drew near to the crouching figure, smeared with blood, dishevelled, his patches gaping and fluttering, she could scarcely believe her eyes. As she stopped the car and sprang out she exclaimed "My poor darling!" just as she had done in his fevered daydream upon Cox's breast. But the villagers began to move back into their houses as they saw her approaching, and Jack Cox had already gone back into "The Marquess of Salisbury," so it was too late for the telling-off even had he not been suffering such atrocious pain. In the middle of the road was the inanimate form of Bill Crockett—who at first Eleanor had supposed must have been her husband's victim.

But Rymer was, it seems, practically inarticulate and she helped him tenderly into the car, saying, "My *poor* darling!" again as she did so. One of the many thuggish tricks included in commando-training had been utilized by the farmer (who had been exempted from military service because of his farm but who had learnt a few of the best thug-tricks for use in civil life). All the facts were sorted out afterwards; Eleanor saw it was no time to ask questions. She turned the car round and with all speed made for home.

His story greatly shocked me. I felt sorry about him as I should with a child. The majority of men are so cunning and practical, such little strategists. *They* would have known exactly what to do. They would in any case never have found themselves with a drunken farmer in their arms outside a public house.

Rymer's departure from my flat was rather sudden. He recalled the hospital hours: I offered to go with him but he would not allow me to do that. He hobbled past the Italian workman who was still glazing though he had stopped hacking. Rymer's back went slowly along the corridor; that was more than six months ago and it is the last I have seen or heard of him. I have written several times but received no reply. I am beginning to wonder whether Rymer exists or whether he is not, rather, a figment of my imagination.

W<small>HEN</small> I entered the train at Paddington station I was absent-minded—indeed I was an automaton. I took my seat in a first-class carriage and it was only when someone coughed that I became aware that I was sitting in a corner seat opposite the only other occupant.

You will assume perhaps that it is my habit to go around in a dream. This is not the case. I had been reading a book I had bought the day before, *Human Rights,* and on the way down in the cab I had been thinking about my "freedom." I had reflected what a wonderful thing freedom of displacement was: what a delightful feature of the individualist way of life it was that I could decide to go to Oxford by the next train and all I had to do was to buy a ticket—or to anywhere in England. *Once* it had been possible to buy a ticket for anywhere in the world: shades of the prison-house were gathering deeply about us in these islands. Today I could go down to the station, buy a ticket, and go to Penzance or to John o' Groats—quite a big prison-yard to exercise in, and as a matter of fact I seldom went further than a hundred miles. But I could *not* go to Calais or Boulogne. To-morrow, it might be, I should have to secure a permit to travel to Oxford. I should then be walking around and around in Rotting Hill.

That I could not go to Calais or to Boulogne without an official permit was no fault of the Government. If anyone is to be blamed it is the selfish greedy fools who pushed England into blood-bath after blood-bath. If a nation ruins itself by going to war on a sumptuous scale twice in a generation its touristically-minded citizens have to be restrained. Also the present government did not withhold its permission for travel to the most distant countries if the journey were to be undertaken for some serious purpose, cultural or commercial. Nevertheless, we were not as free as we were, and, having said that, I reminded myself that it was only the middle-class that had *ever* been free—had ever gone anywhere, so it was only they who suffered. I was very philosophic—but strangely preoccupied.

As I went along the carriage-corridor I was thinking of that middle-class. And I was still thinking of the middle-class as the cough called me away from it. I looked up. I saw the working class.

These railway-carriage *tête-à-têtes* in the first-class carriages of English trains can be rather disagreeable; and as the train left the station it was still a *tête-à-tête*. There are fewer people every day who travel first class in England. Some Englishmen in such a situation bury their countenances in a copy of *The Financial Times* or *The Economist,* or look coldly out of the window; make it quite plain that they object to conversation and will pull the alarm-chain if you compel them to do so by remarking that it is warm for the time of year. This man in front of me, however, looked at me fixedly. I did not need, therefore, to examine him furtively. I looked in his eyes and found them grey, self-satisfied, and aggressive. I noticed that his head was rather narrow, of an English pink—that he was probably approaching forty. What a man *wears* is no longer, in England, any indication of his economic status. It is not a classless society yet, but it is a uniformly shabby one.

I did not like this face but I thought I had better break the ice.

"England is becoming the rat-catcher of Europe," I said.

He gave a frosty, superior smile.

"I was obliged," I continued, "to call in the Ratin Company. We are infested with mice. The Ratin representative informed me that Ratin flew an outfit over to Reikjavik last week, at the request of the Icelandic government. They get many such summonses from abroad. It appears that we have ten times as many rats and mice here as formerly. So the ship cannot be sinking, can it?"

"There are plenty of rats still in this country," he observed disagreeably.

"And mice—who think they are rats and behave as such," I told him. "You would never have thought that *ours* were mere mice."

I knew that I could say nothing to this individual that he would not be superior about, even scornful. The train was a non-stop to Oxford. What was he doing at Oxford, or was he "a commercial"? In the days when there were classes he would have belonged to some section of the working class. His aggressiveness might be on account of that, alone it would not account however for his smouldering alertness.

"Are you at Oxford?" I asked him.

"Yes. I'm an undergraduate," he informed me (as if to say "any objection?").

"Ah," I looked mildly at his watch-chain. No doubt demobbed late and rewarded for his martial watchfulness in the Azores or in Madras by a University education, like so many others—as they said two years ago that half the undergraduates were "old married men" and that Oxford was full of perambulators and the screams of children-in-arms.

"I see you have the *Unesco* book, *Human Rights*." He pointed at my book, which I had placed on the seat at my side.

"I bought it yesterday," I answered. "It interests me."

"Does it?" immediately he said, in a tone that left no doubt as to his feelings about this publication. But he never left one in doubt as to his feelings about anything, and they were invariably strong and intensely disagreeable.

"Yes." I reaffirmed my interest.

"I can't see how anyone can find it interesting," he proceeded—for it was a subject that evidently interested him.

"Why?" I enquired, smiling.

"I can't see how a lot of lies can interest anybody."

"You think it gives an untruthful or misleading account of the problem of 'human rights'?"

"Untruthful!" He gave a grating little cackle. "It gives no account at all. It is anti-Soviet propaganda, that is all."

"It surprises me that you should say that. The views on the subject of human rights of exponents of all schools of thought, from the communist to the liberal, are to be found there."

"No they aren't!" he said with some violence.

"You feel that the communist philosophy is unfairly reported?"

"I am not a communist," he said indifferently—as if he was tired of saying it: "just fair-minded. If there is a war I and my friends will be asked to fight the Russians, that's all."

Like other classes of men, communists are not uniformly agreeable or disagreeable. But since the stalinist doctrine is absolutist, and has its roots sunk deep and fast in an ethic—an angry ethic—naturally in conversation stalinists are, on the whole, apt to be intolerant and tough. For communism a sensible man must have mixed feelings. He must feel respect. He can only abhor its brutality—but he must concede that a great deal that occurs in our Western societies is implicitly of great brutality too. He may regard its moral indignation as phoney: but he must recognize that horror at the wickedness of others is not a communist monopoly. He may ask "Are they such children as they act and talk?"—but he must allow that to see things with the eyes of a child is very popular, too, with us. And so on and so on. Such good sense may seem to lack force. But good sense has nothing to do with force or power. That is its beauty.

I looked over at my fellow traveller to Oxford as one must at a human squib or obstreperous toy one has been handed, and would gladly put down. But he was a walking idea with which one has to come to terms—or the earth will blow up.

"You are wrong in regarding this book in the way you do. Everybody *knows* that this next war will be an even greater crime than the last—though there is no war that *somebody* does not think he is going to get something out of."

"You *certainly* are correct about that!"

"Yes. But although everyone except that *somebody* to whom I referred, loathes the prospect of this lunatic blood-bath-in-the-making, we go about averting it in a very half-hearted way."

"Have you heard of the Congress Against War?" he enquired. I did not say: "But that is partisan. That would not remove the causes of war—all it seeks to do is to secure immunity to an aggressor for all the 'peaceful penetrations,' guerrilla wars, coups d'état, etcetera, that one of the parties wishes to indulge in": instead of this I proceeded with my argument.

"An influential minority in every nation, and in *this* nation at present a majority, are agreed that economic collectivism, in some form, is necessary, and certain very soon to be realized everywhere. Russia has such a system; in this country another variety is being developed. Mr. Truman's 'welfare state' policy—his Fair Deal following on the New Deal—is a first step towards economic collectivism. It may be at some distance yet, but the G.O.P., the Republican elephant, is finished. Let me say that it would be hypocritical for a man like myself to express enthusiasm for multitudinous politics *tel quel*. But industrial conditions and the massive populations ensuing upon them impose such politics. The small world of Jefferson or Locke was more human (but do not quote me as pointing approvingly at its economics—only at its size!). But this monster is here—and socialism of some variety, as much in America as here, is the appropriate political technique."

At the mention of Mr. Truman a sardonic grin fixed itself on his face. I stopped and looked at him. "Go on?" he said.

"As to an international political community, that is a subject upon which, unfortunately, the intelligent minority is divided. We will not talk about that. In this book," and I placed my hand on the *Unesco* symposium, "human rights is described as the 'king-pin' among contemporary issues. I am sure that it is. *Unesco* has laid out side by side, as it were, the competing theories—for the U.S.S.R. as much as the U.S.A. is of opinion that human beings *do* possess 'rights.' The quarrel is as to what kind of 'rights' are the essential ones.

"These 'rights' are of two classes. One class we refer to as *political rights*—the other—the so-called 'new rights'—are the *economic and social rights.*

"The first class, the Political Rights, are the traditional rights familiar to Englishmen—those derived from the classical individualist conception of man, as a being inherently entitled to a number of rights.

"These Western rights are the earlier—the best known of these rights and privileges are, of course, free speech, freedom of assembly, freedom of movement, freedom to work where and how you please, the protection given by the writ of *habeas corpus.* Those are the *Political* rights.

"The socialist view is that these rights are empty. You may have heard the old French jingle:

> "*Liberté de ne rien faire*
> *Egalité en misère*

and so on. It was a reactionary rhyme, directed against the slogans of the French Revolution. It exactly expresses, however, the present-day socialist criticism, directed against the same group of 'rights' as was the reactionary rhyme.

"The second class of 'rights,' the economic and social rights, are specifically socialist rights. They are the kind of which the Health Insurance Bills of Lloyd George and Bevan are a recognition. The right to be cared for when sick and when old, to be suitably born and buried: and then there is the right to a proper education, the right to full, adequately remunerated, employment. Such are the *economic and social rights*—the 'newness' of which Mr. Maritain, I think unsuccessfully, contests in his excellent introduction. Whether it has always been recognized that men are entitled to these advantages, or not, such recognition to the socially awakened mind of our day appears a minimum requirement—and the second class of 'rights' must, of course, be joined to the already existing political rights.

"I agree with the Russian criticism, that political rights without economic and social rights are very imperfect. I agree with Dr. Johnson (the great lexicographer) that *habeas corpus* is the only one of the classical English 'rights' which, *by itself*, is worth boasting about (how he put it was that it was the only liberty possessed by the English not possessed by other nations. According to world standards there has always been a great deal of liberty in Europe). But . . ."

I stopped for a moment and looked at my companion, and before he moved into the gap I continued.

". . . I hope you have followed what I have said—but I am bound to disagree with the communist philosophy when it implies or contends that *economic and social rights* are all that is required. No 'rights' are worth having *without political rights.* There is no right you could give me I would exchange for the right to speak freely and to move about freely. Remove these rights from me, which are called *political,* and I certainly should not be consoled by being tucked up in bed every night by a state-nurse, given perpetual employment; being examined weekly free of charge by a state-doctor and state-dentist, given state-pills and state-teeth, and finally by being buried in a state-grave. Those *by themselves* are slave-rights. The man who barters his liberty for a set of false teeth and a pair of rimless spectacles is a fool. In the slave days of the southern states of the U.S. all sensible slave-owners took good care of their slaves—saw that they came into the world without mishap, did not die if possible when they got ill, and that finally they were decently buried. In antiquity the Romans and the Greeks did not find it necessary to draw up a Bill of Rights of *that* sort: they cared for their slaves as a matter of course.

"So that second class of rights *alone* I reject. And if these 'new rights' are to be regarded as *substitutes* for political rights, as apparently they are, let us not be taken in by the word 'new.' Of course it is a *new* thing to call the care one naturally bestows upon a slave, or upon a horse or a dog, a right!"

My travelling companion, who had been scornfully lolling back with a disdainful smile while I had, with prudent care, sorted out the *rights* and labelled them in their respective historical compartments for him, now had sat up and was practically baring his teeth. The dialectical torrent was seething behind his dental plate.

"One moment!" I cried, holding up my hand. "There is one piece in this book to which I would like to draw your attention—pages one hundred and fifty-one, two and three, the name of the writer is John Somerville." I picked up the book. "He points out that the primary emphasis of the Western democratic tradition has so far been on political rights, whereas 'the primary Soviet emphasis so far has been on social rights.' Listen. It is those words *so far* that are the saving words. And Dr. Somerville on the next page writes, 'Our hope should be that Soviet society, as it grows, will extend its conception of human rights more and more to the political sphere, and that Western society will extend its conception of human rights more and more to the social sphere.' And he gives excellent reasons for believing that this hope will be realized in the case of the Soviet. As to the West, in this country we are far advanced in the procuring of economic and social rights to match our political rights, and other nations will follow suit. So where is the conflict? Must we regard the state of development of Communist Russia as eternally fixed? As we rapidly develop, will not Russia develop too—as it has already, up to and beyond the 1936 Constitution? Cannot the Russians, if they are sincere allow us a little time to draw level with them in one category of human rights, to develop our collectivist economy, though upon our own lines: and should we take it for granted that their citizens will *always* be as politically unfree as at present they are? What will be the motive for this war anyway that is being so busily prepared? Will it be the old motives, disputes about territory, about markets, about power? Is it not possible to reconcile Eastern and Western democracy?"

My fellow traveller to Oxford as I stopped burst in with angry impetuosity.

"Where your pretty plan of kissing and making friends breaks down is right at the start. You are wrong from the word go about the 'new rights.' They *are* new. Russian democracy postulates a totally different conception of human life. It is a totally new civilization—a Russian communist's nervous system, his entire cerebration, is upon a different plane to that of a Western democrat. It is impossible to compare, even, Western and Soviet ways of feeling—they are unrelated upon any level. It would be no use speaking to a contemporary Russian about *rights* in the Soviet being defective in the Western sense—he would not understand what *rights* of our sort mean. A Russian would have no use whatever for political rights. Why should he? The Western conception of political 'rights' and civil liberties came into being to enable the capitalist to do what he liked, freely and without interference, with the worker and with the coloured 'native.' Political rights gave him a free hand, that is what *liberty* means in the Western sense. 'Free enterprise' is freedom to exploit.

"Charles I of England deserved what he got—but it was not the people who executed him for his crimes, it was as big criminals as himself. The Merchant Adventurers and other seventeenth century monopolists plotted to get him put out of the way—out of *their* way. They also rigged the building up of a code of defensive 'rights' behind which to operate. Political freedom is individualist freedom. The Russian does not want to be an *individual*. No thank you! the Russian would say. I don't want to have the 'right' to be an individual and to *starve*. I wish to be an integral social being. The socialist organization of the national economy produces a new kind of individual, one who ceases to be an individual in your sense, so I should not know what to do with the anarchic liberties of *your* individuals. That's what the Russian would say! Our liberation from capitalist slavery, he'd say, that is *my* liberty—the abolition of private ownership of the instruments and means of production has put me beyond the need of your protections. My body is part of the socialist body, what can *habeas corpus* mean to me? That was invented to protect an individualist against a King. There are no Kings and no individuals of that sort in Soviet Russia. Your 'hope,' my dear sir, of a 'development,' as you call it, of the communist philosophy towards individualism, and its corresponding 'rights,' makes me laugh. I'm sorry."

"Thank you," I said, "for explaining my error so fully."

"Not at all."

"You talk as Boris Tchechko writes," I told him amiably.

"That's an insult!" he expostulated. "P'raps you don't know it but that's an insult! Tchechko's an agent of the U.S. government. I have never read such dirty tripe as his. That *would* be the kind phoney *expert* they would get to explain the 'Russian point of view' to people."

"I know nothing about that."

"I hope you don't. Yes, it's a *very good book*. A *very* good book! Good for whom?"

"If what you say is true, it is unfortunate. But such criticism of the experts selected does not affect what I was saying. Such a publication is of great value unless you wish to banish reason from the scene altogether. To know what a war would be *about* is of some importance.

"Irreconcilable ideologies, sooner or later, would attack one another. But when I look around me, in this country, and see a socialist state being rapidly built up, the leaders of which are by no means fundamentally opposed to Soviet Russia—even inclined to imitate it—then I cannot for the life of me see why England should go to war with Russia, or Russia with England, except for *imperialist* reasons. And what would socialism be doing with imperialism? That is a horrible perversion. In the past it has been inherently and essentially international—from my standpoint that has been its strongest card. The moment it ceases to be international, it becomes national-socialism—a most perverse theory of the state."

"You have forgotten the U.S.!"—with a sour smile he reminded me. "You didn't mention that!"

"No, I have not forgotten it at all. The New Deal, and now the Fair Deal is killing capitalism in the U.S. slowly but surely. The United States will not go communist. Why should it? There is a danger that *this* country may. Unfortunately in England socialism has taken over a ruined society, drifting towards conditions of want and helplessness, which makes the problem more like that confronting Lenin than it would have been possible to believe twenty years ago. What we must fear here is that although the English people acquire those economic and social rights which were not there before, they may in the process *lose* the political rights, without which the economic and social rights are a fraud."

"We must *fear*, must we . . ." he was beginning, when a tall man considerably his junior stuck his head in at the door.

"Ronald," this man said.

"Oh, hallo," said Ronald, and got up. He moved out of the carriage grilling me with a passing gaze of fierce sarcasm.

Minus Ronald, I went on turning these things over in my mind. There is a great deal too much *Ronald* in the Soviet position. All the same, the directors of Russian policy are not Ronalds luckily. The arguments that Ronald used with me are a crude distortion of the official polemic. Yet there is something harsh and rigid, undoubtedly, even at the highest level. Is a working compromise possible, of the kind the *Unesco* publication has in mind? The answer to that seems to lie not in the realm of ideas, where *Unesco* could play a part, but in the iron-curtained regions of Soviet imperialism.

CHAPTER 3 : The Rot

THAT there was much rotting of the spirit in this
blistering period, of what we pretentiously term history, was not
hidden from me exactly. But I must confess that it was with surprise that, resting my hand carelessly upon a windowsill at our
apartment, I found my nails sinking into the wood. The wood in
our flat had up till then behaved on all occasions like wood. It
was a week later, I think, that putting my hand out in the dark
to turn on the light, my finger plunged into the wood of a door.
These were my first contacts with the rot.

The following are the main facts about the rot. As might be expected, or it may be better to say, perhaps, as is not to be wondered at, something like a pestilence is ravaging the London
buildings about here. They call it "dry rot"—a fungus that con-
sumes the wood. Even the reddest and most beefy-looking buildings are rotting away where they stand, except for those within
which the builder is blasting at the affected part with his blow-
lamp, putting in new wood for rotted. For one house that is
derotted, three remain in a state of rot. The builder is restricted
to what can be done with scraps. Wood is a shortage as much as
fats in England, and it is the wood that rots, since it belongs to
the living order. A black market exists in wood as in everything.
It is but a trickle of illicit timber in Rotting Hill.[1]

[1] A friend in Washington now calls this quarter of London "Rotting Hill,"
since hearing of my ordeal with the rot. I have adopted his expressive
substitution to maintain a proper anonymity.

Hundreds of streets in London were uninhabited during much of the six years of war, the houses shuttered and fireless. In the damp winters the fungoid condition, the dry rot, developed in the beams, joists, architraves, jambs, window-frames, floorboards of these unlived-in places. As it is, when decomposition has gone so far that you can poke your finger into the wood of a mantelpiece as if it were made of cheese, an order may be obtained for a few slices of timber out of government stock. The condition of flagrant rot is checked by a sceptical inspector.

Compared with Hamburg, or Dresden, London is unmarked. Then the Nazis were such great gentlemen they mostly bombed the poor. Yet every district has its quota of gaps or of ruins, and these wet draughty weed-gardens—rain-filled cavities of cellars that have lost their houses—serve I think to prolong the rot. Many of the gaps and ruins we know will remain. The present rulers are in no hurry to reconstitute London as it was: they have not much love, in fact, for Dick Whittington's city. If actually it *did* drop to pieces it would not break their hearts. So there it is, a monstrous derelict of a city—always the first to be bombed, the last to receive its allotment of bananas when a shipment of them docks at Bristol (the manufacturing North because of the big labour towns is favoured) and so it is with all unrational delicacies: unpopular as a capital with the ruling intellectuals as the traditional headquarters of the Court, too redolent as well of history—womb of the Mother of Parliaments in an age impatient of parliaments; haunted by the stout shades of those parliament men Hampden, Eliot, and Pym—reeking in their nostrils of freedom: London, built upon a bog and cursed with world-famous fogs: every house in it that has a crack from the blast of a bomb and dies at last of chronic dry rot, and is carted off to the potter's field for decayed old buildings, is to be congratulated.

Like Vienna, this city has no meaning henceforward. It is too vast a head for so puny a body—since most of the gargantuan colonial padding that made Britain (Great Britain!) look so enormous has been shed—as an actor playing Falstaff, the play done, unhooks his make-believe belly and unpacks his bloated limbs. So we get down to the actual modest dimensions. True, we still swell airily *in vacuo,* an immense bubble of 50 million souls, blown out with American dollars. But that will burst. It cannot do otherwise—when the next war comes, or the next American slump, or even without them—than explode with a sickening roar.

Up on Rotting Hill, beamed on by Negroes, shadowed by Afrikanders, displaced in queues by displaced persons, ignored by Brahmins, run over by hasty "fiddlers" of various extraction, we are foreign (or like a town in the U.S.) and people come and go. The shops are full of xenophobic growlings but there are no bitings. The houses are camps, towering brick camps, with gouged out clammy basements, packed with transients. We are famous for our *spivs.* But that is a disreputable élite, and there is the rank and file. A newsagent where I deal divides our co-citizens into two main groups: (1) Those who bet; and (2) Those addicted to spiritualism. This he bases upon the papers and magazines most in demand, and of which he stocks and sells fantastic numbers. The second of these passions, the occultist, finds its votaries mainly among the English. But with those who play the horses there is nothing so narrowly national.

Better lose your money on a horse or a dog than be fooled out of it! They speak like that. As to mysticism, and its big vogue (five "lodges" in Rotting Hill): people troop as they are now doing to sit entranced before pythonesses who bring tidings from the other side of death to enable them to turn their backs if only for a while upon life—more vile and ill-smelling daily. Not the stench of power-politics alone, of which the press is full, but the decomposition of the public will is perhaps the worst wretchedness of all, Aneurin B.'s version of a will-less society being too exclusive. Though the occultist fans do not proceed to analysis, anything but—they merely feel that "nothing is worth while."

On Rotting Hill the rubbish is still collected Saturdays, but nevertheless the pavements are littered—with Rotting-hillers. Some get stuck in doorways. I picked one up under a lamp-post the other day and took him up to draw. He sat well, staring blankly at the blankness of my walls. He had practically no will

left. Had I boxed his ears—instead of giving him half a crown—
he would have wobbled about a little but that is all. The public's
reactions are so jaded that it has sunk almost to coolie levels. The
English had a public conscience as big as a house. But its fibre
is devoured. It is completely rotted. Sanctimonious busy-bodies
no longer, they are very callous, their own lot exciting them as
little as that of others. If you informed the public that fifty thousand Finns or Italians had been massacred—by anybody—it would
have as much effect as if you informed it that fifty thousand mack-
erel had been caught. Take away tomorrow all its sugar, for
instance, and all butcher's meat (without replacing the latter by
anything, except what only the richest can buy). Nothing would
happen, except that people would develop complaints for which
a sugarless and proteinless diet is responsible. And of course there
is no tax you cannot impose upon the English. They expect it.

This picture is only overpainted if you wish for an underpaint-
ing of it. For there is no moderate image of atomic politics, national bankruptcy, murderous taxation, blackmarket immunity,
jobbery, world-inflation, populations drained of hope. But *no picture at all* exists in the case of massive sections of our society.
These reactions—even largely it might be said these conditions—
do not apply to a massive minority of our people. For of course
there are those who have so little they are hardly taxable: even
some who—talking of meat—never had much meat. (Their wives
might beg a scrap off the fat butcher. But there were no ration-
books as today, conferring *a right* to the best meats in the shop.
The slum butcher too is officially allotted under rationing the
same quality meat as the butcher for the Ritz or for the King
and he gets it.) If the untaxables, and lower than them the oblig-
atory vegetarians under Victoria, got to themselves a *picture*, it
would be starry-bright in 1948. The ration-book is their charter.
Supertax is a tax levied for their beautiful eyes. But at all levels
the working class, even the quite taxable, is elated: the source of
the elation being even more sentimental than economic.

I find I have been providing with a deeper perspective than I
had intended my narrative of the rot. One rot truly is involved

in another rot. From the epidemic ravaging "better-class" houses to the decay of the classes for which they were built is a logical transition. Returning, finally, to the immediate business of the rot in our apartment: up to the time that one of the windows began to leave its socket and the wind to rush in I made no move. Then of course I did. Upon the telephone the landlord, or more exactly his deputy, informed me sighing that he knew what it was. Oh he did! I remarked disagreeably. But he answered gruffly that in other parts of the building—comprising a number of shops and apartments—there were very bad cases. I was not unfortunately the only one—he wished I was.

His builder's specialist, a cockney carpenter, was at hand; in fact he was at work upon a rapidly rotting off-licence. He presented himself at once, and flung himself into the tracking of the rot with the avidity of a ferret. Upstairs and downstairs, in this "maisonette," he tracked it down, charting his progress upon a piece of soiled paper.

The carpenter looked me over this first time—I had answered his off-hand knocks—as if probing for symptoms of the malignant fungus which was disintegrating our premises. Evidently he found me built of some substance inhospitable to the rot. He lost interest. The little fires went out in his eyes. But the fact that I was uninteresting because unpleasantly free of dry rot did not endear me to him, or cause him to forget that with a fraction of the money I squandered on my books, he could build an A One rabbit hutch and get Minnie (daughter) the openings to make her a Screen Star. Young Fred (son) might shine too, in some capacity, if less glamorously. Now, to indulge this urgent son of toil, Fred (the carpenter's name as well as that of his son) had been led to understand—not by me—that *yes*, in forty-eight hours, work on part of the nether premises could begin. I now said *No*. He evinced no surprise. It is only nice people with dry rot in them somewhere (as in one mood he would feel and from one angle) who can be depended on to say *yes* all the time. The rot softens the fibres of the will. Dry rotted yes-people are as clay in the hands of carpenters.

As I listened subsequently to this man amok in the bedroom underneath, I recalled the humped humanity that shuffled off, cool and relaxed, when he found I was a *no*-person. He had shrugged his humped shoulders and snarled a cockney half-smile at me, with one evil tooth, saying, "Very good, sir. It's as you wish." Actually I was worse as he saw it than the rotten, in and out of whose residences he moved with such dark satisfaction. I belonged to the rot—to a rotted social class: was tenant in a building rotted down to its cellars, lived after an outmoded pattern (a "blooming artist")—rotted and was answerable for rot— rot which began to hem me in, madly nourished by my antidiluvian life-habits. That the dry rot was the landlord's affair was, of course, a major factor. I did not pay. Not paying, I was at most an obstruction, not a source of authority.

The carpenter stood out from the rest of the workmen by reason of the fact that he worked. He must have had a big crack in his palate which he had cemented up, he spoke stiffly, where his mouth writhed up on to his cheek, out of a bitter hole. He had dirty eyes—the face was so untidy no eyes could have looked otherwise, to be sure, but they were blood-shot themselves, and of tobacco-colour green, with embers of hot red. The public house and the blow-lamp between them had perpetuated facial eruptions. An uncut moustache served as a disreputable valance for the mouth. The chin in its cockney droop marked him as a spectator of his own aggressions.

As it was very difficult for me to leave London at that time, the arrangement was that while the builders were downstairs we should live upstairs. The downstairs finished, we should change places, they coming up to the studio floor. And such was the order followed. When the carpenter began work it was in the nether premises, in some respects the more rotten of the two. We had, according to plan, gone to live on the upper floor.

When first we were informed that our apartment must be de-rotted, we had not the remotest idea of what awaited us. It only slowly dawned on us that this was a major operation, at which we were to assist. But we did not have to wait long for enlightenment. As a fact, the carpenter moved in to pull down, weeks before the building-up again could start, the order not having come through from the Town Hall releasing the necessary material. Neurotic as this man was, he could not keep his hands off it. He would have demolished the entire building had it lain in his power to do so—the entire quarter, too: and, on a particularly good day, all of Greater London.

The realization of what we had let ourselves in for involved a dual shock. First we saw that we were to cohabit with earthquake. Secondly came understanding of the time factor; in other words, the immense mouthfuls of time demanded by this inane operation, because—oh, because of the same crass agency that eats up all the rest of our time, in wars, in queues, in rot, in all the subsidiaries of the central inhumanity of man. We had some such figure as three weeks in our minds at the beginning, or a little over. But a sleepy lazy gang (living in a Dalton daydream of booming wages, cheap money, short hours) could make such short work in every sense of three weeks that if you told the time by their handiwork it would seem to be three days that had passed, not three weeks.

The preliminary stripping of the place, parking of furniture in a grey mass, was unexpectedly disagreeable. There are different ways of stripping a life, of disintegrating a domestic organism. There are seemly, even ceremonious, undressings. There is everything, between an invitation to a pleasing *déshabillé,* and a brutal *debagging.* There is a way of turning a chair upside down (if that chair has known all its life the pressure of your bottom) that is an effront, or of handing down an oil-painting of a Buckinghamshire backyard from its nail that is an outrage.

The invasion actually began—with the stripping and stacking for its breathless overture—when we were only half awake. The carpenter and his mates, this first time, were shuffling about outside the front door long before 8 A.M. At 9 we left them, Mrs. Clark having set out our breakfast of "hot roll mix" (from a friend in Baton Rouge), Cuban Honey (a friend in New York), fried eggs (from another friend, in Montreal), and tea on the ration;

expressive of what the tea-merchants of Colombo think of their ex-lords and masters. At ten we sat in our vast roof-room digesting the disagreeable reality downstairs. "I feel like a bruised grape in a basketful of glass marbles," observed my wan wife, quoting a Canadian tulip.

Then—preceded by a brief silence, upstairs and downstairs, and as it seemed outside as well—the first blow fell. "Ye olde Cottage" effect, produced we discovered partly by authentic wooden beams (now turning, of course, into mushrooms), in part plaster boxes masquerading as beams—all that went first. This we divined at the time, and afterwards inspection confirmed, since the ceiling eight or nine inches under the soles of our shoes jumped violently. We were glad the rot had found out so palpable a fake as the archaic rafters, of which we were ashamed if anything: but the carpenter thought his blows fell upon our hearts. The plaster boxes, beneath repeated blows from his axe, and the hammers of his men, came crashing down. We recognized immediately that we, and not the plaster, were the true target of the assault.

With what frenzy of accumulated resentment this stunted man, deformed with toil, flung himself upon us. The rot was, no one could doubt it, his master passion. But he was socially minded— he knew how to give his rot an historico-economic perspective too, being no fool like the painters (without exceptions) and deeper than the plasterer. We and the rot were one, we were involved as if we had been wood. Was it not *our* rot? The rot existed for us. If there was a fungus here instead of the wood which honest workmen forty years before had lifted into place, we had produced the fungus—an emanation of social decay. Were it eventually necessary to pull down the house, *we* ought to be demolished with it. Such was the line of feeling at least of the mastermind among what eventually became an army of invaders.

The token liquidation was taking place in the room in which we slept, so we congratulated ourselves upon having so thoroughly emptied it beforehand. A shambles of plaster and wood must suddenly be there—though when later we actually saw the rugged landscape of piled-up débris we were astonished: and now it sounded as if the carpenter were savaging the walls. But almost buckling the floor, the timber of the chairs in which we sat recording a maximal shock, they burst out into a short passage, and, in an exceptionally paranoiac rush of the carpenter's a cataract of plaster which must have shaken Marble Arch smote the floor of our nether premises.

"Is this in fact token class-war?" was my question: and my life-mate answered and laughed: "It is so to speak token class-war." "Is it not getting out of hand?" I pondered aloud. "There is, in effect, a sensible deterioration," came the response, "in the situation, as that regards the workmen in our nether premises." I recommenced: "Is this in fact hatred for those who dwell in posh dry-rotted flats . . . ?" "Not posh. Dry-rotted." But I resumed: "Of relative magnificence, in select neighbourhood—yes, in this fringe of Rotting Hill we rub up against admirals and generals and tread on brigadiers—in their turn they bathe across the mews from Millionaires. Comparatively modest as our abode may be, it exceeds the limits of his dwarf exchequer." (I cast my eye down through the ceiling at the carpenter.) "We are economic giants to his pigmy purse. If men were their money he would reach to my knees."

So, thinly disguised as care for the health of buildings, it was reaching the point of open confessions—when, axe in hand, the carpenter would appear at the head of the stairs and snarl:

"You can keep your plaster and your rotten wood, Mr. Lewis! *You* are the dry rot I'm after!" At the latest mountainous fall of plaster underneath, I allowed my eyes to rest upon a drawer where an old, rusted, practically token, revolver probably was.

Having engaged for some days in unrestrained and wholesale destruction, the carpenter and his mates melted away. They left behind them exposed and mutilated ceilings, gaping floors, bald patches, gashes, rents, and holes everywhere; tottering doors, unframed windows. I had not had much contact with the carpenter. So far as I was concerned one day he and the others failed to appear, that was all. The usual noises failed to occur. There was peace. And so day after day, peace. Still this peace of course was outrageous too, because we wanted to occupy our apartment, not remain camped in a corner of it. On the telephone the builder acquainted me with the true position. Nothing could be done until the order came through.

For the rest, the carpenter had done just as he pleased. Provided he did not injure my goods I could not—as he knew—stop him from knocking the walls down if he liked. There was no supervision. No one in Rotting Hill in 1947—landlord or builder or anybody—cared enough about what happened to climb a flight of forty stairs, or for that matter to cross the street. My own outburst was awaited. With sultry anticipatory glee the carpenter slogged unnecessary objects unnecessarily hard at inconvenient times. Apart from clearing him unceremoniously out of the toilet where invariably he took up his stand, blow-lamp at full blast, around the time he knew access would, to late breakfasters, be imperative, no scintilla of criticism could he carry off to magnify for the purpose of complaints-about-complaints: "As usual, interference on part of tenant with work of man doing his job!" He interested me too much for me to feel anger. Still I was in no mood to furnish amusement. Otherwise I might have cursed him for making an uncalled-for noise, or ignoring the little fact that I after all paid the rent. That was what he wanted.

Now all the lower region of our apartment was a shrouded place of dirt and gloom. A plasterer's mixing table straddled where a comfortable bed should be: for the plasterer and his mate had joined the carpenter upon the last day of the destruction. The Christmas blackout was the next thing to happen. So it was in fact a month or more before we saw a workman again. The plasterer came first of the main group: with him men carrying breeze cakes and sacks of cement. Then our new life began in earnest: except that often there would be a blank of two or three days, or once a week: the non-delivery of long-overdue wood-substitute accounting, they said, for the idle week.

The workers in general were sleepily, carelessly "respectful," distant, except for the odd reader of the *Daily Worker*. All English workmen were and are a little intoxicated with events. At long bloody last their government was in and was socialist. The days of the classes over them—calmly squatting on top—were numbered. Building trade workers as ours were—*they* knew. Didn't they go into all kinds of homes: of the rich that once was (pots o' money!) who used to keep two housemaids, a cook and a chauffeur and now had a dirty old char! Startling changes—they came across them everywhere.

Slow, halting, and meaningful spoke to one these cockney eyes, blue, brown, green and grey: indirect, still cowed in the presence of the "educated," still with their old superstitions about rank, submissive as ever to a Lady Jingle Jones—they spoke in flashes. An exultant gutter-tongue, talked by dancing eyes, language of the small sooty shells of the cockney family unit (the blackened doll's-house with white washing on a line seen from the Golden Arrow) radiantly hailing their novel status in the new day—inferiority lifted from them for keeps. Sun-dazzled earth-worms—slaves in the Senate. Might for the Midget—Madness—MILLEN-NIUM.

The awakening, one felt, was of something of extraordinary age. Was not this the liberation of a being accustomed to restraint since the days of the theow, laet, esne, or earlier? So it was a little terrible. Has not most "liberation" in our hypocrite century proved phoney—to use the proper cheap and ugly word for what is thus exactly described? Their behaviour was in any case that of prisoners set free, or of birds released from a cage. Has England then been a concentration camp for the "lower orders," the third estate; and was the barbed wire removed and were the sentries marched off in 1945? They disported themselves, to celebrate the end of bondage, and I was too friendly toward them and too sorry for them to complain. But they relieved me of my small steel chopper.

Our section of six flats does not enjoy access to or give access to the other parts of the building. Upon its large autonomous stone stairway six or seven painters were at work. Their songs, shouted conversations, betokened a natural buoyancy, at having won the war, won the election, won the right to sing rather than paint. Like much joy, it was ugly. Everybody recoiled from it. But it had the pleasing effect of silencing the artificial buoyancy of the contralto Star in apartment 3, which she shared with a Czech woman-doctor, unlike herself a pessimist. It was her custom, taking herself up and down the spacious stairs, to do so with *brio*, and full-throated song—to demonstrate how beautiful, youthful, and successful she was, though in fact none of these things, as all of us knew. Or if the remains of youth were still hers, it need not, one felt, have chosen to die so noisily. As it was, if a watery English sun gazed blearily in at the window, she would richly and brilliantly exclaim "What a *glamorous* day!" Well, the painters put a stop to both the singing and expressions of youthful ecstasy: and neither, after the painters' departure, were renewed. They out-sang her and out-shouted her. They out-youthed her: and lastly they out-successfulled her too. For were they not Dalton's boys? And they were the merriest, noisiest, laziest in this bankrupt land—where "too much money chases too few goods" but what of it? On the Utility level nix is in short supply. We live on Utility level, for ever and ever—what of it? there won't be no other. Hurrah for Utility-life, with money to burn in Austerity Street, at the blooming old pub at the corner. Hurrah! cried the painters as they smoked their Weights, Hurrah! Hurrah! Hurrah!

Why men should work any harder than that (for the painters hardly worked at all) or be any less merry I myself can never see. What is life for—to make carthorses out of monkeys? People invent objects for life. They attempt to drive us on to what they label "targets," as if we were bullets. I secretly applauded these slothful and light-hearted workers—and almost forgave them for deliberately making it so difficult to get in and out of the house and attempting one day to ruin a glorious overcoat they resented my having. But they had better luck with the musquash of a neighbour, to which they did a lot of damage—partly high-spirits of course. Yet every morning I would open the newspaper and, harsh and minatory, the words of Cripps, economic Czar, would challenge my easy-going humanism. Just the opposite he argued to what I felt. Men must work themselves to the bone, most monotonously he repeated. To close the gap between exports and imports. To close the gap. To CLOSE the GAP! There was evidently no gap in the building trade, or no one was conscious of any gap to fill, except in the belly and the bladder.

Here, in outline, was our workmen's working day. At 8 A.M. the workmen were supposed to arrive and start work, and the staircase painters were subject to the same time-table. In practice our workmen arrived not at 8, but 8.30. By a quarter to nine usually noises would be heard: the day's work had begun. At 10 they left in a body for tea. They returned at 10.30. At 12 o'clock they knocked off for dinner. At 1 o'clock they returned. This was the longest spell, namely two hours, passed of course in talk and in work mixed and alternating: in visits and counter-visits between rotworkers in different apartments, or flat-workers and painters, or outside friends working across the road or round the corner, or plumbers at a loose end, or marking time between two assignments of burst pipes or stuck plugs. At 3 they left for tea. At 3.30 they returned. At 4.30 they began tidying up and preparing to leave. At 5 o'clock they left. The day's work was over.

After a few weeks we grew tired of their joy. But when at last work moved upstairs, and we had them *overhead*—plasterers, painters, electricians and carpenters on occasion all at one time—their joy became for us an agony. One day I met the master plasterer hurrying out. Through his cement-grimed lips, coldly cross, he muttered: "Nothing but a blooming boys' school up there. The noise they're making I shall be glad when they hop it, all of them!" The plasterer alluded to two diminutive boy-electricians and a friend—the firm seemingly had no grown-up workmen to spare in that department. With what misgivings I had watched them for a moment gambolling and frisking as they attended to our lighting system! The boss looked around fourteen. No wonder boys are impossible to get for messenger offices as bell-hops, or to do errands. Later I could hear their shrill shrieks of delight and bumpittybump went the ceiling. Because these noise-makers were so minuscule, in so remote an age-class from himself, the plasterer could see them and hear them. Even he left the house in disgust. But when the whole place rocked with heavyweight lightheartedness his eardrums recorded it, if at all, with indulgence.

But to finish with these problem-guests—my big house-party to hunt the rot, which, like barbaric celebrations, endured for many weeks. The end came in pandemonium. Finally it was to heavyweight aggression I succumbed. I had been writing, and I was reading by myself in the lower flat. The book in my hand bristled with examples of injustice, the poor man wronged, the worker cheated: whether authentic or not who could say? A propagandist record of experiences in Stalinist Russia, for which a Trotsky adherent was responsible.

I put down what I was reading very often to reflect on the inner meanings of this sort of book (if you chopped away enough of the humbug of politics to contact the inner truths); of the material with which power worked, the human mass namely, and the numerous disguises adopted by power—disguises imposed by the sensitivity of the human material, by the dangers involved in handling energies so disproportionately vast compared with the physical insignificance of the "master mind." Power does not like to have a bronco beneath it—meaning a violent or spirited people. Problems of political liberty presented themselves of course. But political liberty is not an Asiatic commodity, and I doubt if it can be a Russian—not as my friends upstairs would have understood the free. You would not have discovered it, in the ancient world, anywhere on the Asiatic or African shores of the Latin Sea. The Romans and Germans practised it at different times. England is eccentric, but it has excelled as a great and celebrated centre of liberty for the privileged.

The English have bred as spectacular a breed of underdogs as any dog-lover could wish! But at last, approaching mid-century, the *whole* of that great dog has been dragged out from underneath in Britain: and does he shake himself and *bark* hysterically! He does that. And shows few signs of wanting to bite the decadent old top dog, who does not seem to mind much either, but queues up for bones and quietly takes those bottom dog doesn't want. It is a superb feat! (I grew enthusiastic as I thought of the *whole* of this vast dog.) He will never go back again—not in the same place anyway, or *beneath the same dog*. Whether in Russia they had ever had, even for a few weeks at the beginning, that grand feeling, was very doubtful: that sensation of being free men which our people . . . *Brrrromp!*

The entire house shuddered with their freedom.

I sat pulverized. There had never been so inconsiderate a fury of undisciplined joy by the upstairs workers. The longer the job dragged on, the more careless they became. But these men were intoxicated with what I still regard as a sacred beverage—liberty. I was ruled by this great liberal scruple. As they scuffled and kicked around overhead, choking with the hysteria of the Harrow Road, gulping with Hammersmith fun, for a ball they used, I imagined, a wad of my old newspapers, tied up in an oil rag. They had before. Their trampling was atrocious. I put my book away and stood up. The shindy grew in wild intemperance. "Goal," panted the fat painter. *What* goal? (Once you unchain one who has never tasted freedom, his wild ego will know no limit. But I did not desire to be the person to recall these men to order.) I put on my hat and moved silently out, as in certain circumstances, rather than strike a man, one would abruptly make haste to leave a room. As I went I thought of bread and circuses, of Clodius who petted the plebs in preparation for the coming of a despot—the great prototype of modern dictators. Not that any of the hills of the Rome of antiquity were Rotting Hills. The rot was in the valleys between. There it was worse than with us: frequently, it seems, houses would cave in, shop-property be demolished by spontaneous collapse. Little wonder when we think of the six storeyed tenements, renting not rooms but bunks, so that easily two or three hundred persons could be packed into one smallish building. I have never read anywhere that the

Romans had the rot: probably their houses dropped to pieces from other causes.

As, still absorbed (thinking of Rome partly I suppose in order to clothe raw realities in a classical remoteness), I descended the newly-painted Roman stairway, the sun gilding the shimmering dust of the windowpanes, the uproar from the open door above receded. But I found myself obliged—if I were to continue at all with my parallel—considerably to deromanize my image of the time. Though a dictator might be expected here long before the century's end, that after all was not because London resembled the Rome of Clodius—which already was like New York or more so. Beside Paris or Vienna, London is a centre, not a city. We improvise ways of civilized living in it, and it *is* a centre, though otherwise a place of about the same natural glamour as Bradford or Nottingham. From our apartment now came a thud, a muffled bellow of blurred noise with it. A goal! The shock-tactics of the fat painter doubtless responsible, the neat footwork of the brick-layer's mate no match for a rushing avalanche of fat. The young plasterer's mate passed at a gallop, with a friendly grimace, wind-milling with one arm as he forced it into his jacket.

Once outside I moved quickly along—no further need to dis-guise the fact that I was in flight from joy. I was met by a con-tradictory sight—to what went on *chez moi*, I mean, a flat con-tradiction. Road-workers were remaking sections of the road. They worked under the direction of foremen, who never left the road, and the men never stopped: they seldom spoke to one an-other, except about what they were doing. I only saw them laugh once: a young elegant from behind a bank-counter loftily sauntered a shade too near where a load of slimy pebbles was being discharged. He jumped—but a neat granitic spray pelted all over his nice new trousers and nice sports-coat. The burst of laughter was unrestrained—not insulting. The road-workers were trained to work quickly, they were the same men who had made the airfields during the war, and remade them at top speed. Eight drills, for instance, each as explosive as a motor-bike, were in massed action, blasting down to the eighteen-inch line of the specification, and though there was no rushing but concentrated deliberation—of progressive unmaking, layer by layer, and then of remaking, from earth-line to the street-level—the tension of the time-table was felt. Were these Irish workmen? People said so in the shops. But this may have only been because it was an Irish contractor and the men were small. Here was the gang: and there was the ganger. This is how my house-party of rot-hunters must work one day, when the honeymoon is over. I do not say this with satisfaction: in theory at least I am all for football and song.

We keep a window box for birds. When there is some sun, watching sparrows rolling in our mould, sparring with one another in featherweight skirmishings upon the rim of the box—but a matter of fifteen feet above the ferocious marmalade cat on the roof beneath: shaking the sooty earth out of their wings, or sometimes asleep, become drowsy in the sheltered warmth—this is very pleasant indeed. The author of *Far Away and Long Ago* did a good job on the London Sparrow. I have always liked the common finch, that plebeian bird, as ordinary as grass. Whatever effort I made, however, I could not, I knew, find the joy of the bricklayers, painters and plasterers, pleasant, or see them as big human sparrows. Their class has no part in this—their dirty clothes and husky voices—there is an obstacle to our sharing the joy of adults of our species indiscriminately, as we can with birds or many quadrupeds. The rich contrive to repel us in *their* way, the poor in theirs.

Crossing to the other side of the street, I reached, in the next block up, the office of Thomas Cook and Sons. Those ornamental places advertised in the window, the archaic glamour of Cook's placard-world, were not my destination. I was going to Llanmaerth. I put my hand up to open the door, but found myself looking at the carpenter and stopped. He had come up close to my side. "Where did you spring from!" I enquired. "I didn't spring, sir, at all. I was walking. I was just behind you." "Ah!" I gave him a stern look. He admitted he had followed me. The carpenter gave in return his half-grin, in the midst of his discoloured cheek. "If you was going away, sir." As if some ugly wind had blown upon them, the embers in his tobacco-green eyes sulphurously sparkled, with their minute red particles of fire. "If you was . . ." But the carpenter was a lone wolf: I felt no responsibility as regards *his* joy—which in any case was confined to destruction. "If I was?" I asked. "Well, there's one place Harry, that's the plasterer, told me I'd missed in the toilet, where the rot. . . ." "The rot?" "Yes, the dry rot, sir . . ." "In the toilet the rot will remain!" I found myself saying, to my surprise. I could never have been rude to the plasterer, or spoken discourteously to the bricklayer, nor have turned my back upon a painter. I turned my back squarely upon the carpenter, as I burst my way almost into Cook's. *I* was going to taste liberty as well.

_____ 1.

THE GRATE in Eldred's study had been elegantly boxed in, and painted milk white. Not far below the centre of the milky expanse the bars of a chromium-plated electric fire had the appearance of a grating. At present the thick and gleaming bars reflected the cold flame behind them, from which came a moderate heat. But the house was centrally heated.

Between lying and sitting, Paul Eldred, on a massive white leather chaise-longue, in a lightish new-looking suit, was stretched level with the fire. A large Buddha sat facing him, benignly gleaming. In a large chair, nearer than the idol, sat a visitor. This visitor was shabby but looked intelligent. He chain-smoked Philip Morris. Seven stubs were in the ash-tray beside him.

"The specialist I saw last week," said Eldred, "informed me that some toxin was destroying me."

Silence.

"Some toxin as yet to be identified."

The visitor then responded.

"Such assertions as that made by your specialist," he said, "are usually a prelude to the administration of a dangerous poison."

Paul Eldred gave vent, after a rumble which gathered strength over a space of some seconds, to a burst of stylized belly-jeers. This was a guttural growl rich in insult, simulating the spasms provoked by the comic.

"You think, do you, Evan, that the fellow proposes to poison me. Just for fun? I should have thought I might be of more use to him alive."

"Oh, he might not intend to hurt you at all. Doctors are malignant or benign, like tumours. However, their benignity is more terminological than real. It does not mean they are not dangerous."

"They admit their ignorance exceeds their knowledge, and where there is ignorance accidents are bound to occur."

Evan shook his head. "It is not their ignorance, it is their humanity. If you are sick, the problem is this: the knowledge and the skills, through the agency of which your health might be restored, are in the possession of certain men—doctors of medicine. But unfortunately they are not morally or intellectually responsible enough for the powers of life and death they wield. Many approach medicine as a business: and then in the very processes of salvation they become brutalized. So the problem is—'How on earth am I to get at the knowledge and the skills possessed by this small-time business-man by whom I am confronted, or by this callous brute?' "

"That is a pessimistic simplification, Evan, I cannot allow. I have known many very decent chaps who practised medicine. I know surgeons who are both intelligent and humane."

"Certainly such can be found," the visitor agreed. "Often G.P.s are quite good chaps. They are the journalists of medicine, who know a little about everything but nothing *à fond*. I can see, however, that your experience has been happier than mine. Medicine seems to me to attract a high percentage of irresponsible people."

"Most people are irresponsible anyway," Eldred objected. "Surely medicine does not absorb a higher percentage of irresponsibles than politics."

"Just as many," the visitor maintained. "If it is medical help you need, I would suggest you obtain a report from a private detective agency on your man. A report on his killings."

A belly-jeer broke out at this. Eldred gave his sardonic nature full play only with a few friends with whom he had been young.

Their chat would be punctuated with coarse insulting noises, as they derided their enemies and mocked their friends or clients, as they sat and drank dry gin.

His present visitor was not of these, though a friend of his young days. He was one who despised the animal in man and would not sneer and jeer and wallow with an intimate. Eldred belly-jeered all the more and figuratively unbuttoned, without so much as a reciprocative chuckle. Furthermore Paul Eldred sensed the critic at watch in the friend. "Just for a handful of silver he left us, just for a ribbon to stick in his coat," was the reproach, Eldred knew, silently levelled at him by the accusing eyes, whenever the presence of his late wife's money accidentally obtruded, or whenever reaction, not to say "fascism," became indecently visible in his conversation.

Eldred sold himself as a fake antique. A thick veneer of age much in excess of what was biologically warranted had been serio-comically created. What the analytical visitor had to say about that may be summarized as follows. When young, Eldred developed a sensitive dread of ageing. His was a feminine make-up. In order to forestall the dreadful moment (and rob it of its sting), when people would whisper "Old Paul is getting on," he began acting old while still a young man. But if this was the true account, the mannerisms had become second-nature.

When Eldred spoke, it was slowly and portentously, in serio-comic judicial manner. With him all serious deliveries were serio-comic in style, so as to disarm mockery. Whenever an opportunity offered, he played the judge. He had collected a young highbrow following for himself as "creative historian": and to break off a young follower's engagement, for instance, to a young woman with money, such a feat would cause him to feel agreeably Mephistophelian—and should the poor little rich girl be discovered gassed or drowned, well, that would make him feel wickeder, that was all. He had no deep organ tones but with the deepest he could muster he would admonish that *money was bad for people,* especially if they were young creative historians—as all his followers were, hundreds of them. People laughed. However he did not need to be told that the more strikingly irrational his behaviour the better material it was for gossip: and Names are nourished with Gossip as plants are with manure, and Names can grow great big Names in an atmosphere of hot air too. He was a hard-boiled gardener, engaged in the cultivation of a certain Name. He had long ago realized that the manufacture of gossip was of far greater importance than the writing of history.

Finally, Dr. Paul Eldred belonged to the not inconsiderable number of more or less learned Englishmen who choose to believe that they are Dr. Johnson. A corollary was that some people saw him as that, regarded the dry comments on men and things, in a thudding delivery, as authentically Johnsonian.

"Once," the visitor said, "I was in a bladder and kidney hospital, in a room, not a ward."

"Indeed? How disagreeable."

"Yes. An unpleasant world, the bladder and kidney world. However the night nurse, knowing I was just a bladder case and not interested in kidneys, spoke with a minimum of reticence about the surgeon whose patient I was. I had said sleepily, 'Mr. Bingham does not do kidney work, does he, Sister?' Whereupon she told me that he was not allowed to remove kidneys any more. Too many of his patients did not recover from their encounter with him in the operating theatre. He had attempted to bump me off, I may say, in mere high-spirits. He kept me under an anaesthetic for two hours and a half, afterwards informing me that a visiting Swedish doctor who had watched the proceedings had observed 'how brave he was.' And he really *felt* brave, too."

"Well!" Eldred enjoyed chatter about doctors just then and looked approvingly at his visitor.

"That particular doctor," the visitor proceeded, "began as a bladder quack in Harley Street, helping a big quack. But he had repented and gone back to orthodox surgery. Straight bladder surgery is plain sailing. It was essential, however, for him to get practice in removing kidneys which is within the speciality of the bladderman."

"I know nothing about it," Eldred said, "but do they not acquire the necessary skill by practising on the cadaver? I understand that is how innovations in surgery are arrived at. But this perhaps is different."

"I don't know either," the visitor answered. "Only the use of the living cadaver, so to speak, provides a man, I would think, with the necessary confidence to take on a patient and charge him two or three hundred guineas."

"Is it really possible that in a great London hospital such homicide could be tolerated!"

"This was not a great London hospital. It was small."

"Ah. You advise a very large hospital!" Eldred summed up.

"Probably it is a bit safer, yes. Personality is a great factor in doctoring. A big muscular high-spirited surgeon should be avoided like the plague."

Eldred emitted a belly-jeer, of three vibrations.

"Mine," he said, "was a little runt of a man."

"A redhead?"

"No, he had once been black."

"Then perhaps you may survive. Bingham, the one I was speaking of, was big and muscular. He had been a rugger international and dodged about as he spoke to you as though dodging a tackle. He had all the qualifications for a popular surgeon, devil-may-care, a merry twinkle in his cold grey eye, his humour irrepressible for was he not a broth of a boy. His high-pitched boyish laugh charmed his victims and made them feel as safe as houses with him."

"However did you manage to escape him!"

"With women he was not such a success as one would have expected and I suppose the nurse who gossiped about him put me on my guard. No nurse liked him, he would treat a nurse as a piece of hospital furniture. He was cold and tough beneath the blarney and the smiling charm was only for the patient."

An appreciative spasm of belly-jeers broke forth, which Eldred rattled about upon a bed of phlegm; applause at the story of the bladderman, and mockery and insults for Bingham.

"Your hairbreadth escapes among the surgeons and the physicians, Evan, trouble me."

"What is your doctor's name, Paul?"

"Shaw-Vaughan," Eldred answered. "They are very partial, I have noticed, to double-barrelled names."

"Just for identification purposes," Evan Jones told him indifferently.

"The same problem which eternally confronts the Joneses!" Lazily Eldred rolled a little towards his visitor, to deliver a friendly belly-jeer or two: to dimple his cheeks, archly to insert his mischievous mask into a thick ring of double-chin like a bird pushed into too tight a nest. This was a habitual disarming social gymnastic, when "saying it with a smile" (*it* being some barbed remark), or when being "well-bred" merely. Evan Jones was unable to decide whether Eldred actually believed him to suffer acutely because he was a *Jones,* or, on the other hand, whether he hoped to induce painful sensitiveness, and to score an advantage over him, by his smiles and dimples, the arching of his vulpine beak, and the fat insult of his double chin.

"Jones is not a name," Evan Jones said dryly and contemptuously. "It is like an algebraic symbol. You are wrong. Jones presents no problems. The anonymity is acceptable. No Jones worth talking about wants a name."

"Of course he doesn't," Eldred said soothingly and woundingly. "I am sorry old chap. I often wish I had not got a name. People sicken me by their name-snobbery."

Here he was rubbing in his fame, and a smile flickered in Jones's face. Annoyed at the smile, Eldred was just going to rub an extra dose of salt into the wound, when Evan Jones proceeded, didactic and unruffled.

"Is a man adequately described by a name—until he makes it mean something himself, like Napoleon, or shall we say Montgomery? And then what happens? Montgomery, as a Field-Marshal, becomes 'Monty.' Napoleon Bonaparte becomes 'Bony,' or, in France still more simply, 'Lui.' Names that have been brought to life by their owners always get simplified. They are

emptied of their pointless weightiness. Such men are often referred to by letters merely, like H.G. or G.B.S. On the other hand
the Joneses start with those abstract advantages. And in my own
case no one can pretend that my first name, *Evan,* adds to my
identity."

"No. That is true enough. No one would say *that.* Yours is an
almost perfect incognito."

Evan looked at his friend as youth gazes with scorn at corrupt,
irresponsible, slothful age. Only a few years separated their birth-
years in the same decade many decades ago, and the difference
was in favour of Paul, not Evan. But for very long now Evan had
had this attitude. Eldred lay dramatically haggard, a smile of
deliberate derision on his face, which he affected to attempt to
hide. (He wished to give the other the sensation of being underneath—rather ridiculously so, and felt cheated of something because apparently this sensation was not produced.) His hands
were clasped upon his stomach. Out of the grey face stuck the
acquisitively-hooked nose (stupidly acquisitive, Evan would have
said) and the massive brow was the brain-trust in the service of
the acquisitive will. Evan remembered when this thin man had
first begun to feel like Dr. Johnson and when the appetite for
petty pomp first showed itself. The shadow of the great lexicographer had fallen on him as he began to taste success, though his
manner had been assumed with a cautious self-ridicule at the
outset.

But now suddenly the visitor caught sight of a new feature
in this room; on the wall on either side of the door was suspended
what looked like a green matting.

"What is that? A tapestry?" he enquired.

"That," Eldred told him, a little aggressively he thought, "is in
order to prevent the sound of the telephone in my secretary's
office from disturbing me while I am working. They make it I
believe from seaweed."

"Ah."

But Evan felt that evidence that his was a busy line would
hardly be disagreeable to him. ROT 5959 was music in his ears,

of that Evan felt sure. It must, on the contrary, be the long periods during which the telephone did *not* ring which depressed him. This seemed, as a first hypothesis only of course, the most likely explanation.

Eldred stretched out, with grandeur and languor, a bony hand, and pressed an electric button.

"You say you want a letter to Henri Meritrois. Why do you want a letter? Why not send your card up?"

Evan Jones did not answer. ("Your name weighs more than mine," or something, his friend *hoped* he would say, of course. He reckoned without the pride of the Joneses.)

Eldred's secretary appeared in the doorway.

"But you would rather have a letter. Miss Cosway, will you please . . ."

He stopped as through the open door a peremptory knock was heard. "That must be Dr. McLachlan," he observed.

Jones got to his feet. "Send me the letter will you?" he muttered as he moved resolutely towards the door, Miss Cosway moving out of his way with a smile he did not like.

Eldred sat up and in place of the belly-jeers reserved for male intimates there was an otherworldly unreadiness, an almost appealing weariness, as he seemingly attempted to gather his wits together in order to cope with a practical matter. The world sought him out in his seclusion with its importunities. Miss Cosway was his go-between—his considerate and sympathetic buffer. Miss Cosway knew quite well that he was never too busy to see some foreigner of no account; she played up, as the efficient secretary she was, to the dramatic resignation with which he consented. She looked tired and resigned herself. It would have been impossible for her not to realize that he took every step in his power to augment the number of these importunities and to swell his daily mail to the point where eighty per cent of it had to be dealt with by her, on occasion practically all. Into her epistolary style had crept the weariness of a long-suffering recluse, and she relished greatly mirroring his pomposity. She could not otherwise have acquitted herself with such efficiency as the secretary of this celebrated recluse, who required at times two secretaries to sustain his correspondence.

Eldred got to his feet, a ham act showing a patriarchal invalid dragging himself up, his iron will alone enabling him to do so. He stood bowed, gazing up sideways from under what should have been shaggy brows, at the visitor's back.

"It shall be sent on to you, Evan. Goodbye, goodbye!" (To Miss Cosway.) "Mr. Jones feels about doctors as some people do about cats."

Miss Cosway and her master exchanged polite gleams. For not only was she never allowed to hear his belly-jeers, but if he shared with her some highly innocuous mirth, the gleam he gave would be one of otherworldly tolerance and compassion, like a man looking back magnanimously from the gates of paradise upon the worldly scene. He had once, by inadvertence, given vent to a belly-jeer of scornful defiance in Miss Cosway's presence. He blushed and fell into an alarming fit of coughing, pretending of course that the unseemly sounds which had escaped him had been a novel prelude to a violent catarrhal convulsion.

The doctor entered, a maidservant appearing for a moment behind him. Dr. McLachlan was a Scot, who, trained at a famous London hospital, had learned in England to appear to forget that anything is serious, which certainly is most agreeable for all concerned. His attitude to his patients' complaints was that they were well-bred jokes. He spoke snobbishly in his throat without a trace of Scottish accent. Eldred's intellectual attainments he knew how to value, as no English doctor would have done: he accorded to his position a dignified deference which the Englishman because he felt "independent" would refuse, even if paid to look impressed. As a physician Eldred had a high opinion of him. Indeed, he regarded him as unique. Dr. McLachlan's reckless frankness astonished him at times. He would discuss a specialist's findings without fear and warn his patient if a diagnosis had a fishy look to him. There was only one class of specialists he was unsafe with, namely those belonging to the great hospital where he had been trained. Where they were concerned he became an orthodox general practitioner.

"Well," said Dr. McLachlan with his frosty professional smile, "how are you?"

Stiffly he seated himself. He was perhaps forty-five, Eldred thought, but his movements were studied and circumspect, like those of an elderly man. He sat down, as if his behind were made of glass and crossed his legs as though they were china legs. His version of the behaviour of a man of the world seemed to emanate from a book of etiquette. Such was the personality this doctor had evolved, though there was one other feature: the population of Rotting Hill probably would identify him most readily with his neckwear. There always appeared to be a lot of white collar about him. It was Eldred's theory that the collar served to conceal post-adolescent carbuncles, traces of which our doctor had been unable to banish from his face. Upon the completion of his training McLachlan had set up shop in Rotting Hill as general practitioner: he had built from zero a brilliant practice but his health had been the price he had had to pay. So, a still comparatively youthful wreck, there he sat frostily smiling with a somewhat startling levity at that most theatrical of wrecks, his haggard patient, as if to say "health to a gentleman is highly ridiculous."

However, he had something more concrete to say than that and he came immediately to the point.

"If," he said, "you care to rough it a little, Dr. Eldred, I can get you a bed in a small nursing-home tomorrow. But I promised to let the Matron know at once. They are nuns, it is non-profit-making, so it has the advantage of being cheap. Most of these places are, of course, extortionate today."

Eldred looked at him with his heavy judicial eye, weighing this proposition dubiously. Dr. McLachlan was a Catholic. Eldred believed it was a Catholic dentist McLachlan had sent him to, as he had seen some nuns at his surgery while his name was O'Toole. To Catholics he had no objection: but the Catholic community in England is small, and it is therefore unlikely that the best dentists, anaesthetists, nurses, radiologists, specialists, etc., are *all* Catholics even if the best G.P. was that.

"Tomorrow!" he intoned heavily. "I should, of course have to consult Miss Cosway, I should have to see what *Miss Cosway* had to say! Yes, it would be necessary to speak to Miss Cosway first."

"Of course." Dr. McLachlan was all understanding. A Prime Minister cannot leave the scene like an ordinary man at a moment's notice, and was not Dr. Eldred in the Prime Minister class? "Besides its cheapness, this place has one great advantage over other nursing-homes. There are no telephones in the rooms."

"No telephones!" Eldred shouted, horrified but incredulous. He recovered himself so swiftly, however, that the transition was hardly perceptible by which he reintegrated his factitious self. "No telephones, now that clinches it!" In the next breath, he exclaimed: "Please engage the room at once. I do hope the Matron has kept it for you."

"I am sure she has done so."

"How wonderful!"

"The room is not large," Dr. McLachlan warned.

"I do not care what its size is. It is a cell I suppose, is it not? It has no telephone—*that* is the essential! I had no idea that it was possible to find a room without a telephone." He pressed the bell-button on the table at his side. "Why did I never think of a nursing-houme before? But it must be a Catholic institution, I take it. All the undisciplined communions, I am sure, have the beastly things within reach of their patients."

"I am afraid that is so," the Catholic doctor agreed, his cheeks pushed up into a chilly jollity. It was perfectly obvious to him why his patient had started violently when he had warned him the rooms had no telephone: and he had been much amused by the corrected reaction which had so promptly replaced the first impulse of consternation.

Miss Cosway entered. Her employer put on his wearier mask and prepared to communicate the big news, namely that the recluse had at last discovered a retreat where the world would be unable to molest him: a beautiful living grave. He passed his hand in an uncertain dithering arc over his lank hair, and, with an obvious effort, spoke.

"Oh, Miss Cosway, Dr. McLachlan wishes to use the telephone. He has been able to secure a bed for me."

"Oh, I am glad, Dr. Eldred!"

"It sounds too good to be true," he went on, "but the room will be without telephone."

These last words suddenly changed the expression of Miss Cosway's face. Its customary look was a genteel reflection of Eldred's weariness. Suddenly it became one of indescribable panic.

"It will only be for six or seven days," Dr. McLachlan informed her, and her glance fluttered in his direction almost with indignation.

Eldred all but allowed a belly-jeer to rumble out and the doctor showed his teeth frostily.

"You will have to get Miss Ford around for a week to help you: and her sister perhaps, too, if she is disengaged."

"I am afraid I shall, Dr. Eldred," she answered faintly.

When Dr. McLachlan returned from the telephone he had imposed upon the piece of wood he had for a face an expression of almost boyish professional satisfaction. Lightly rubbing his hands he went towards his chair.

"That is all arranged," he said. "They will have the room ready at noon or just after. As soon as you have had lunch you will have the first penicillin injection."

"Where is it? In Rotting Hill?"

The doctor coughed. "I am afraid not, but it is not so very far. Actually it is in Putney."

"You will inform O'Toole?"

"I have done so. I did so just now."

"Capital."

"He will be there at one on Wednesday for the extractions. You will have two injections tomorrow, and another the following morning."

"That will take care of the sepsis."

"Oh, entirely. It is a reinforced penicillin. Those are terrible teeth, Dr. Eldred. You should have had them out twenty years ago. Both Vaughan-Shaw and myself believe they may be responsible for your condition."

Eldred threw himself back. They relaxed, Dr. McLachlan permitting himself a filter-tip cigarette.

"What fools you doctors have been, handing yourself over unconditionally to those political monopolists."

"That is putting it mildly," said the doctor.

"They will have you tied hand and foot in a half-dozen years."

"Unless . . ."

"I am afraid there is no *unless*. Someone (who?) opened the gate to the enemy. An army of G.P.s will have the status of druggists' assistants."

McLachlan nodded, delicately puffing out a little smoke. "I should not be surprised," he said, "if in the end doctor and druggist became one."

"True. Yes, that would be it."

"An abbreviated hospital training, a rather longer pharmaceutical training. That is the logical evolution. A National Health Service doctor with his four thousand patients, dealing perfunctorily with each, ultimately would be supplied with a rigidly standardized set of labelled bottles, printed instructions for the patient on each bottle. Instead of a prescription (as now) the patient would receive a bottle. And the druggist-cum-doctor would waste no time on diagnosis. 'Pain bottom of the back? Here you are. Number 39. Next please.'"

"Ghastly." Eldred shook his head.

"Not very different from today, except that now there is the complexity of the large and often luxurious chemists' shops, to which the panel-patient takes a prescription. Also the doctor at present possesses a quite unnecessary amount of knowledge of the treatment of disease. The little state-clerk who diagnoses and dispenses in one movement will point to the instructions on the bottle if asked any questions. And people, of course, will wear spectacles from birth, and dental plates as soon as their teeth sprout up."

"You are giving a prognosis of the course the disease called socialism will take that is amazingly accurate."

"It does not require much skill to do so. At present they are splashing money around like water. I have just come from one of the big London hospitals. It is swarming with newly-appointed clerks."

"Jobs for the boys," said Eldred.

"I suppose so. In this hospital there used to be *one* clerk. All the bills went out to time, the patients' reports were punctually completed. Today there are *fifteen* clerks, and the clerical work is always in arrears. What is worse, a ward has been closed to provide accommodation for these clerks. There is a waiting list of one thousand sick for this one hospital. And they close a ward."

Dr. McLachlan delivered his propaganda with a desiccated gaiety. He paused, and they both laughed bitterly.

"So the vote is built up for the Party," Eldred commented. "The 'spoils system' in the United States was recklessly inflated under Franklin Roosevelt. Millions of unnecessary jobs were created for his supporters, or for those who had not been his supporters but thenceforth would undoubtedly be so in order to keep the job. A standing army of voters was thus enlisted, ranged under the banner of the New Deal. Our socialist administration here has learned much from the New Deal—and of course works in the closest harmony with Truman's 'Fair Deal.' German national socialism made every smug little political monopolist's mouth water and still serves as a model. The clerks you mention are the drones that the ruinous taxes pay for. It is the reckless bribery of the last days of parliamentary democracy."

The doctor listened with pleasure and respect. "Of course you as a historian, Dr. Eldred," he observed, "are conversant with the anatomy of many political techniques. You have a deductive grasp of these matters. I merely observe what is under my nose."

"You are a remarkable observer."

So these two malcontents had the little talk in which they usually indulged after Eldred's colon, his bladder or his insomnia had held their attention for a while. Several further illustrations of the iniquities of the administration of the National Health Act were furnished by the doctor. He was a tireless polemist against the Act, he had a big repertoire of atrocities. There was the case, for instance, of the wild-eyed young man who had come to the nuns, the day before, with tears in his eyes, and of course his prayers did not go unheeded, although the nuns themselves are short of beds and have to crowd extra people into their four small wards. The mother of this poor young man had suffered a paralytic stroke. She was helpless and among other things incontinent. He had appealed to every hospital in London but none would take her in. They did not regard themselves as places for the old to die in. And she was incontinent into the bargain. All the clinics were full as well. She now was recovering from her stroke in the care of the kind Sisters.

Dr. Eldred's indignation visibly waxed as he listened to this story.

"How outrageous it is the way in which they discriminate against the old," he exclaimed. "The majority of our Cabinet Ministers and Civil Service experts are old men, the most eminent hospital doctors likewise. But an old person will be turned away from a hospital as if he were a leper. It is to treat a man as if he were a machine. When a machine wears out you push it on to the scrap-heap. When a man's body wears out there is still a man inside it. And as for us as Christians it is the man that is valuable, not the machine. It is a heathen generation."

Dr. McLachlan gravely assented, though very doubtful whether his patient's sympathy for the old was anything but political.

"For myself," Eldred pursued, "I would rather have Ranke old than a million young machines. Life is not an economic machine. But when the mechanistic millennium is consummated they will superannuate at forty-five at latest—except in the case of politicians—and kill shortly afterwards. They may kill outright, or they may prefer to starve and torture to death, as they are beginning to do now."

The doctor looked up with a touch of alarm at his patient. The latter had been going far beyond what politics dictated.

Could it be that his high blood-pressure was exposing him to an invasion of humanitarian bacilli? Not Paul Eldred! he decided. The cause must be looked for elsewhere. The doctor now rose, like a scrawny bird levitating from its nest, as he left his chair vertically.

"Well, I must be moving on," he said. "There are two women with pneumonia I have to go to first. Tomorrow I shall see you at the nursing-home. You will find your room as warm as even you could wish."

_____ 2.

DR. ELDRED, his secretary, and a reporter stood on the miniature stoop outside the front door of 27, Rotting Gardens, the flowery tip of Rotting Hill. At the foot of the six spotless white steps stood the uniformed car-hire driver—the uniform shabby, the car none too clean. It was noon on the driver's wrist and at the end of a gold chain in Eldred's pocket.

"No," said Eldred to the reporter rather nastily, fixing him with his eye. "No. A few days, no more. Down in Gloucestershire."

Every opportunity for contact with the Press was eagerly seized upon by Eldred, but on this occasion the Press was actually *de trop*, and the Press sensed the abnormality of its reception.

"Shall you be speaking while you are away, Dr. Eldred? May I know what are your subjects?" The reporter put great respect into his voice.

"I am-not-speaking!" Eldred ground out, pausing between the words. "In Gloucestershire I shall remain absolutely silent." At this point Eldred almost allowed a belly-jeer to escape him. It was able to mobilize down below before he nipped it in the bud. With professional inquisitiveness the reporter directed his eye immediately towards Eldred's gastric centres.

"You will be resting, Dr. Eldred?"

"No," Eldred droned ponderously. "No, I did not say I should be *resting*."

"I see, Dr. Eldred."

"I don't know what you *see*," Eldred scolded. "There is nothing to *see*."

The reporter laughed. A telegraph boy arrived at the foot of the steps.

"Eldred?" he called up at them. "Eldred?"

"Yes," said the reporter. And the boy handed him the telegram.

Paul Eldred had stepped hastily down and said to the driver, "You know where to go?" at which the man rapped out (the reporter, behind Eldred, committing it to memory): "Nursing 'Ome. Fifty-five 'Astings Terrace, Putney 'Ill." His interest now thoroughly aroused, the reporter this time took down on the back of an envelope the number of the car. "I wonder if it's a prostate?" he asked himself. "He said he was going to be *absolutely silent*. What could that signify? Operation on the tongue? Malignant? Or just benign!" Secrecy of any sort being what most excites the pressman, this young fellow laid plans as he went down Rotting Hill on a bus.

The mock-chauffeur, leaning into the hired car, attempted to drape the unclean rug over the knees of his two passengers, both of whom stoutly resisted, pushing it off each time till he desisted and closed the door, while Eldred muttered to his secretary: "Did that young reporter go off with my wire?" In eloquently smiling silence Miss Cosway held up the telegram.

Having crossed the river they found themselves in that pleasantest of riverine districts, where the first of the Cecils was a publican, where the Oxford and Cambridge boat race starts, and where Swinburne was imprisoned by Watts Dunton—Putney. They found the nursing-home somewhat difficult to get into. After many summonses by knocks and bell a nun opened the door. She seemed willing enough that they should come in but unable to guess what might have brought them there and at first at a loss as to what to do with them. However she turned another older nun out of a small room, placed them there and closed the door. In the room they remained until perhaps ten minutes later a third nun appeared. She stopped, taken aback, she seemed about to leave them, but she changed her mind. She possessed much more administrative genius than the first nun. Having enquired if they were expected as patients she said, "You had better go to your room, I think." This was evidently a rather revolutionary idea, but, it seemed, there was literally no alternative. All the rooms and the wards as well were upstairs. "Go upstairs," she said, pointing the way. "Up?" asked Eldred, with great courtesy. She smiled brightly and nodded genially. Although dreamy and numbed with religion, as were most of the nuns downstairs, her smile and her nod were intact, even if her words were of the scantiest.

When they reached the top of the stairs there was a brief blank corridor. The corridor was L-shaped, they turned at right-angles and were in a gloomy hall and saw a man's back bent over a table. He was absorbed in something which turned out to be a temperature chart.

A nurse carrying a tray came out of an open doorway. She said: "Are you Dr. Eldred?" and the man doubled up over the chart abruptly straightened himself, and it was Dr. McLachlan smiling a frosty welcome. "Ah, I did not hear you," he said. "How curious." "Not really," said Eldred. "Miss Cosway and I are not a clamorous pair." They all laughed genteelly. "Well, let us come to your room, Dr. Eldred. It is just here." They moved down a fairly long windowless corridor. One door was open, from it came an authentically sepulchral groan, which increased Eldred's respect for the home (it might be small but it groaned like a hospital), whereas it caused Dr. McLachlan to cough censoriously while stepping up their progress.

Eldred's room, however, was the next and the doctor led the way in jauntily, rigid but jocular. "Admittedly small but it is quite pleasant I think," he remarked as he looked around. Eldred looked around as well. "A bright box for a toothless historian to lie in," was his view. "And a hot box, too." "Ah, but you asked for heat," the doctor reminded. "I asked for heat"—in his usual way Eldred, for answer provided a deep significant echo—the same words his interlocutor had used, but loaded with a supposed meaning of almost limitless profundity. Half of Eldred's conversation was made up of such reverberating echoes.

"I will get into bed," the patient abruptly announced. Miss Cosway moved towards the door quickly, casting an anxious backward glance over her shoulder.

"Yes, do so," agreed the doctor. "I will remain with Miss Cosway where you found me just now," and Eldred was left alone. Evidently no room for visitors, he thought. You have to stand around in the space between the lavatory and kitchen and study the charts, or else leave the premises. Contact with the profane is reduced to a clinical minimum. He smiled in the midst of his shirt, which he was pulling over his head. As he stood in his undergarments the door opened and a nun of severe aspect entered. She looked at him absent-mindedly, turned loiteringly as if attempting to remember something, and left. Eldred gave a belly-jeer with much real gusto. "Am I of glass?" he asked the air. "Do people see through me—but do I make them remember something they had forgotten? Am I a transparent remembrancer?"

Once in bed Eldred pressed the dangling bell-button and secured the return of his doctor and secretary. It was his wish to get rid of them quickly and to be alone with the nursing-home; away from everything with a lot of nuns—bathing in their remoteness from the vile and worthless world of the malignant commonplace, of vociferous nonentity, and to stop there until he had learned the secret of their apartness.

After apologizing for the absence of the Matron, Dr. McLachlan offered to drive Miss Cosway back to Rotting Gardens. To a few last anxious, indeed desperate, appeals from his secretary, Eldred answered: "Tell them I am dead."

Miss Cosway accorded to this the hysterical laugh indicated. Recovered from the spasm she said: "I have sent the telegrams to New College and to Wilfred Bull. There was nothing tonight . . ."

"Nothing tonight!" Eldred echoed angrily, glancing at his doctor.

Apprehensively Miss Cosway glanced at the doctor, too, slightly flushing. "Well, you know what I mean, nothing really *important*, nothing that cannot be arranged. But *tomorrow* . . ."

"Ah, tomorrow!" echoed Eldred significantly.

"Jennifer Robinson was coming to tea, and she will be so dreadfully angry."

"She does allow her temper a bit too much rope. And she grows arrogant."

"Yes. She bullies me when I say you are engaged. She doesn't think you are! It's quite absurd."

"Absurd!" Eldred frowned.

"I know," said Miss Cosway, "but you know what she is! She will go away and describe you somewhere, in a gossip item, as 'the greatest historian since Froude'!"

Eldred was becoming increasingly uncomfortable, under the sceptical gaze of his doctor. No engagement tonight!—and merely a publicity interview with a gossip-writer tomorrow! "Am I not supposed to be dining with Sir Christopher Smith tomorrow?" he demanded.

"No, Dr. Eldred. That is next month."

"Ah, next month. Next month it is!" growled Eldred, giving his secretary a rather nasty look.

"But what can I do about the address you had agreed to give on Monday? The Charterhouse Literary Society." She was wringing her hands over this unpaid talk to an obscure group. "And there is that Canadian historian."

"Canadian historian?"

"Yes. The one you said had cribbed your last book. His name is Dr. Burnaby Harry. I think you said he had a Chair in the Arctic Circle."

Eldred stared fixedly at Miss Cosway, attempting to mesmerize her into silence. "Please do not allow these problems to worry you," he said, spectacularly relaxing. "Tell everybody—and I mean *everybody*, to go to hell."

Dr. McLachlan beamed frostily upon her. "Excellent advice!" richly and throatily he told her. He then, with a frigid pinch of jauntiness and Scottish gallantry, carried her off, protesting.

_____ 3.

IN describing Paul Eldred it is very easy to make him seem a clown and nothing else, and this even without succumbing to the temptation to select what may possibly entertain. His mind was at times blotted out by his frantic vanity, but of course a mind was there. The inferiority feeling of a provincial, it was believed by the wisest of his friends, had rotted his personality and even eroded his intelligence. Jones, his most sceptical friend, had had an unpleasant experience on two occasions. It was not the waspish ferocity of the little feverish ego that darted out on him that surprised him. The subterranean existence of such a spiteful animal he had been dimly aware of. What surprised him was that Eldred no longer troubled to check it, but allowed it to have its way and dart out and bite people. Of course what provoked these sorties had been connected with old Paul's *work*. Jones had ventured a criticism of something. But he found that what had begun as a young man's resolve to run himself, in the Intellectual Stakes—and quite good-humouredly while youthful still —as a "great" something or other, had developed, as time went on, into a pathological self-esteem. It is true, "greatness" had come: which no one was better qualified than what Paul once had been to evaluate. But *that* Paul was no longer there. "Greatness" corrupts. From that time, after the *second* of these disagreeable episodes, Jones refrained from all reference to the *works* of his old friend. But he still respected a certain flickering integrity, and loved the image of his youthful companion which haunted this celebrated ruin.

Almost regenerated in his present isolation, Eldred even came to look ten years younger. Having climbed out of that Cigar Store Indian, the Great Dr. Eldred, having found, by accident, a place where it was impossible to be that anyhow, he lay in his bed an *undressed* personality, as it were. The patient-in-bed situation helped. He never had felt so free since he was a schoolboy. He embraced that anonymity he had always dreaded.

The nurse he had already seen entered.

"Good afternoon. I am Nurse Tanner. Here is some lunch."

A hard-boiled egg, a tea-cup full of tapioca, and a thin grey slice of bread was placed upon the glass table with long chromium-plated legs which straddled the bed. The fare of the anchorite! He beamed quietly on the savage repast. Nurse Tanner interpreted this as sarcasm.

He ate the egg and was looking at the tapioca when a nun entered with her mouth open, holding a hypodermic syringe. It was obvious she was toothless: her eye-sockets were empty, in the hollows lived her eyes.

"I am Sister Giles," she told him, aloofly but aggressively.

"And I am Paul Eldred," said he.

The nun was in a white conventual uniform, the much-pleated skirt needing a dozen petticoats for it to balloon around the nether limbs—or how else could it be so pneumatically expansive and beautifully circular? (This applied to all the massive myriad-pleated skirts in which the nuns discouraged the idea that nuns have legs.) Sister Giles was the nun who had intruded and gazed through his underwear at the window beyond: and for her he was still obviously vitreous.

Eldred smiled sweetly, Sister Giles's blank expression was unchanged.

"Please lie flat on your tummy," she said.

Eldred dutifully heeled himself over, pulled down his pyjamas and presented a buttock to Sister Giles, enquiring gently and even a little archly: "Is that all right?"

"No," said the nun gazing away, "flat on your face please. It's no use if you don't, you know."

"I see. That makes it clear at once," said he understandingly. "The muscles have to be relaxed, haven't they."

Sister Giles rubbed a spot on the buttock with wet cotton-wool.

"She's a shy old girl," he thought. "It is natural. I should be frightfully embarrassed if I were an old monk and had to do this to a lot of worldly matrons." To her he said gaily over his shoulder: "Novocaine, I can smell it."

She jabbed in the needle.

"Thank you," he said. When she had gone Eldred ate the tapioca. Afterwards he felt a little sick. Nurse Tanner entered, collected the lunch-tray, and suggested a little sleep. She was a stream-lined hospital nurse for whom patients were a species distinct from nurses. She saw him close his eyes with satisfaction and left the room giving him an *up* stroke in her mental chart. Sleep was just sealing his eyes but the door opened and a nun came in and moved up to the side of the bed. "How do you feel, Dr. Eldred? I am the Matron. Are you comfortable?" She apologized for appearing on the scene so late. As she spoke her hands were interlocked in front, but the two thumbs circled rapidly around each other. All of their faces appeared at the end of a tunnel of white lawn and looked strangely small. This miniature face looked at him along its white tunnel with a painfully placid aloofness while she talked, her thumbs revolving as though a small propeller, perhaps to sustain the smooth flight of her mind in the profane dimension, perhaps to preserve an equilibrium naturally threatened in commerce with the world, which must be an artifice demanding effort. She was a very sensitive educated woman. Undoubtedly it was an effort for her to be normal yet abnormal, to be worldly at the end of a white tunnel, to reintegrate her presanctified personality for the occasion; she moved back into it with stiffness and distaste. Again, the *quantity* of chat each patient might receive was rigidly rationed. After she had expended, say, a hundred words for a maximum, the interview would not be broken off but would fade out. If the patient said anything further she would not answer as if she had not heard it. She would wheel, in her bulbous voluted skirt of dark blue, like a clockwork figure, and move quickly out of the room. The words were well chosen and sensible, perhaps thanks to the whirling of the thumbs.

After the Matron's departure Eldred turned over and thought again of sleep. His eyes were rolling up, his limbs relaxing, his blood was leaving the surface vessels and his mental images were beginning to behave drunkenly when someone entered. It was one of the many stunted female gossoons, Irish nationals, attached to the nurses. Muttering something she thrust her hand violently into the foot of the bed. After a lunge or two she seized the hot water-bottle on which his feet were resting and drew it out of the bed. Next she pushed in a hotter bottle. This taciturn intruder having shuffled out he took up a book and read for a few minutes. The door opened and a startled Irish face appeared. "You rang, sor?" panted this girl. Very sweetly smiling Eldred gently shook his head, adding a musical "No." "You did not ring!" the girl cried frantically and charged out. Five minutes later the book began to slump down and his eyes to close when Nurse Tanner entered briskly. She put down a slip of paper on the bed-table. "Your signature is required," she said with her efficient smile. "Ah, yes," said he, picking up the paper drowsily. "Yes, I think you may administer any anaesthetic you like. Ah yes, and my nearest relative. You want to know that of course." He signed the printed form, and returned it to the nurse as though she were an autograph-hunter. "You should try and get a little sleep now," said Nurse Tanner, giving his pillow a push. "A capital notion," said he with a smile that was a shadowy reminder of his old sardonic self. A most appalling groan, followed by a cry of anguish, came from the neighbouring room. "That woman sounds rather ill," he observed. "Yes," said Nurse Tanner as if he had broken some regulation. "She is very ill. She will probably die." There was a cry from the other side of the thin partition—"Merciful God!" came the distracted voice. The nurse, of a neat dark prettyness, with very dark brown curls, looked very faintly annoyed and carried her neat little body away, self-righteously erect, as if all the good were healthy like herself. Eldred felt that this was much too real a nurse. She was the only discordant note.

He now knew that however often Nurse Tanner recommended a little sleep, that sleep was out of the question. Up till eight o'clock, when the night staff came on, someone or other was always doing something in his room. The Matron moved in once more, looked at him distantly but tolerantly, asked when his teeth were to be extracted and did he sleep well, and removed herself silently. Tea at four and dining at six were the big events: but a considerable time was taken up in making the bed. He went to sit in the arm-chair from which he watched the two diminutive Irish helps on opposite sides of the bed swinging the bedclothes and pyramiding the pillows. He became conscious of an incessant hissing sound for which at first he supposed the pipes were responsible. But it was the two girls hissing at one another across the bed. He could not have sworn it was this, for their mouths did not move nor did their expression change and whatever they were doing—if one of them stooped down, for instance, to pick something up—the noise continued. But when they left the noise ceased. They were evidently able to converse with one another almost inaudibly.

Finally, before the night session, Dr. McLachlan showed up, as stiff and formal as a Prussian Geheimrat, though sitting on the edge of his bed in a frosty familiarity. Eldred reflected how he fitted into the Home. After all, the Matron and he belonged to the same ethos. On his side, the doctor consulted with himself. He had expected a lofty exasperation on the great man's part with everything, just because it was not the London Clinic. To his surprise he heard criticism of nothing. He had never seen his patient so calm—yes and so happy. He went away pondering this paradox. And just before he left Eldred gave him a slip of paper, on which he had written a message for Miss Cosway, to the effect that for the remainder of his stay he did not wish her to visit him or communicate with him in any way. He wished to be completely alone. This message the doctor was enjoined to deliver by telephone to ROT 5959 the first thing in the morning.

One thing that would not be apt to enter into the doctor's analysis was the fact of the excessive acuity of Eldred's time-sense. Could he have been carried back in a time machine to the England of the fifteenth or sixteenth century, he would not—as did Erasmus on a first visit—have been disgusted with filthy rush floors, never renewed, but fresh rushes put down on top of the old. The time-sense would have restrained him from finding fault with the backward islanders. His attitude towards the Catholic

Home where he found himself was that, to the best of its ability, it was in the Middle Ages. (Which does not mean, it was otherwise than clean and comfortable.) Of course, as to Eldred's *other* feelings his doctor could not have divined what *they* might be. He simply regarded his patient's attitude as fortunate, but perversely incomprehensible.

Dr. McLachlan before going checked on the pulse, pulled down his lower eyelid, raised his upper eyelid, and informed himself as to the stool. Lastly he asked him if he had managed to get some sleep. Eldred smiled and shook his head.

"I think Sister Bridget, that is the night Sister, had better give you something."

"Perhaps it would be as well," the patient agreed. For if the night staff had anything like the vitality of the day staff he would certainly, he reasoned, require a sleeping draught.

The doctor looked at him sharply. This new docility and quietistic temper (if it was not a pose) began to worry him. He coughed—as if to say *Achtung!*

"I expect you are terribly bored, Dr. Eldred," he observed, as one man of the world to another.

"Not at all."

The doctor brushed the negative lightly aside.

"Of course you must be. A man like you, always surrounded by people. . . ."

He got no further, for this galvanized Eldred into automatic action. "Surrounded by people!" he protested, with gently raised eyebrows. No man, alas, is a bona fide recluse to his doctor.

"Well, you *would* be, of course, that is what I mean, if you did not employ two secretaries to hold them at arm's length. I know how many admirers you have, Dr. Eldred. Some of them are my patients. Loaded with engagements as you are, it must be a strange experience to step out of it all, suddenly like this. To be in so uncompromisingly—er—insulated a nursing institution as this is too."

"A blissfully strange experience," Eldred told his dubiously gazing medical adviser, who then approached and gravely checked once more the blood's faint thump in the wrist. Next morning, he explained, O'Toole the dentist and Dr. Tomlin the anaesthetist, and he himself, would gather well before one o'clock in the operating theatre. He and Eldred would not *meet*, properly speaking, until later, after the mass-extraction: and at length he left with a throaty *Good night.*

It was 8 p.m. Sister Bridget arrived, hypodermic syringe in hand. There was a smile which was a bitter-sweet rictus forever upon her still lovely waxen face. Half heeling over Eldred presented his bared buttock to the nun. "Is that far enough over, Sister, or shall I flatten out?" he enquired. "Ach, no!" she genially dismissed the exactions of the day-sister martinet. "That's arl that is necessary of course it is." Hearing the accents of Cork or Clare (John Bull's Other Island English) he responded with a friendly smile. "Ah," he thought, "Irish, so with a more elastic and graceful puritanism. No *Get on your tummy* stuff with her!" But the injection hurt quite a lot—far more than with the day-nun. But Sister Bridget was so kind and had so much beauty that he did not mind if her ministrations caused pain. His temperature came next, and after that she gave him a powder which took effect with great dispatch. It was not until five in the morning that he awoke, and lay listening apparently to a dromedary charging up and down the uncarpeted boards of the corridor. It was Sister Bridget with her long legs, in her ungainly shoes, rushing to and fro in response to the summonses of the distracted patients. The groans, and the agonized protests against the fierce pain, were clearer than ever at this early hour. He lay wondering what this poor woman could have done to be racked in that way. The partition was so thin he could hear her clutching at the bedclothes and grinding her teeth, calling on God in his mercy to spare her these agonies.

Soon afterwards he had another penicillin injection and Sister Bridget's tribe of little snub-nosed helpers proved to be quite as agile and officious as Nurse Tanner's. The lowest in rank of the personnel, the floor-mopper, was also the newspaper girl. Eldred enjoined her *under no circumstances* to bring a newspaper into the room. She gave him a kind of frightened leer for answer. Then at eight came breakfast, and from then up to noon some gnome or other, or a nun or a nurse, was weaving in and out of the room.

There was one thing which especially attracted his attention during these four hours. The Matron and Sister Giles both came in twice. Sister Giles as usual wandered in casually as though she had forgotten something and had come in there in order to remember it. But she drifted up to the bed and gazed into his face. He was even able to see that her eyes were blue. This proceeding almost startled him. He said to himself that her face was like that of one of the horsemen of the Apocalypse in a German church. The Matron, on both occasions, seemed to be peering at him very inquisitively. It would be all right, she said—though he did not know exactly what she meant. "Am I pale?" he asked smiling. Her answer was that the Sister would give him something at twelve o'clock. That was always done, she said: over significantly he thought. He considered both these women a little odd.

At noon Sister Giles strayed purposefully in, and ordered him negligently to go to the operating theatre. "For dope?" he asked, succinctly, like herself. She nodded. "Not *here?*"—he expressed his surprise. "No," she said and left the room. (Ah well, he thought, they are wise to put her on in the daytime. I should hate to have her around at night.) He put on his dressing-gown and went out. Hundreds of Hibernian gnomes were charging up and down the corridor, with food, flowers, bedpans, and hot water-bottles. After walking through the territory of two other nurses he came to a stairway. This was to the rear of the building. At the foot was a much broader corridor. A few yards and it terminated in an obviously important and sinister door. There was no stink of ether, which usually announces the proximity of the theatre. But he pushed the door and it was an unmistakable theatre. There was the stage, like a glorified ironing-board, on which a recumbent performer went through his limp and speechless part, except for an imprecation or a dark mutter escaping the drugged body like speech from a corpse (though in this strangest of theatres there are some who consider the Star to be the so-called Man in White). There hung the hooded lamp above the stage to illuminate the performance, with its cold false daylight, often the last light the entranced actor is to see on this earth. This most tragic of all actors is carried in and out of the theatre, if the play is a tragedy, Eldred thought, and not a comedy like his.

The room was lofty, a large north-lighted cube, filled with the clinical gadgets of surgery. Probably it had been a garden-studio. Once the bearded painter had here attacked his canvas, his fist bristling with brushes: and here a fair Victorian, corsetted like a swollen wasp, giving a little precious gasp of alarm had been overcome by faintness, collapsing like a monstrous toy upon the painter's throne. The good historian almost smelled the sal volatile or eau de Cologne all Victorian painters would have in readiness, with, as a last resort, scissors to snip the murderous "stays."

Sister Giles, as he entered, was stolidly stationed beside the operating table. She at once began propelling it towards the window. She placed it exactly under the window and then turned in his direction, her eyes directed towards the door in the middle distance. "Where," he asked, looking around for a chair, "shall I sit?" She gave the operating table two slaps. "Get up on this," she instructed him with impeccable boredom. He walked over, and smiling almost meltingly at the venerable religious dragon, objected "Up there, Sister?" "Yes." "But I shall roll off." The nun however administered two absent-minded slaps to the operating table. "You must do as the doctor says," she told him, in a flat impatient voice; "you have to lie down here." She tapped to show where and stood looking away. It was not at all easy to mount this high and narrow resting place: once he had done so and stretched himself out, it was intolerably hard, for it was impossible to adjust the body to the hardness without tumbling off. "You must lie on your back." The old nun was dully peremptory. He smiled. Evidently she did not know who he was. He wished she did, but wriggled upon his back, his rigid body violently protesting. The voice of cold command sounded again. "Roll up your sleeve." (Ridiculous and incredible, thought he, that Dr. Paul

Eldred should find himself cut off from the world, alone in this obscure operating theatre, obeying, as if he were a taxi-driver, this rough old nun.) He rolled the sleeve up and she dug a needle into the arm.

A beautiful tropical drowsiness immediately began to pour into his brain and invade his limbs, the warmth of a potent obliteration. Ah, the boon of anaesthesia! The board was no longer hard, he was quite indifferent as to whether he fell off or not, death itself would be merely the infinity of his sweet anaesthesia, the putting to sleep of the will. And the nun was a good old fairy nun. All the same, even at that moment, he realized it was far too strong a dose he had been given. The last thing he saw before his head lolled over—and what will was left to him was a will to sleep, there was no resistance—was the Sister pushing a large white screen towards him, such as they screen the dead with in a hospital ward. It grew larger—whiter. He thought "Good old cross-patch!" and that was all he knew for the best part of an hour.

A very imperfectly functioning consciousness returned to him, numbed and devoid of more feeling than a man would have about a cricket match if he was not interested in cricket, merely regarding it as a handful of white figures slowly changing position on a green field. A cocktail party might have been going on the other side of the screen. The theatre seemed full. Though it was true their hilarity was muted, there was polite mirth. But the atmosphere was electric too. The people the other side of the screen were excited. He felt like the Star actor out of sight of the expectant audience: or the Christian martyr in the echoing pens beneath the amphitheatre. Violently, as it seemed, two men pulled the screen aside, and he began rolling out into the room. He found himself beneath the closely impending hooded circle of the lamp.

He hardly looked at all the people. Dr. McLachlan came up and whispered in his ear. "You feel quite comfortable?" "Perfectly," he answered. "Why all the concourse, doctor? What an audience I have got." McLachlan disregarded this. Eldred was aware of men in white, with white masked faces. One was doubtless the O'Toole, concealing his forceps behind his back; and even McLachlan had been in white. A red-faced man like a doctor, he noticed, was lying across his legs for some reason, as if to get a good look at him. He stared fixedly. Eldred's head, it seemed, was hemmed in with people but he could only see their stomachs. Two men grasped his left arm. They had rolled up the sleeve and held his arm stiffly out from his side. Why on earth were all these people milling around him? he wondered. It was like being Gulliver, intoxicated perhaps, only mildly curious regarding the antics of his captors. Or images of the Inquisition visited him perforce. The Catholics had never liked his histories, they were all on the Index, it might be that he was about to be ementulated, or blinded. The nuns he saw betrayed this image for they ought to have been monks. Or was it a *woman's Inquisition*? The needlessly brutal hands of the two kneeling house-serfs tightened upon his arm, he felt the plunging of a needle. The world stopped where it was for a second or two and then clicked out, like turning off an electric light.

When he awakened he was in bed and a pleasant girl stood over him, one of the army of nurses' mutes, but this one had a tongue and a beautifully expressive face.

"Ah," he said thickly, "the show is over."

She gave him a mug and told him it was to spit the blood in. Hours had passed since the extractions, he learned from the girl. But he still was stupefied. McLachlan hastily entered, his face flushed, no smile. He came over and warned Eldred he had bled too much as if it were his fault. "You must not touch your gums. The bleeding must not go on." He asked to see his gums. These seemed to give him unexpected pleasure. "Doctors are always surprised if they have not seriously injured you," was one of Jones's sayings. But McLachlan's comment was, "O'Toole has made a good job of it." It seemed indeed that he had: apparently it was Dr. McLachlan who had been at fault. Since the events in the theatre Eldred had had, in his doctor's absence, what almost amounted to a dangerous haemorrhage.

_____ 4.

THE doctor gone, the humane girl continued her ministrations
while the rest of the staff were rather (for them) mysteriously
aloof. She lifted the veil, too, on the hours during which he had
been unconscious. She was much impressed by the excessive
bleeding; dish after dish had to be emptied until the doctor was
summoned. Eldred had also decorated the wall with some of it.
His most serious escapade, however, was connected with the Matron. She and Nurse Tanner were interested spectators of the
blood-bath when unexpectedly he began blowing, it seemed, like
a sea beast—but blowing blood. He puffed blood all over the
spectators. The Matron, dabbing herself with a towel, had beat a
hasty retreat followed by Nurse Tanner, who since then had not
put in an appearance. Eldred was gravely concerned as he listened to the report of this eyewitness of his bad behaviour, but
the girl was discreetly amused. He, of course, could appreciate
the comic stimulus to a young mind, but he did not feel certain
what the Matron's reactions would be. Were these people to see
him as a boor who blew blood over those who were kind to him
he would be deeply mortified. On this score his conscience was
soon set at rest. About six o'clock the Matron came in, spotless
and unruffled. She began at once to point out how necessary it
was to bleed, in order to enable the septic content of the gum
to be carried away. What she seemed mainly concerned to do
was to white-wash her little doctor. Eldred smiled at her: for
while _he_ had been worrying a little at what her reactions might
be, _she_ had been preoccupied with what she felt must be _his_
reactions, at the excessive haemorrhage.

As she spoke of the necessity of much blood Dr. McLachlan
appeared and on seeing his patient's benign expression, he grew
very excited and jocular. His wit and gallantry was side-stepped
by the Matron as if she were ducking to avoid missiles. She
plunged her eyes from one corner of the room to the other, refusing to meet his gallent glance or to give him smile for smile.

He attempted to intercept her plunging gaze, piqued at her un-responsiveness; but she flung her head bodily over in the opposite direction, and he quietened down after that. And soon they both departed.

Eldred found that he was unable to stand. The bed had to be made with him in it, by a couple of dwarfish hissing gnomes. The day's goings and comings were succeeded by Sister Bridget and relative peace. As he lay there and was able to look back upon what had occurred in the theatre without distraction, he perceived how far from the normal the proceedings had been. They partook unmistakably of the nature of a rite. A blood-sacrifice had been enacted: and it must always be in that spirit that the theatre was used, even if it was only an appendix that was involved. Their theatre was the obsessive emotional centre round which the existence of these secluded women revolved. The peculiar interest he seemed to awaken in the nuns on the morning of the operation, which at the time he was aware of but could not understand, was explained in the light of this analysis. It was *his* blood that was going to be shed that day, it was he that was about to have an agony.

Then there seemed to be a theory governing the actions of everybody in this institution that a patient invariably was in a state of the liveliest terror during the hours immediately preceding his operation, however insignificant that might be, and even that he was apt to become dangerous. Sister Giles's attitude was explained in some degree by these circumstances. The *danger*, as it was felt, inhering in the terrified victim accounted for the un-necessary potency of the drug administered as a *quietener*. Actually it had more the effect of knock-out drops. Lastly there was the mobilization of all the available man-power to hold down and if necessary to restrain the victim about to be sacrificed. Eldred enquired of the friendly girl (one of a family of converts from the Putney-Wimbledon district) whether patients were always held down in the theatre or whether he had impressed them as a singularly violent type of man. Her answer was that patients on the operating table often kicked and struck out. Once a Sister had been injured by a violent blow in the stomach.

Of course all this, far from prejudicing Eldred against the Home, merely confirmed him in the view that he was *really* in a medieval *pocket,* as it were preserved by means of disciplines and incantations. These good women had evolved a biological mechanism deeply Christian, centering in a sacrifice and an agony. Then death noisily abounded beneath their roof. Eldred discovered that several of the rooms contained relatively poor people, in which respect it differed from Protestant nursing-homes, run strictly for profit. In fact these poor creatures had crawled there to die. It was not easy in the utilitarian England of 1950 to find a place to die in, outside of the poor house, which is the terror of the destitute old. They all believe that the infirm are given a mercy-killing there. Unless you are rich, it is highly inconvenient to die where you live. But death is the element in which these women of course had gone to dwell. They have gone to live next door to death, away from the world which pretends there is no death or which forgets it. They live in saintly proximity to the indestructible regions into which death admits the penitent and impenitent. Their minds steadfastly fixed away from the temporal, at night they lay themselves down in a grave. Souls are always flying past their ears into blessedness or damnation. So, dedicated to the care of the sick, the nuns had no objection to the moribund. On the contrary. Having died to the sensual life themselves, a person in the act of abandoning it, involuntarily, became akin to them; though it was a constant source of astonishment to them with what noisy reluctance their dying patients took the final step and died.

That morning at dawn an approaching bell tinkled in the corridor and a hurrying tread came to a stop at the door of the neighbouring room. Then through the thin partition came the flat rapid expressionless recitation of prayers for the dying. There was a silence and afterwards the bell hastened away. Considerably later a man's voice was heard in impassioned supplication, a supplication as old as the catacombs, modulated in such a way as to make it evident it was a text that was being said, not a man speaking. How splendidly that was read! thought Eldred. There was soon a dead silence. The groaning had diminished and at length had stopped. The priest prayed. Then suddenly breaking the silence, his voice was heard laughing heartily, a rather startling sound in the early morning. He was talking with great gusto. Eldred supposed Sister Bridget must be there now.

This patient died three days later, Eldred assisting through the partition, at the rite of extreme unction. He stared at the ceiling as there were sounds that must be the confession. Almost simultaneously, through the partition behind the head of his bed a poor woman violently entered upon the last stage of some painful disease. He was told nothing could be done for her, and several times she embarrassed Dr. McLachlan by her yells. It was her habit to scream with pain for a while, but otherwise she was relatively quiet. Eldred assumed they gave her a drug, she was at peace for such long intervals.

_____ 5.

AS Eldred was not a strong man it was some days before he could even take a few steps. But Dr. McLachlan was visibly elated. He took all the credit for Eldred's surviving his bad doctoring.

On his side the patient was well pleased with his physician. For had he not introduced him to a community of expert recluses, who daily demonstrated for him an immemorial technique, enabling you to give the impression that you are a mile away, when in fact only separated by a yard or so from another person. Eldred began to practise under the bedclothes, twirling his thumbs while he chattered with Nurse Tanner, as an aid to self-abstraction.

One evening patient and doctor, as usual, engaged in a little frivolous speculation: Eldred imparted, in the first place, how vastly he esteemed the nuns and the good work for which they were responsible. He went on:

"When these execrable monopolists, the socialists, have abolished by taxation all the other clinics and nursing-homes outside the state-hospital system, the Catholic clinics will still be there. They will be the last refuge of free medicine. One will still be able to be ill like a gentleman, thanks to them."

"There is the Masonic Hospital," McLachlan observed. "That is outside the National Health Service too."

"Is it indeed?" Eldred looked up quickly. "How did they manage that?"

"Some influential Freemasons went to see the Health Minister, who quite likes *influential* vermin! It is a wonderful well-appointed hospital—the best in England in fact—and particularly difficult to get into."

"For non-Masons."

"No, for Masons!" bleakly the little doctor laughed. "Patients of mine who are Masons have been unable to get in, though I tried very hard for them. Were they indignant!"

"Ah!" Eldred seemed to be interested.

"Then I believe—I am not sure about this though—that the Labour Hospital has been left outside the National Health Service."

"What is that? I suppose a hospital for members of the Labour Party."

"I do not know."

"In the Welfare State there must be privilege!" By a hairsbreadth the patient escaped a belly-jeer.

The Matron entered.

"How are you tonight, Dr. Eldred?" she enquired.

"Feeling much better," he told her. "Much better. Oh, Sister, there was something I had to say. I think you should all make a novena to your patron saint for me."

As he was speaking her expression changed in no way, but before he had finished she had turned away and quickly left the room.

"I fear I offended her," Eldred observed.

"No. Evidently what you said reminded her of something. She is very forgetful."

"She misunderstood me, I think," Eldred explained. "What I was about to say was this: I propose to write a short history of the order to which she belongs. That was why, I meant, they should make a novena for me, or some other suitable devotion. For I shall need all their prayers."

"Oh, I see," McLachlan laughed distantly. He went over gravely and sought information of the clockwork in the patient's wrist, taking out of his waistcoat pocket a massive professional man's gold watch. Eldred, smiling, lay quite still. This was always McLachlan's procedure when his patient said anything he did not like. And he had not liked the request for the novena any more than had the Matron.

For the rest, as Eldred lay there, day after day, during the maddening hospital routine of cleaning, nourishing, evacuating, and he steadily refused to look at a book or much more a newspaper, he immersed himself in a luxurious barrenness. Was he not buried alive? He was buried deeper, hour by hour, by these Irish dwarfs, hissing as they worked. Would he ever be so happy in any other mode of existence? Since the days when first his ambition began to impose its idiot disciplines, he had known no relief. *Here* he had found it. The hissing dwarf that solemnly scrubbed his face, and the grinning one that tickled his feet, were all the company he ever wanted.

Often he spoke to the friendly girl of her conversion, and that of her parents. He wished to peer into her mind and discover how conversion affected the thinking of the Movie-bred twentieth-century young: an injection of the medieval into one of Hollywood's spiritual brood. But it was the nuns who were of course his principal study, from the immovable Matron to the gay but equally evasive Sister Bridget. "Ah, God bless ye!" she would say with fervour after he had said he would send her a gold crucifix he had seen in one of Rotting Hill's antique shops. But she was not to be bribed into departing from edification of Irish gaiety. There was no other mode.

His first opportunity of trying out the techniques he was acquiring occurred about seven days after the haemorrhage. Still decidedly unsteady (and, according to his habit, exploiting his infirmity) he was dragging himself back from the bathroom, most theatrically the Invalid. A familiar figure suddenly appeared, and he heard himself greeted in a vaguely familiar voice, in tones of deep surprise.

"Dr. Eldred! A nursing-home is the last place I should have expected to find you, sir. Nothing serious I hope?"

The reporter whose face he had last seen, and fled from, a week ago in Rotting Gardens stood blocking the corridor. What was *he* doing here, the rat? Running *someone* to earth. His was the least welcome of visages: Eldred put on his usual mask for reporters; namely, suggesting that the stench of an exposed cesspool had suddenly reached his arching nostrils and curled lip, but that stoically he was smiling it off.

"What are you doing here?" he enquired of the reporter, rather in the manner of Sister Giles.

"Well, Dr. Eldred, that was precisely what I asked you just now?"

"I am just resting," he growled, the old manner returning. "I am just resting here for a short while. Yes, just *resting*. I was absolutely worn out, you know." And he squinted up at the other sideways, his head lolling forward.

The reporter expressed deep sympathy and confided that sometimes he "felt rotten" himself.

"Yes, you feel *rotten*," Eldred said heavily, "because of the *rottenness* of your life. But my life is rotten too."

The reporter expressed hilarious scepticism.

"No," Eldred heavily insisted, "rotten!" But he had become more lumbering and Johnsonian every moment. Though his frame lacked flesh, he *felt* bulky in his voluminous dressing-gown, so had started rolling from side to side as Boswell described his Master as prone to do. Alas, affecting to be a bigger man than he was, at least in girth, he was overtaken by the weakness ensuing from his loss of blood: at the end of a long roll to larboard he almost fell over. The wall of the corridor saved him but he fell heavily against it. He shook off the reporter's helping hand.

"My life," he growled angrily, "has been rotten. I am taking up the monastic life as soon as I leave here."

"You are becoming a monk, Dr. Eldred!" cried the reporter, dancing with delight.

"Perhaps a friar. It may be a friar."

"A friar!"

"One of a mendicant order, yes."

"Would you beg in the streets, Dr. Eldred?"

"That would be where I should beg."

And he crawled away dramatically, bumping the walls.

The following evening Dr. McLachlan entered with a newspaper beneath his arm. In his fruitiest, throatiest "social" voice, and with his frostiest smile, he said, advancing airly—"I see, Dr. Eldred, that you are proposing to become *a friar* when you leave here." He opened the paper and read: "If we are approached in Piccadilly by a gaunt austere figure in the dress of a Franciscan friar, and solicited for arms, that will be the great historian Dr. Eldred. He shuns the world as other men shun a contagious disease. But now, he tells your reporter, he is going a step farther. He can no longer tolerate even that degree of worldly contact; he spurns the comforts of his home in Rotting Gardens—he asserts, indeed, that he is tired of Rotting Hill and of our *rotting life* as well!"

The doctor placed the open paper on his patient's bed. There was the headline:

GREAT HISTORIAN TO BECOME A MONK.

Eldred shrank away from the shouting headline, pushing the newspaper away from him with horror. He whispered hoarsely: "That vile Fleet Street garbage fly I met in the corridor! Will you remove that yellow rag! I shall be sick. My stomach is not so strong as it was."

"Yes, but I suppose you *did* say something to the fellow, didn't you!" The doctor, for once outraged by that humbug which he had learnt to expect of Eldred, registered disapproval in his un-laughing eye.

"I told him that he *stank!*" Eldred shouted almost. Then drop-ping his voice dramatically: "But I said I stank too. I—do—*stink.*"

Dr. McLachlan coughed.

"I suppose I said *something* to him, to get rid of him. They are a pest, they poison my life with their lies."

The doctor looked very sceptical indeed, as he watched his theatrically writhing patient, but he said no more.

_____ 6.

ELDRED had now been sixteen days in the nursing-home. The Matron the nurse, and everybody else had *When is he going* written plainly upon their faces. But he showed no sign whatever of moving. There was nothing to prevent his going except his dis-inclination to take up his own life again where he had left it to have a lot of teeth extracted. In the end they were obliged prac-tically to push him out. His doctor gave the first push, humorously of course.

"If you wish to enter upon a monastic life," McLachlan told him jocularly, "*this* is not the place for that. This is a nunnery."

He packed and left, but only after many representations had been made to him, to the effect that (1) he had now recovered and had even been seen running up the stairs; and (2) a queue of sick people was waiting for his room, and one was in a dying condition. So he had said farewell to Sister Bridget and Sister Giles, and to the Matron, with great emotion, and, after a con-valescence was back in Rotting Gardens. The house had been redecorated inside and out. Black was the predominant colour.

Miss Cosway sat in her office as usual. She was dressed in what amounted to a black uniform. She looked very despondent. Black did not suit her, she considered; formerly she had shown a taste for gayish frocks. Also she liked the bustle of life. But the bustle of life had ebbed from Rotting Gardens. As Eldred no longer spent the major part of the day writing letters and telephoning, letters had stopped pouring in at the letter-box. As to the tele-phone, it sometimes stood there silent for hours together. For that reason Miss Cosway jumped slightly as it now burst into life, with its loud cross bell. The call was from Evan Jones. Miss Cosway said "Oh, yes" as she heard the name. She was disap-pointed. Naturally she took her tone from her employer, who exhibited a submissive weariness when anyone was announced, but added a kind brave smile when it was Evan Jones. However, after a short absence from the telephone she informed Jones austerely that the doctor would see him at six the following day.

The tall figure in shabby black that entered Eldred's study punctually at six was far more monastic in appearance than Eldred could ever manage to look, with his leathery lawyer's face, though this would not be for want of trying.

The visitor sat down in the same chair as upon his earlier visit, when he had expounded the risks inherent in commerce with Doctors (M.D.).

"You appear to have escaped injury," he observed. "At least physical."

"Ah, yes, that was only an affair of teeth. Just a little dental show, doctors in secondary roles."

"Dentists are not greatly to be feared. They can break your jaw. That is all."

"They cannot do much more than break your jaw. My dentist was the O'Toole. He left my jaw intact. But then I did not tread on the tail of his coat."

"Good."

"Yes."

There was a silence, during which they both looked at one another. In each case their thoughts were uncomplimentary. Jones noticed that the Buddha had been removed. In its place was a large engraving of a Madonna. He turned away his head, watched by Eldred. He then found himself looking at a Descent from the Cross.

"Are you," he enquired, "for Grasmere or for Ambleside?"

With a smile of hawk-like sweetness, of an overbearing and

superior douceur, his head inclined as if condescending to a child, Eldred said: "What is that, Evan? What is Grasmere?"

The visitor shrugged his shoulder.

"Grasmere? I see you have not read what has happened in connection with the centenary of Wordsworth's death."

"Has there been a centenary?"

"You are so out of the world! The newspapers have been splashing it as if it were a child-murder by an erotic homicide. You see the people of Grasmere, and those of Ambleside, both claim that the authentic Wordsworth Shrine is their town (or is it village). Celebrations have gone on simultaneously in both places, with mutual recriminations and denunciations, in which members of parliament and archbishops have been involved. It is, I imagine, a matter of the first importance to the hotel-keepers, lodging-house keepers, garage-proprietors, caterers, and tradesmen of the rival communities. It is a case of a shy little 'violet by a mossy stone half-hidden from the eye' no more. Yet it had to hide behind the mossy stone in the first instance . . . just as 'trade follows the Flag.' "

"I suppose so," said Eldred politely, twirling his thumbs and gazing at his visitor as if the latter had been vitreous and as if glassiness bored him. He, of course, had read the newspaper reports of the Wordsworth Centenary disturbance and, while he read, had speculated as to whether the people of Rotting Hill would be the victors when it came to *his* centenary. He would put his money on the Rotters, though his birthplace would no doubt put up a good fight and do all they could to attract pilgrims: though his birthplace was frankly a repulsive spot and he doubted whether more than a few hundred devotees would collect there. It was such problems as these that he was turning over in his mind when his visitor began speaking again. He then listened, twirling his thumbs at top speed.

"It is generally agreed, I suppose, that Wordsworth was one of those men who outlive their genius. As a young man he preferred human liberty as understood by the men of the French Revolution to the hypocritical liberties of the Anglo-Saxon middle class."

"Rubbish."

"I beg your pardon? A commonplace or a conventional man outliving a bit of vision—for the great visionaries see 'the light that never was' to the end—a worldly person who has been visited by some muse in error, naturally exploits this visitation for ever afterwards, like some little businessman. When the age of poetry was over the prosy old moralist naturally proceeded to exploit his dead self just as one hundred years later the Grasmerites and Amblesiders are doing, who follow his example to the letter. 'Greatness' is at times a sweet racket. Some are the pioneers of the racket growing up around their dead virtue. They build their own *Shrine*—when their genius has departed. A Shrine-builder of this sort always builds a *sham* or phoney Shrine. Victor Hugo, for instance, was really *all Shrine*. It would not be fair to mention Tolstoy in the same breath with Wordsworth. . . ."

"Have you ever read Wordsworth?" Eldred said tonelessly, looking away. But his visitor understood that unwittingly he had been treading on someone's toes—or perhaps trespassing on someone's Shrine!

"Yes." Jones nodded. "I read him last night." Then he changed the subject: only his choice of a subject was unfortunate. He spoke, and in somewhat partisan terms, of the Crusade to Prevent a Third World War. Eldred grew more and more remote, until at one moment Jones actually registered the sensation of being alone in the room.

It had not taken this very observant visitor long to realize that Paul was pretending to be a new Paul. He would, he felt certain, have given a fruity belly-jeer at a certain moment, packed with insult, had he not superannuated his abdominal Jeer, which was a revolutionary step. It had not been lost on him, either, that Eldred had been conducting himself as though his visitor had been a large piece of animated glass. Needless to say the twirling of the thumbs had been remarked and marvelled at: he had attempted to assign a cause—unsuccessfully. What impressed him most forcibly, however, was that Paul Eldred was *elsewhere* (realizing of course that it was in all probability a *deliberate* absence): successfully self-abstracted.

Eldred had acquired so skilfully what he interpreted as the nun's technique of self-abstraction, that everyone he came in contact with now felt he was not really there, or uncomfortably remote. Evan Jones found it so oppressive that his stay was an unusually short one. As was his custom he rather abruptly rose. For a moment he stood looking down on his oldest friend, not unaffectionately.

"Paul, are you becoming a monk, as the newspapers say you are?"

"No," Eldred answered carelessly. "That is just a silly lie."

"Whose?" was all that Evan Jones said, as he moved towards the door, in a tone that indicated he did not expect an answer. As he descended the steps of 27 Rotting Gardens he communed with himself almost thinking aloud: "I can take old Paul neat, I can take him with soda, I can take him with tonic, orange, or lime, and I can even take him, and often have, with vinegar. I fear I cannot take him with holy water. That is an innovation against which my stomach rebels." A fire-engine rushed across Rotting Gardens. It brought instant relief, it released something which had got obstructed somewhere within, and Jones's eyes shone again. "Thank Beelzebub there is a fire somewhere!" was what he thought as, smiling, he stepped briskly away.

CHAPTER 5: Time the Tiger

——— 1.

IT WAS, as usual in London about that time of the year, endeavouring to snow. There had been a hard frost for days, in fact it was so cold that in any other country it would have snowed long ago. The sky was a constipated mass, yellowed by the fog, suspended over a city awaiting the Deluge. It was eight-thirty in the morning. The streets of Rotting Hill were like Pompeii with Vesuvius in catastrophic eruption, a dull glare, saffronish in colour, providing an unearthly uniformity. The self-centred precipitancy of the bowed pedestrians resembled a procession of fugitives.

Mark Robins was standing at his bathroom window. His eye followed with displeasure the absurdly ominous figures moving under mass-pressure to be there at nine o'clock, passing on through the hollow twilit streets towards the swarming undergrounds. It was the urgency that jarred, their will-to-live as a machine.

He could see into the lighted baker's shop. The lady known in his private mind as "bum-face" arranged yesterday's and of course the day before yesterday's pastry in the window. Whenever he saw the old pastries ranged in the window he thought of that air of uprightness and invincible integrity owned by the little master-baker. Why were his loaves the least white, the greyest, of any in Rotting Hill? He held very strong opinions on the subject of the socialist administration: perhaps cause and effect. His bread became as hard as a brick within forty-eight hours. It became like that in the stomach too if you failed to expel it promptly. This baker's views on the socialist government were as forcible as a pick-pocket's are regarding the police force, only the baker's had the added force of moral indignation.

Then, as Mark idly watched, "Fringe" (in his private mind she was known as that) erect and white in her chemist's uniform, came out of Willough's. She moved like clockwork, as steady as the swan on the surface of the lake. Whenever she turned she turned abruptly at right-angles with the precision of a Royal Marine. She had been a she-soldier. Mark approved of "Fringe," and regretfully noted how she stopped, pivoted to face at right-angles, and entered the baker's shop (as she did every morning) and selected an ageing pastry. However, she worked in a chemist's and no doubt kept her bowels open.

In several windows of the lofty Victorian houses—all Private Hotels—where the diligent refugees of Rotting Hill were already at work on their biographies of Goethe or of Meyerbeer, there was electric light. The silversmith and diamond merchant was (typical of his class! thought Mark) the latest riser of the tradesmen of Rotting Hill. The last snores of the night blew out of his nostrils upon the little fluttery moustache as his head lay on the pillow beside that of Mrs. Silversmith. Both the Silversmiths and Mark had a low opinion of the other's morale: their flats so situated that nothing that went on in one was exactly a closed book for the other—especially in view of the prohibitive cost of material for curtains and the veils that in happier times shroud our domestic interiors.

Mark withdrew from the window. He sighed. He did not know why he sighed. But a large white "Ascot heater" stood in a corner of the bathroom which no longer produced hot water. Three months earlier the mechanic of the gas service had called for the routine clean-up. Since then it had been out of action. Mark boiled some water in the kitchen and washed: then he filled the kettle again, and again put it on to boil. After that he went to his guest's room, knocked at the door, and put his head inside.

"Charles! Stop dreaming and get up. I have put some water on to boil for you."

"Thank you, Mark. Whooah!" Charles yawned.

"You slept well?"

"Perfectly."

"Good."

"Whooah."

As he went to his room Mark was smiling. "Whooah!" was so like Charles. Seeing Charles in bed "whooahing" had caused him for some reason to think of Ida Dyat, Charles's sister. He thought of her, as he always did, in repose. Action was not her element: so, though on horseback her hair was dramatic as a maenad's, he preferred to think of the stationary cloud of dull gold as she lay back in an armchair reading a book. The indolent red lips he would see for preference at their most indolent, when she had been too lazy to smile and had smiled with her eyes instead—which was less trouble. Her beauty was preraphaelite at its best, brooding or dreaming in some equivalent of the mirror of the Lady of Shalott.

It was a certain inactivity in Ida's composition which attracted him most, and it was that, too, that accounted for his romantic attachment remaining in a state of abortive repression, contained within the forms of youthful camaraderie: Mark being one of those men who needed, if not to be hunted by the female, at least to be reminded that women are sexual phenomena. But always a warm wind from the past rushed into his mind when he had, as now, these images of her. Then the image suddenly dissolved, his smile faded. For Ida must be a hag of forty-five, he thought. Thinking of Ida as greying and pathetic was so immensely distasteful that he began moving quickly and noisily about. Old Charles stopped young though, he thought. "Whooah." Mark smiled again.

But he soon forgot Charles's sea-lion cry, for he became grimly absorbed in dressing. His bedroom was a far more efficient refrigerator than the "Ascot heater" was a heater. However, the Briton regards chilliness as next to godliness. Mark would have been quite as displeased had the refrigerator failed as he had been at the defection of the "heater."

Taking a fresh shirt out of the drawer he identified it—as the one with the smallest buttonholes of any. This abnormality was revealed by all new shirts to some degree. With the shirt in question the buttons refused to go in. Each buttonhole had to be forcibly entered, the one at the top entailing as much sometimes as five minutes strenuous thumbing. Unquestionably this afforded him that grim satisfaction the Briton experiences when senseless obstacles are placed in his way or life bristles with purposeful mischance, all food for his "grit." But in this case there was another factor: namely the credit and good name of a socialist Britain. Probably it would prove a better advertisement if British manufacturers turned out serviceable shirts—easy to button up and with such conveniences as are prized by self-indulgent foreigners. It was like our taxation. Few foreigners understood *that*. Taxes such as *we* can stand up to would cause a revolution anywhere else. Only *we* have the guts to "take it." Besides, the obvious explanation of the smallness of these buttonholes aroused Mark's party-zeal: the motive was *profit*. It saved labour and time in the factory to make them small. It was a relief to one's feelings to reflect that the days were numbered of "free enterprise" shirt manufacture.

Even the best shirts tended to shrink and the buttonholes lost width in the wash quite as much as the sleeves lost length, if only a little. But the button naturally was unaffected. Any slight dilation of the buttonholes attendant upon the constant passage, in and out, of the button, was less than its shrinkage in the wash. It *had* of course occurred to Mark to purchase a few dozen shirt buttons, smaller than those on the shirt. But although there were many sorts of buttons in the shops, shirt-buttons (oddly enough) were practically unobtainable.

As he pulled on a sock one of his fingernails caught in the wool. With an almost new pair of nail-scissors he attempted to cut off the chipped nail. But the scissors were already loose and of a metal formerly unknown to cutlery. The nail was bent by them, it was not severed. He fell back on his nail-file. After a little he gave that up, and stuck a band-aid over the nail.

The quality of all goods supplied by the sundriesmen had inevitably deteriorated. Then he knew about the small piratic factories that turned out the defective steel goods, inundating England with gimcrack merchandise, and felt grateful that their days were numbered in a collectivist society.

Mark was superstitious. To start the day in slippers appeared to him almost an ill-omen. The shoes on which his choice fell, on this occasion, were his recently-acquired £5 brown pair. Of these he was still rather proud—an emotion the shoes were not fitted to inspire. And Charles had assured him that there was no pair of shoes to be had worth putting on your feet under seven pounds ten.

With these shoes he invariably attempted, completely without success, to tie a bow. The shoelaces were too short. In England today the statutory length for shoelaces is fourteen inches. It is illegal to supply laces longer than that. Mark was not aware that he had to thank the Government for this idiotic difficulty, and put it down to some dishonest manufacturer selling short weight on the plea of a non-existent "shortage." As usual, for all his stout finger-work, he got nothing but a solitary loop, one for the left foot, one for the right.

He rose to his feet, the petty frustrations involved in the act of dressing done with. A tweed jacket hung from a peg. No peasant weaver could ever have been responsible for the vulgarity of the colour. Mark, who had paid twenty pounds for it, eyed it dubiously. It was about the maximum price for a ready-made tweed. All first-quality tweeds, of course, must be reserved for export. But *why* (the question had once forced its way into Mark's mind) need what was left for the home-market be so ugly and vulgar?

Another question: Why should all ready-made jackets, cardigans, jumpers, be made for small and frail men? Mark was tall and muscular, so *that* question it would have been inhuman to ignore. But it was easily answered, too. Far less material was required for a small man or a child than for someone of Mark's size. Consequently the manufacturers preferred to think that Englishmen, with a few exceptions, are stunted and emaciated.

Mark took the jacket off the hanger and a phoney smell of ersatz peat assailed his nostrils. It was with no possessive glow he put on this practically new garment and as he left the bedroom he registered depression. He could not guess why *sans amour et sans haine* his heart was so full of a low-grade pain.

There was no sound of Charles, so he went into the kitchen to prepare the breakfast. He took the "Strachey loaf," as Charles cheaply called it, out of the bread tin. Officially it was one day old, but when he applied the bread-saw it was like sawing brick. He sawed off four slices and grilled them two at a time. The kettle had been refilled and was acquiring a little heat. He threw the remainder of his butter-ration into the repast, added a few pinches of alleged Darjeeling to the pseudo-Ceylon in the teapot: placed on the tray the two dishes of cereal, a teaspoonful of sugar for each. Sugar was always a bad shortage with him. He took down a jar marked "Strawberry Jam," recognized by housewives as mainly pectin and/or carrot pulp, given appropriate local colour of course and flavour to match. There was neither nourishment nor pleasure to be had from it. Charles appeared, yawning and smiling.

"Why no Mrs. Bristers?" he enquired.

"Oh, *she* does not come when I have 'flu."

"Why?"

"Because—I *believe* this is the reason—Mrs. Bristers thinks I am putting it on. Swinging the lead."

"When you quit malingering she comes back."

"Yes. Of course she malingers herself meanwhile. She calls off her malinger as soon as I announce my recovery."

"Anything I can do," Charles said, "in Mrs. Bristers' absence?" He was given the kettle to carry.

"How do you feel this morning?" The guest put the question.

Mark hesitated a moment. "Depressed!" he confided. "Unaccountably depressed."

_____ 2.

THEY both moved into the living-room, the lightly laden Charles in the van.

"What a poisonous day," Charles shouted, and the room was in fact so dark that when a match was struck to light the gas-fire it was like a miniature firework display.

"A bit of fog," Mark conceded with didactic firmness.

Where the weather was concerned Mark was always on the defensive, because people were apt to blame the Government for the weather. Then, he had a feeling that very bad weather (of which there was an awful lot) *was,* in fact, compromising in a brave new day.

They sat down facing one another and Mark poured out the tea.

"Ah, that is a capital idea." Charles picked up a piece of toast and examined it. "The dreadful bread arrives disguised as good old-fashioned toast."

"Let's see, you like sugar?" Mark looked up, a cube poised above the cup.

"If you think it won't spoil the tea!"

Mark laughed. Even a bureaucrat laughs sometimes on such occasions, as a clergyman would consider it politic to laugh at not *too* coarse an anecdote. Besides, he was fond of tea. "It is certainly not good tea," he said in a firm voice. "I have tried to coax some decent tea out of my grocer. But I really believe he had none."

"Have you tipped him?"

"Good gracious no!" Mark protested.

Charles shook his head, dogmatically flourishing a piece of toast. "I am afraid you cannot expect to get anything if you don't oil their palms."

Mark's was a damp smile.

"Do you," he enquired, "go around oiling everyone's palm? I know that is done. But it does not strike me as very nice. You may get the lion's share that way but it is the behaviour of a less noble animal. I will not say a *rat*."

"A pig, you think, eh!" Charles laughed, drinking with relish. "Best to drink this stuff while it is so *hot* you can't taste it."

Since Mark had worked at the Ministry of Education and since Charles had become a farmer of a rather lurid black-market type, they had started arguing differently. In their discussions in the old days nothing more concrete or subjective, as a rule, was touched on than the present Catholic revival or the currency of the Incas. Also when, in easy-going debate, Charles's opinion prevailed, Mark did not mind in the least. Today, however, he would defend his position, at times, almost acrimoniously, particularly where the issue was political. This was very unMark like.

Mark Robins and Charles Dyat had known one another as schoolboys, been at Marlborough, then at Oxford together. Neither had formed any close friendship except this one of theirs. But its rationale was not likemindedness. Charles was what is labelled "a leader-type." Mark had little taste for responsibility. These two facts alone may have provided the essential ingredients for a friendship.

Theirs was not quite the comic marriage-of-opposites, instances of which are so common. Leaving aside physical contrast—Charles who was fair, being only of middling height and Mark being a tall black-haired man—Charles looked at life from a certain social eminence (an imaginary one), whereas Mark was uninterested in social distinctions. Where intellectual distintions are concerned he was rather romantic, from which circumstance Charles had benefited. Charles he considered very brilliant, unquestionably destined for great things. Again, were one to investigate and collate, their roots would reveal a common soil exploited to different ends. Both came from the prosperous professional middle class: but Charles's father had been a successful and a pretentious country lawyer, who ran at one time a butler and footman, his large house, Tadicombe Priory, standing in half a dozen acres of pseudo-park, a small satellite farm completing the picture: Mark's father, on the other hand, was a Manchester doctor with a big practice, with neither time nor inclination to emulate his most snooty patients.

So the conversation had taken the acrimonious turn it nowadays was always liable to do. Mark ate his handful of cereal, inadequately sweetened with the teaspoonful of sugar (although the Jamaicans were starving because nobody wanted their sugarcane). Charles noisily tested the friability of a blackened and gritty crust, smeared with ersatz jam. Then Charles sat back, and after a minute or two took up again the question of tipping.

"Of course I go around oiling palms," he began aggressively. "Your masters don't need to—they have their farms like Stalin's commissars and their privileges. But you and I have to exude pourboires or our health would suffer. You can't live on one ration book without tipping. Tipping is the black market of the poor."

Mark no longer hesitated to recognize the political gulf which yawned and gaped between them. Charles smiled his tough gay smile, belonging to his cavalier complex, as he glanced into the yawning chasm. The white hairs in his brushed-off-the-mouth moustache were not numerous enough to make it "gray," the gold-gray of the temples he kept clipped. In the yellow gloom he sat up, eyes dancing, a gallant little daguerreotype darkened by the fog of time. Mark returned his gaze, with a bit of a waver, across the grim period-piece of sham-tea, sham-jam, "processed" butter, grey bread scorched into toast. He admired, as he had always done, the lawless eye, the witty mouth.

Charles was too monotonously destructive, however: he had an *individualist itch to pick holes*, in Mark's phrase. Where Mark would be apt to respect the most pernicious by-law, Charles would be quite certain to break it. Was he not (in imagination) of the class that made the laws? As part of his synthetic "aristocratic" outfit he despised all laws and the law-abiding. But the great social changes since 1945 of necessity complicated the role of the synthetic "aristocrat." Charles was towered over by a hostile Zeitgeist. Mark saw quite well this menacing shadow looming over his friend as he argued: for the natural law-giver had become a potential outlaw.

"In our young days, Mark," Charles said softly, "it was *you,* you know, who were the little Tory, I the little radical. Do you remember?"

Mark agreed that he had been a dreadful reactionary and that Charles had been most frightfully advanced. "A perfect devil, in fact!" he laughed a little derisively.

Charles pushed his cup towards the teapot. "May I have some more of that bloody tea? Yes, you were quite shocked at my red tie."

"*I was!*"

Flushed and animated, Charles had laid aside his imperious technique—he had chosen to soothe and to charm. For the second time that morning Charles forcibly recalled his sister—the submerged sexual asset in this friendship was brought into play. Mark softened at once in response: and it was with eyes still moist that he looked up and cooperated in recalling the pleasurable absurdities of undergraduate youth. "You did really alarm me at one time," he confessed. "We nearly parted company for ever on the subject of Trotsky, for whom you had a most irrational admiration. Do you, I wonder, retain any vestige of that obsession?"

"He would be better than this lot!" Charles answered. He emptied his cup. "For what we have received by gracious permission of the Ministry of Food may the Lord make us truly thankful."

"Amen," said Mark. Charles lighted a cigarette, then rather abruptly he announced:

"No, I am no Tory. I am just a defeatist."

Frown lines returned to Mark's forehead, he bent a questioning eye upon the peccant Charles.

"You should not be that," he said.

"Why not?" Charles asked, with amiable truculence. "We are not going to win the Peace on monkey-nuts and black bread, whether as socialists or Churchillites. I suppose I am, after all, *not* defeatist. I don't want England to degenerate into a slum, presided over by a sanctimonious official class. If I despaired as you do and sold out to Beelzebub, then I should complain no more of course—I should say *yes* to bad tea, to bad bread, to the purchase-tax, to the income tax, to no petrol, to three-and-six-pence for cigarettes, and to a doctrine of servile submission."

"If you think it is the way to win the Peace, Charles—to use your ridiculous expression—to find fault . . .?"

But Charles broke in impatiently.

"Of course one must find fault, Mark. You work for them, that is another matter. But why on earth should *I* swallow their rotten tea, and smoke their extortionately-priced cigarettes (two shillings and tuppence of the three-and-sixpence goes to the Government) and say it is heaven? Besides, mankind cannot dispense with fault finding, or call it by its proper name, criticism. If an inventor were enraptured with every model he produced, even his first rough draught, if he dispensed with the principle of trial and error—if he tested but *never discarded*—he would not get very far."

"Nor would he if he listened to every ignorant suggestion."

"The trouble is that all the experts are outside, not inside, the Government and its committees."

"Quite untrue, but go on."

"These people are not *trying*, however, that is my main complaint. They have in mind something quite different from a prosperous society. They have in mind an object society. When you and I yearn for good tea and for white bread, that is 'reactionary'."

"Which is utter nonsense, Charles. There *is* a world food crisis. I am sorry, but there is."

"Do you really believe that? Are you incapable of using your reason, have they deprived you of that, my poor Mark?"

"No. It is not I who am irrational. . . ."

Charles gathered himself for an assault upon the citadel of Unreason, and Mark, smiling nervously, manned the walls.

"I am as sure as that I am sitting in this chair—it seems to me

self-evident, that the most irksome of the restrictions and shortages are not economic but ideologic; political. A Government
which wanted to create an atmosphere differing from that of a
Poor House, which is what we experience, could do so without
risk of any kind to its economic stability. Why is there no rationing in Switzerland, a country which imports proportionately just
as much food as we do? Why are things more 'normal' in France,
Italy, Belgium, Holland? The answer is that our rulers do not
wish for a return to normality. They desire to maintain abnormality and 'crisis.' Even in Western Germany there is much more
food than here."

They had both pushed their chairs back a little from the table,
the glow from their cigarettes sometimes lit up their faces in the
yellow gloom, which the electric light did not banish.

"Is it really necessary for me to point out why England appears
worse off than neighbouring countries?" Mark asked testily. "It
is easy enough to explain, and it is very much to her credit that
she does so appear."

"Oh, yeees?"

"Yes. In other west European countries Marshall Aid has
reached the top crust only, the idea being that it would somehow,
some of it, trickle down to the bottom. A return to normal *luxury*
was in that way rapidly achieved. You mentioned Western Germany. The most dreadful contrasts exist there—of a new *Schieber-
tum* in stark contrast with an indescribable poverty. They have
just fixed prices so high that only the rich can buy the best food—
and then they abandon rationing! So could we easily if we were
so inhumane as to adopt that method! In England rationing
stopped the well-off from getting all the food. It is a façade of
immoral luxury in Paris that makes the French seem 'better off'
than the English to the tourist. Underneath the gilded crust those
countries are *worse* off. You ought to know better than to believe . . ."

"So ought you, so ought you!" Charles yelled delightedly, waving his hands. "Don't you believe all that stuff about a thin gilded
top crust, with famine underneath. In Paris restaurants fre-

quented by taxi-drivers you feed better than at the Savoy. *Anywhere* in France one can eat far better, far more, and far cheaper, than here in England. *And* there is no filthy purchase-tax either. You forgot to mention that!"

"Really old chap . . . !"

"Be patient. We English are in the presence of a Great Design. The big idea is to push this people down to a living-plane strictly that of the average manual worker. That is the first phase. When they have us tied up with controls so that we cannot move hand or foot and have drugged us with dogmas, the idea is to push the entire mass down lower yet, to a carefully regulated peonage, paid possibly with scrip, all shops state-owned. Nothing must stick up above the primitive level decreed except the Party. Even such tiny protuberances as us, Mark, with our hankering after good tea (of the old middle-class days) are an offence. The 'crisis' atmosphere is of the same kind of as the wartime black-out. All are now agreed that the black-out was grossly overdone in England if not totally pointless. It was 'atmosphere.' This tasteless tea is *atmosphere.* So is that ghastly bread!"

Mark had been listening more attentively at last, but his expression became much more severe. He examined his friend—the eloquent moustachioed mouth, the eager ideologic eye, the inflexion of the "county": he watched as if engaged in making a diagnosis, with a patient who revealed symptoms more and more disquieting. As Charles stopped his host suddenly stood up.

"Charles, you are hopeless," Mark told him quietly—in a tone in which a doctor would wind up, "and I fear it is *malignant.*"

"Incurable. I am chronically sick of the present Government."

"Where on earth did you collect all those batty beliefs? A Great Design! Socialists are sparing you, Charles, the exquisite inconveniences of a bloody revolution."

"Fiddlesticks. Like Kerensky they are paving the way for communism."

Mark shook his head.

"You get your politics from the *Daily Express.*" He stretched. "I am going to get my mail."

"Postman doesn't bring it up any more—pops it in a box down-stairs—have to fetch it yourself—serve you right!" Charles chanted, lying back, his face to the ceiling and puffing derisive smoke through his moustache.

Mark stopped at the door. "Egotist! Why should that poor devil climb fifty flights of flat-stairs every morning and get vari-cose veins and fallen arches!"

"He did before!" Charles called after him. "And—he's varicosed already. His feet are as flat as a pancake!"

Mark roared back from the stair-head. "You will be a postman yourself in your next incarnation."

"Not going to have any more lives," howled Charles. "This life is quite enough for me!"

When Mark got back, muttering "excuse me" he tore open a buff envelope, glanced at the contents and hastened to the tele-phone. He dialled a number and waited. With an irritable sigh he hung up and redialled. After a minute or so he rehung and dialled a single number.

Charles laughed. "Telephone not working this morning? The Exchange will see what they can do! Dial O."

"Will you try and get me Whitehall 6688? . . . Yes, I have dialled twice. There was absolutely no sound. . . . Thank you." (A long pause.) "Number engaged? But there are twenty lines at least. . . . Thank you." (A long pause.) "What? . . . The num-ber is Whitehall 6688 not Whitechapel 8866. . . . No, it is *not* 8866. . . . All right."

During this pause Charles chattered. "It keeps a lot of people out of mischief playing telephones. An American woman wrote to my paper the other day that it took longer to get through to Brighton than to Buffalo, New York."

Mark was speaking at the telephone. "Yes. I am having a blood test at twelve o'clock. . . . No, they think it is all right. . . . I will. I will mail it tonight."

Mark looked at his watch, quickly dialled again. Then he ex-ploded.

"Are you Temple Bar 5032 or *not*! . . . Oh, 8976. I see. Sorry."

He rehung and dialled again. A short pause. "What is your number? . . . Not 8976 *again!* . . . Oh damn. Sorry."

Mark rehung and dialled a single number.

"The symbolical number Zero!" observed Charles as he went to the door. "You are showing the Dunkirk spirit, stout fellow. You haven't left your post at the telephone. You have to vacate all numbers except Zero. So you go and live with good old Zero. Why not always dial O? Why have any truck with anything but Zero?"

Ten minutes later Mark was setting off, a brown paper parcel held against the stomach. Charles joined him.

"Going to be bled?" said he.

"If you care to call it that."

"Just what you need as a matter of fact, bleeding."

"You think so, Charles?"

"What we all have to put up with, *you* deny the existence of. *You* bottle up the curses to which I give vent! *You* suppress more than I spit out. One of these fine days at that rotten old telephone you will explode, the bad blood you bottle up will tear you apart —*bang!*"

Mark laughed. "You have got it all wrong! The telephone staff are . . ."

"Wonderful—I know, I know, all ought to have a Victoria Cross and a Nobel Prize. And so ought you—so ought you! Come along and be bled—quick."

Outside the flat-door before pulling it shut, Mark stood still and fixed an Ancient Mariner-like eye upon Charles.

"Let me tell you something, Charlie!"

"Yes?"

"All the intelligent people I know—*intelligent,* Charles, intelligent—are socialists. They have discovered suddenly that they are socialists."

"You mean all the smart alecks."

"Oh no. For it is *stupid,* Charles, to be a little black-marketeer. Not very intelligent, Charles!" And Mark poked Charles with a stiff forefinger.

"And, Mark, my lad!" Charles poked an expressive forefinger into Mark's midriff. "The winning side, eh! Cowardly cowardly custard!"

Mark growled with sporting glee and his eyes sparkled as he flattened the tip of his square-headed forefinger upon Charles's chest. "Not so, Robin Hood! Not so Dick Turpin! You will end with a price on your head!"

"Ha! And *your* head"—and Charles flattened his forefinger upon Mark's cheekbone—"won't fetch a farthing if it ever comes up in a witches' auction. *This yes-man's skull one farding!* No bids."

"I suppose, Charlot, you pat yourself on the back," and Mark flattened his forefingertip on Charles's arm. "You outwit the police, yes? Rich Americans get their black-market eggs, illegal rashers, and what not, thanks to good little Charlie! Fine intelligent work, what!"

"And you, my smart man," Charles poked him pointedly with his finger, "you have one egg a week and crow as though the millennium were here!"

And they went shouting down the stairs, jabbing each other mirthfully with their forefingers.

_____ 3.

DURING the remainder of that day the two friends might be found in various parts of the town, up to 11 P.M. when they returned to Rotting Hill. Their cab took them up Wimpole Street on the way to the Heppel Laboratories. As they ascended one of the two celebrated streets of costly medicinemen Charles reacted characteristically to his surroundings. "The art of medicine," he said, "will decay in this country. The National Health Act writes *finis* to fine work in surgery and dentistry, and doctors will sink to the status of druggists—with more responsibility and less pay." To which Mark replied, "Charles—rubbish! When medicine ceases to be a profitable racket as it is at present it will be far better placed to make real advances. They may even discover a cure for the common cold."

The man with the dirty white clinical-coat who let them in said: "I suppose it's for a blood-draw?" "I imagine so," said Charles. "My friend is badly in need of a *letting*." The man himself looked like a blood-donor in the last stages of pernicious anaemia, but he was a hectically talkative Cockney.

When Mark's turn came to go in to be "drawn" he expected to find himself in a laboratory, spectacularly antiseptic, white jars and tubes containing human blood, labelled and ready for diagnosis, lined up on glass shelves. The tools for "the draw" would be much in evidence. But this was a Socialist dream. What actually happened was so much the reverse that Mark supposed a preliminary interview was considered necessary.

A dingy sitting-room of the Trollope period was where he found himself. No vacuum cleaner ever came near the dusty shelves and decrepit leather arm-chairs. The doctor would have been all the better for a little mechanical suction too. But he was unmistakably a doctor: he invited Mark, with great urbanity and kindness, to take off his jacket and to be seated near him beside an untidy desk: and when they were both smilingly seated close together by the desk he invited Mark to roll up a sleeve. This was it, then!

The doctor, still smiling, examined Mark's left and right arms, well stocked with muscles and fat. "I think we will take it from the finger," he announced with quiet affability—he could not have spoken more softly or smiled with better breeding. "Your hands are very cold," the doctor remarked sympathetically. And indeed, the room was so cold that Mark's hands were like ice rather than flesh. The doctor was evidently used to this complication. He led his case to a wash-basin. There the hands were practically boiled, and they both went back to the chairs again. The doctor smiled with exquisite courtesy and kindness. "Warmer now!" he said. "Yes. The *hands* are," said Mark. The doctor apologetically took his right hand and gently stroked the middle finger with a piece

of wet cotton wool. Then rather unexpectedly he jabbed an instrument deep into the ball of the fingertip.

The doctor drew out the instrument and proceeded to squeeze
the hole he had made quite viciously. He murmured a complaint
about the paucity of blood, then jabbed his instrument in again.
"Sorry!" he murmured (he was a very perfect gentleman) and
started squeezing again and collecting the red trickle.

"My blood," said Mark, "refuses to visit so exposed an outpost
of my body. It lurks in the well-covered trunk until I get into a
warmer room. Then it may come out."

The doctor smiled gently and indulgently as he fixed on the
band-aid and said "I am so sorry the room is not warmer. When
we throw out this Government, Mr. Robins . . . !" Mark looked at
him severely as he put his jacket on and very coldly observed: "It
is not the Government that is to blame, sir, as you know quite
well! Good day." As they were being shown out by the hysterical
anaemic Cockney with the dirty white coat, Mark enquired, "Is
this a National Health Service place?" to which the answer came
with a laugh "No, sir . . . not by a long shot. We *do* have
National Health Service patients, sir, when the other laboratories
are flooded out as I might say with them. Let me see, yes, sir,
there was one of them this morning, sir." Charles burst into a
laugh which caused the doorman to jump almost out of his dirty
white coat.

"I," said Mark sternly, "am that National Health Service patient.
I shall immediately report the filthy condition of this place, and
the lamentable disregard of sepsis. Why do you not send that
coat to the wash? Good morning!"

Charles remained on the doorstep holding his sides, which a
gargantuan laugh threatened to split. He stamped about gasping
for breath.

"You are growing into an idiot!" said Mark.

"But I would not have missed that for anything. 'Why don't
you send it to the wash?' Ha, ha! Sublime! The Welfare State in
action. An informer!" And he pointed at his friend a trembling
finger. "Snooper!"

"Shut up." Mark walked smartly away.

But Mark had not lost Charles. As he entered the marble halls of the Richelieu near Piccadilly, Charles was at his side—or he was at Charles's. This most famous establishment has always specialized in poor food. But the grill room lunch was a carefully calculated insult to the British palate, delivered by a staff of deaf but noisy Italians, who flung the plates down on the table, and rushed away, deaf to the protests which at once arose. The "soupe brésilienne" was dirty yellow water, the "foie braisée mode de Mayence" was literally a piece of blackened shoe-leather, the "pommes soufflées Richlieu" had never "blown" and tasted of last month's fats, and the "baba au rhum" had no rum and was not a baba. The coffee tasted so rancid and bitter that one sip was more than enough.

"If you put a five shilling ceiling on what may be charged for a meal . . ." said Charles in answer to Mark's muttered apology, lighting a cigarette. "A man has to live."

"He does not have to live at the expense of the community. *This* is bad behaviour!"

"Report 'em!" Charles winked at him.

Mark eyed the wine list with distaste. "What will you have, Charles?" They had a double "Fine Maison" and Mark spoke of Ida. "I was thinking the other day," he said, "we haven't met since . . . when *was it*? Being out of England most of the war years in the East damages one's time-sense, deflates the perspectives or something."

"It was 1936 I believe, down at Tadpole's."

"So it was, so it was!"

"As a matter of fact," Charles told him, "she is coming down to stay with me and is coming to London tomorrow."

"Is she really—you didn't tell me, Charles. . . ."

A mixed expression came into Mark's face, which he struggled to conceal. It was the outcome of inharmonious emotions. In his effort to shut off the true expression he acquired one of sheepish benevolence. "How is old Ida now?" he asked, frowning in sympathetic puzzlement, as if he had asked a pretty difficult question.

"I have often meant to get you to tell me how she spends her time. You don't see much of her, do you, but *I* haven't seen her for over ten years. I was awfully sorry to have missed her last year. That was your fault! Has she altered . . . I mean become a blue-stocking or anything?"

Charles smiled enigmatically. "Come along with me tomorrow to her club; she would like most awfully to see you, I know."

"May I, Charles? An excellent idea, I still have a day or two's sick leave. It will be most exciting seeing Ida again. Another snort? I'm going to. Waiter!"

A half-hour later the two friends stood in one of London's largest stores, the brown paper parcel still held by Mark rather carefully, against his left-hand breast pocket. The thick and sluggish stream of shop-gazing charladies, finding an obstruction, bumped it and rolled around it. For Mark and Charles stood together muttering in the middle of the MEN'S SHIRTS. They examined attentively a batch of shirts of most attractive soft check, conspicuously displayed.

"Sixty shillings," said Charles pleasantly, "of which fifty per cent, I expect, is purchase-tax. You bought two. So you paid Cripps sixty shillings when you fell for this pretty checkwork."

"Try not to talk like the *Daily Express*," Mark observed.

"Oh, well, you love Cripps so much you probably feel patriotic about it."

Mark asked a tall shopman where the manager of the department was to be found.

"I am the assistant manager," he was politely informed. "The manager is away."

A young man came up to him with a bill which he initialled or something. Mark opened his parcel and revealed a shirt identical in all respects with the attractive pale blue checks displayed on the counter. The assistant manager gazed at the shirt and then looked enquiringly at Mark.

"Have you had any complaints about these shirts?" Mark asked him.

"No, sir. None whatever."

"I bought two of these here recently. Have you a room where I can put this shirt on?"

Mark and Charles were conducted to a small room and Mark changed into the shirt he had brought in the parcel. Not only his hand but all his bony wrist and a piece of his hairy forearm protruded from the cuff. "When first I wore this," he told the assistant manager, "it was rather embarrassingly long in the sleeve, the cuffs almost reached my knuckles. This has only been washed *once*. You can see for yourself what has happened to the cuffs. They receded at least four inches, leaving my wrists high and dry."

The A.M. produced a tape measure and adjusted it to the area in dispute. "Yes, sir," he agreed. "Two and a half inches."

"I call it four inches," Mark corrected him.

"We, of course, will give you another shirt." There was to be no unseemly dispute, the A.M. made it clear.

"It was this shirt I bought, though. I do not want just *a shirt*. I was not short of a shirt."

"Of course not, sir, I quite appreciate that. No shirt today as I dare say you know, sir, is 100 per cent safe, most unfortunately. The trouble is in the factory. In the weaving of the fabric if they do not weave it close . . . well, there is a space between the threads. Naturally, sir, when you *wash* this cloth the space between the threads tends to close up. The cloth *shrinks* in other words. It is the work people. They will not work as they used to. Since the war it is terrible. Not that we don't insist, sir, that goods we buy are *tested*. Oh, yes. As an instance, in the Swiss factory where these shirts come from everything is thoroughly washed before it is made up."

"These cuffs must have extended well over the fingertips mustn't they before *that* wash!"

The A.M. tittered politely. "That's right, sir. That's what puzzles me."

"Are people, customers, still too timid to complain?" Charles asked him. "If they take home an article of this sort have they not the spirit to bring it back and raise hell? Do they think *any-thing* is good enough for them? Because they are merely English?"

"A year ago they were, well, a little like what you say, but they do complain now. There are people bringing back things all the time. But I wish they *would* complain more!" protested the assistant manager. "You would be surprised the kind of goods we get sometimes. A consignment of thin vests arrived this summer. We opened up one vest and there was a blooming great hole the size of a half-crown right in the middle of the back. We opened up a few more and I'm blessed if there wasn't a hole in every blooming one! All had to be condemned of course, but I'm bothered if I can explain this Swiss shirt."

He affected to muse for a moment. "It is just possible, of course that these shirts come from here."

"What!" Mark was indignantly alert. "From England?"

Charles lay back in his chair and laughed. "*Never* from this land of competence and integrity! What are you saying!"

"I don't say it *is* so," the A.M. corrected. "It is possible, that is all."

"Do you mean that *material* was sold by us to some Swiss factory," Mark demanded, "which that factory proceeded to make up into shirts: and that when the first of these shirts began to be sold to the Swiss they duly shrivelled up (like this one) in the wash? As you see I cannot even *button* this collar. And did the Swiss—is that your theory—then send the whole consignment over here?"

"To sell them to the poor boobs of English—that sort of thing?" Charles added.

"Well it's you that put it like that you know, sir! I know nothing about it at all, I only think that perhaps the shirts themselves were made here for export to Switzerland. The Swiss are fond of checks you see—the way we like stripes. But" (catching sight of the displeasure which Mark did not seek to hide) "remember I know no more than *you* do. I am only trying to put two and two together." The cloud on Mark's face made the man nervous. Could he, he wondered, be a shirt-manufacturer?

"Your explanation seems to me an exceedingly plausible one," Charles told him. "You are to be congratulated on your brutal frankness."

Mark was silent. Thoughtfully he took off the shirt. "Will you please let me see what you propose I should take in exchange."

Back at the counter the assistant manager muttered obviously confidential instructions to the young man serving at that counter. At last two shirts were produced from some secret recess and laid side by side for Mark to make his choice. One was of exceptionally cheap and garish blue, coarsely striped, the other white.

Charles said in Mark's ear, "They keep these for such occasions. You would look well in that *blue* one!" Mark shortly left, his shirt beneath his arm, informing the assistant manager that he would write to the management. "It is disgraceful!" he added, in a rather official voice. As they marched away Charles affected to be concealing a smile which Mark affected to ignore. When they reached the street Mark said his head was aching badly, which indeed was the case, and that he thought he would go back to the flat if his friend didn't mind. In an offensively "understanding" voice Charles advised him to rest up for a while. They arranged to meet at a downtown restaurant for dinner and Charles took a cab to keep an appointment with an eye-doctor. This had been the main purpose of his visit to London.

The eye-specialist, who was one of the leading consultants in this specialty, possessed a large, brilliantly-lighted residence, eloquent of wealth, health, and a beacon-like eyesight. Within, it was sumptuous. The young woman who answered the door (one of the doors of Death, after all) breathed an expensive friendliness. The strains of "Cosi Fan Tutte" came down from halcyon regions above, also brilliantly lighted, at the summit of a vast staircase. "How fortunate it is," thought Charles—as he passed into the costly and cosy waiting-room (which was actually *warm*) and took up a copy of *Life*—"how fortunate it is that I only suffer from astigmatism."

This was one of the many eminent specialists who had refused to take service under the State. "Cosi Fan Tutte," Charles approvingly reflected, "does not belong to the same dimension as the Welfare State!" But when he found himself in the presence of the large preoccupied man, with a shock of white hair, he received no response to the first of his disparaging remarks about socialized medicine. The man he had come to consult went down in Charles's estimation. "Whatever did Williams want to send me to this old fool for?" he grumbled internally.

His was a routine eye-test, "no thrills," as they say in Harley Street when no pain is to be inflicted. The massive and clumsy frame used for tests was stuck upon his nose. The big anguished-looking red-faced man then delicately placed lenses out of a box in the empty sockets of the frame. He dropped one of these, which later was discovered in the cuff of Charles's trousers. The lenses of course were revolved and Charles was asked what he could see. There was sometimes an embarrassing absence of *rapport* between what Charles saw and what the doctor thought he ought to see.

The doctor, twisting the lense slowly towards him would comment, "Now that is better like that, isn't it?" Charles would answer, "I'm afraid not." "Not?" the doctor would ask with surprise. He then would place another lense in one of the sockets and say confidently, "Now *that* is clearer, isn't it?" When Charles would answer "No, that is worse" the doctor would observe gruffly, "No, it can't be *worse*. Let us try again. Now I will put back the one that was there before. Remember what it looks like through this. Now"—and snatching one out and placing the disputed one once more in position (and it was during one of these lightning exchanges that a lense flew out of the doctor's hand and nestled in the trouser cuff)—"now is that not better? You can see better with that can't you?" "No, sir, I am afraid not. I cannot see so well." This happened more than once. Charles naturally concluded that the great specialist was no magician. The doctor, on his side, decided that Charles was one of those insufferable patients who always try and put the doctor in the wrong. At the end of the test he was even less talkative than before.

When Charles said, "I suppose I shall have to wait months for these bifocals," the doctor said: "Probably. That, however, is not my affair." "You could not," Charles asked, "use on my behalf, sir, one of the priorities they give you?" But the only answer he got to that was: "It is dispensing opticians who are the people to talk to about that, not doctors." Meanwhile the specialist was making out the prescription for the spectacles. "Do you mind where you go?" he asked Charles. "You don't mind where it is?" A curious question. However, Charles declared himself indifferent, and the specialist said, "Then go to Davis and Merks. You have on this envelope their address." And Charles saw that the name "Davis and Merks" was printed on the envelope. (The old devil gets a rake-off, mused Charles.) "I will telephone them and see what I can do."

Charles would of course have preferred one of the spacious and dignified Wigmore Street Opticians' saloons, where a staff of impeccably mannered male mannequins still fit spectacles upon one's nose as though it were a historic nose and as if Debrett were their bible. But he sat in Davis and Merks modest premises in an insignificant side street for a long time before he realized the sort of place he had been sent to—before it dawned upon him that the treacherous old eye-doctor (obviously playing a dirty game, with one foot in both camps, but his *left* foot having precedence over his *right* foot) had sent him to a National Health Service shop.

When he first went in he sat beside a woman in a fur coat with a well-dressed youngster. They seemed to him quite nice people until the fur coat *spoke*. He was deeply shocked to hear the accents of the Harrow Road. There were a couple of bald men who looked like clerks in his father's office. Although deploring the presence of what Mr. Orwell called "Proles," and wishing that the eye-doctor had better taste in opticians, he was still a long way from understanding the dirty trick that had been played on him. The eight tables, at which client and shopman sat face to face gazing into one another's eyes, were huddled together, and at each were two figures, their intent faces a foot or two apart. Charles became increasingly fascinated in the problems of a young charlady having her spectacles adjusted at the nearby table. Charles watched the expressions in the assistant's face and studied the extraordinarily expressive fat little back of the youthful charlady.

A mirror stood upon the table, placed there that she might gaze into it. As she studied the revolution her personality must endure, the addition of a pair of ultra-gay spectacles doing strange things to her face, alarm and doubt were expressed by her back muscles. As the quizzical eye of Mr. Charles Dyat was trained upon this bauble, this festively-coloured nose-toy, he reflected, "That's what gets their silly votes! God, why did those dratted fools of Tories never think of *spectacles*—coloured like sugar-sticks? Thirty million pairs of cheap specs would have won for them a hundred seats!" But now came the buxom young char's leisurely (everything luxuriously leisurely) terminating of the proceedings. Time was made for slaves and slaveys—and Britons were *no longer* slaves. She poked several short black neck-curls back under her bulbous tammyish cap. And oh with what delicate restraint the assistant advised her: "Always clean them with water—with—well, tapwater."

The little shy respectful hesitation before actually referring to anything so plebeian as a *tap*—and then the little laugh of comradely complicity. "Why *not*, after all?" he might almost have said. "A little lady like yourself is broad-minded enough not to mind my mentioning the tap over the sink!"

At the street-door there was another leisurely palaver, shopman all smiling charm, as he deferentially yet a little flirtatiously held the door open. Charles heard him reassuring her. They would, she would find, *quieten down* with use. Yes, the canary-yellow would no longer, er, be quite so painfully canary (no longer scream at you, my dear, *"I'm cheap!"*—Charles supplemented these adieux under his breath).

The shop was emptying and refilling all the time and Charles missed his turn twice because of his absorption in the *tap-water* episode. It was now that he began to say to himself that *there was something wrong about this place*—something terribly wrong! After all, there were *too many people* in it, to start with.

A dark baldish individual, Charles noticed, was sitting alone at a table. He walked over and sat down in front of him. Charles did not like the face of this man, nor did Charles's face appeal to the assistant—who made no pretence that he was a "younger son" who had gone into trade, who obviously would say *tap-water* without a modest pause beforehand. But he was not uncivil. It was a skimpy table, it was close quarters; Charles silently handed him the "Davis and Merks" envelope.

"Bifocals," said the assistant, staring at the prescription.

"Yes. Bifocals," Charles repeated.

"You know, don't you, sir, that the earliest you can expect these, or any bifocals with as large a reading segment as this, is three months?"

"Three months!" Charles scowled.

"That is the earliest."

"Oh, dear." Charles looked disagreeable. "What is the *smaller* reading segment you spoke of?"

He was shown a bifocal with a round spy-hole for reading at the bottom, of about the diameter of a lead pencil.

"Why does it take so long to get these glasses?" he asked angrily. "Is it a result of the National Health Act chaos?"

A tough look came into the spectacled eyes opposite his own. "It is nothing whatever to do with the National Health Service."

"Oh, you deny that!" Charles said disagreeably.

"I don't deny anything. I tell you what the situation is regarding bifocals. It always has taken a long time."

Charles reached over and took the prescription from the assistant's hand—not without a certain difficulty.

"This is mine—excuse me!" He pulled.

"You cannot get them made quicker anywhere else."

Charles and the assistant darted a nasty look at one another, and Charles left the shop. He made his way as quickly as possible to Wigbome Street, and entered the first luxurious opticians he encountered, Craxton and Dawson, Opticians to H.M. the King of the Hellenes. It was five times the size of Davis and Merks, discreetly lighted—and completely empty.

"No blasted National Health Service *here!*" Charles told himself with satisfaction.

A tall distinguished grey-haired gentleman (he turned out to be the manager in person) approached. They took to one another at once. Both suggested by their demeanour that they had been born in a Palladian palace in a vast park, in which deer drifted from tree to tree: and naturally Marlborough and Magdalen in the clothes of Savile Row defeated with great ease the Secondary School and an Austin Reed suiting.

There was complete harmony—but alas the reality of popular government in its ultimate totalitarian phase imposed its ugly presence, inasmuch as the manager was sorrowfully obliged to confess that he had no influence whatever with the factory that makes bifocals. That factory is the only one doing bifocals: it has literally tens of thousands of orders to be executed before it can deal with any new order. Nothing any shop says makes the slightest impression. Such was the gist of the manager's information. Asked whether the National Health Service was responsible for these conditions, the manager answered, a little surprised, that of course that and nothing else was the cause.

"Why does not the Government set up a *second* factory?" Charles enquired idly.

"Why does it not do a great many things!" the manager countered. These two supporters of the old order parted on the best of terms. "Not a gentleman, but a damned sound feller!" was Charles's mental comment. The manager without realizing what he was doing, wrote "Major Charles Dyat, Tadicombe Priory" against the order though Charles had laid no claim to military rank.

_____ 4.

SINCE their return from the cinema in an attempted snowstorm —a fiasco resulting in very dirty soft hail—the two friends had sat in front of the gas fire. A French existentialist film they had gone to see after dinner—"Time the Tiger" was the English title—had predisposed Mark, in the brief halt before re-entering his un-made bed, to a deeper discouragement than he had known for some time. The past fifteen hours pressed on him in this relaxed moment, in the way a crowd pressed on you as soon as you stand still. Mark's mind was now accessible to the day's frictions, against which it had been shut firmly all day in spite of Charles's propaganda. The 'flu, he told himself, still lurked in his blood-stream and perhaps some further toxins as the doctor suspected. He grilled his feet before the red-hot elements superstitiously.

Charles sat at his side gazing at the stream rising from the water placed in front of the fire. He thought of what "the actor-feller" had said: "Time is not passive—it is like a tiger devouring its prey." Its prey is *us*. But its prey is temporal, like Time itself, for we are merely time-stuff, existential ephemera. It is not some-thing timeless it devours how could Time do that?) nor is it something timeless devouring something temporal. It is Time de-vouring itself, time eating up time indeed. But *is* there in reality any devouring? Is not everything we see just something fizzling away like a firework, which we call *time?* This verbalism has mis-led us, we create an abstract entity.

Arguments of this sort had been going on in the film and were now prolonged lazily in his mind. He excogitated dimly an ob-jection to Time seen as a Tiger. Our existence is more like the water, he thought, in that bowl—a small and limited quantity. The active principle is like that fire, which slowly disperses the little body of liquid placed in front of it, until there is nothing left.

Mark at all times was liable to be visited by the discontents which—both because of inherited stoicism, and of a repressive ideology lately acquired—he daily smothered. This was a very severe attack, not unique. But day's discontents came not singly, as disagreeable memories—for he would not have admitted them into his memory any more than he had done at the time: they came as an anonymous *cafard,* an exquisite depression. On the other hand Charles was subject to no attacks of this sort: he was more analytical to start with and a truculent perfectionist. For Charles, life was a silly wrangle over a shrunken shirt: life as he saw it was waiting months for spectacles—so life becomes a struggle *to see* which ought not to be the case in the twentieth century): was a struggle *to eat*—as if we were paleolithic: he thought of life as charged with toxins no blood-test could isolate —he saw life as a struggle not to be poisoned by all the *ideas* that were injected as anti-toxins into it by malignant quacks: he saw life as a hysterical chemist obsessed by problems of antisepsis. But he never had the rough philosophy or the detachment to say "what is one man's meat, etc." The man who was being poisoned was *himself,* that was sufficient. But at least he *knew* he was being poisoned, he knew what was poison for him.

At Oxford they had sometimes sat like this, Mark and Charles, at the end of the day: and as their discussions used to start then, so now one started rather suddenly, with Charles looking up and saying:

"Do you think Time is a tiger, a ferocious beast of prey?"

It was an undergraduate opening, how people talk when they are young.

Mark shook his head.

"No," he said magisterially, "nothing forcible and palpable like that. More like the bacteria of a disease."

"It is rather a fierce malady!"

Mark shook his head again. "I don't think so. I know you do."

"At least," Charles said, "it moves at an accelerated tempo at present. Perhaps Time has contracted a fever."

Mark looked up, his handsome eyes of a mildly-stern big-dog losing their lethargic droop.

"A *fever*. Perhaps." Mark passed his fingers through coarse dark hair. "Time has certainly shown itself in the tiger class dur- ing this century. The immense explosion of technical creativeness has torn the world of two millennia apart."

"You call that tiger *Time*. You are sure the tiger is not Man?" Charles asked.

"There were men there in the eighteenth, the seventeenth, the sixteenth century and so on. No, I prefer to say *Time*. In 1900 the bee was in the clover. God was in His Heaven, all was well with the world. Fifty years ago the scene was amazingly different. The radio, the automobile, the airship and airplane, the tele- phone, television, the cinema—these revolutionary techniques did not come one at a time with decent intervals in between. Four decades absorbed this stupendous cataract."

"The advent of energies out of scale with man, as if a race of giants had been born the size of skyscrapers." Charles shook his head; "1900: a blessed time."

"In some ways, yes," Mark agreed. "Though neither of us was born yet. We are like the cinema and the telephone in that respect."

"I am neither like a telephone nor like the flicks." And they both laughed. "Tonight," Charles proceeded, "we have been to a movie play. Forty years ago it would have been living, sweat- ing, actors. Much better!"

"I too prefer the mime in the flesh: as I prefer a concert hall to a radio," Mark again agreed. "However, the cinema has its uses and beauties. You would not deny that? At present it is *mis*used in the most disgusting way by Hollywood."

"And don't forget what is done over here."

"All right. But once the profit-motive is banished—as it will be in a socialist society, then there will be nothing but an intelligent standard of movie. If nothing else, its educative power will be enormous. Today it miseducates and corrupts. *Then* it will . . ."

"No it won't," shouted Charles, "not if you have that pack of vulgar nobodies still there! By *education*, which you stress, they would mean *propaganda*. And as for *art*! In the company of some film magnate they lap up the vulgarest rubbish the cinema can produce. No Hollywood horror would be too stupid for *them.* One would say that they identify *socialism* with *philistinism.*"

Mark laughed nervously. "You have got that all wrong too, Charlie. That is not bad taste, the minister involved is a man of sensitive culture. Alfred Munnings and he, for instance . . ."

"Yes, yes, and Augustus John!" Charles laughed boisterously.

"Augustus John?" A rather grave look came into Mark's face. "I don't know about Augustus John," he said slowly, "but the responsible officials are not philistines whatever else they may be. No. It is DOLLARS."

"Nothing but dollars," echoed Charles. "You believe that on the sly these great ministers of state slip out to see films of the type we have been to this evening? Who knows, that fat man at my side may have been Bevan."

"Highly probable," snapped Mark. "I know Bevan likes good films."

"Don't speak to me of *vermin*! There are vermin in *all* movie houses."

"Poor Nye."

"You will really have to get a new type of politician, Mark, for your brave new world. Do be serious about it if you must go in for it! . . . But I have been thinking about what you said—the last forty or fifty years you know and Time going berserk."

"Well?"

"Well," said Charles, "I of course agree that Time has packed a millennium into a half-century. But what should interest us most, purely as citizens, is not the terrific stepping up of man's power over nature but the fantastic power conferred upon the politicos in this new era of radio, automatic weapons, atomic bombs, and so on: of man's power over man. The power of a Sultan or a Mogul was absurdly limited in comparison with that of present-day Iron Curtain rulers. And the fact that they rule *for the rulees' good* (so they say) does not make it a more attractive proposition. Upon what they might think was *for my good* we should violently disagree, were I a Pole or Roumanian."

Mark groaned and placed his hand effectionately on that of his friend. "Charles—chum. . . ."

"Please!" Charles looked up with alarm.

"All right!" Mark laughed, "I thought you'd rise to that. But we *are* very old and very great friends."

"Yes, indeed," Charles responded gravely.

"I was not born a socialist—quite the contrary."

"Anything but!"

"Well, Charles, what I suggest you remember is that I have *made* myself a socialist—just as you might do."

"No thank you!" Charles told him. "When you see me in a 'Liberty Cap' you will know I am on my way to Colney Hatch."

"I understand perfectly. It was not at all easy at first in my own case. I felt just like you. *Inside* I still feel in many ways as you do. Habits acquired in one's young days . . . oh, of eating, dressing, and of thinking: don't I know their power! They form an unbreakable framework—I can never be a socialist like Bevan. . . ."

"I hope not."

"But cannot you see, old Charles, that all the moulds are being broken *for* one? Do you feel intact yourself? I feel sometimes like an oyster without a shell" (hastily.) "I know you will *say* you do. There is nothing left of the world we both grew up in. We have been forcibly, violently, reborn. I am not a *convert* to socialism: I have been re-born a socialist."

Charles blew, to denote disgust. "Well, I *haven't*," he said, and put a match to a new cigarette.

"You're a pig-headed blighter, Charles. But force your mind open a fraction. Consider! The right word for what you hate is not 'socialism,' in fact. It is not a theory of the state I have been re-born to. It is a set of *quite novel conditions*. But, for those conditions, like it or not, socialism is the necessary political philosophy. The society that was here in 1900 is as utterly of the past as the England of the Wars of the Roses. You have omitted to be re-born or have escaped re-birth, that is all."

"Thank God."

"All right, Charles, but you move about in this world like a ghost. You are, my dear Charles, a ghost from my past life. You are not a creature of flesh and blood!"

Mark laughed heartily, gazing affectionately at his friend.

"No?" said Charles. "I am not of flesh and blood?" At the same time he administered a pinch of considerable force. Mark started and caught Charles's wrist. "Such demonstrations," he observed, "prove nothing. A poltergeist is still a ghost."

"What you *say* proves nothing either, for it has no logical support."

"You think not."

"No. First of all, the word 'socialism' needs to be defined of course. What you mean is Marxism. Its prophet flourished a century ago. Marx's 'class-war' is the sociological complement of Darwin's lethal biological vision."

"Is life not a nightmare battle of organisms to survive? But go on."

"Marxist socialism comes to us from the past as a sacred text. It has been imposed upon this age by means of a ceaseless propaganda. As to Marxism being the only doctrine that is compatible with the air age and the ether age, that is rubbish. It is arbitrary and irrelevant. It is just as archaic as those other things which continue to be foisted on us such as the credit system, the Texas hoard of gold, Cabinet rule masquerading as parliamentary democracy—there is a long list of these obsolete institutions and techniques deliberately preserved. It is a very eccentric theory that television, rocket-bombs, radio and X-ray oblige us to accept Marxism."

Mark lay back and yawned nervously. "If," he said, "you find yourself unable to accept my solution of your difficulties . . ."

"What difficulties?" Charles interrupted.

"Wait a year or two Charles and you will find out. But here is something else. Socialism is so solidly entrenched that no Blimp crusade is likely to dislodge it."

"So you think."

"So I know. Its leaders are *de facto* rulers of England."

"What if the Tories come out on top at the general election?" Charles asked.

"If they were the strongest party? They could hardly secure a working majority. But if they did—if they do—they could not rule. There would be a General Strike, a violent one. Should the Tory Government succeed, for argument's sake, in breaking the General Strike, that would not be the end. In suppressing it there would be bloodshed. A nascent class-war would be on. There would be great bitterness, nation-wide plotting and agitating, half the country permanently strike-bound. Do not delude yourself: the old party-system see-saw is at an end in this country. Not to adjust yourself, Charles, to this new situation is hopelessly romantic. Are you impressed with Lord Woolton by any chance? Are you an admirer of Mr. Anthony Eden? Or are you go-ahead, and a hot Butlerite?"

Charles laughed as he got up and stretched himself. "Now you are on sounder ground," he said. "The winning-side argument— the best I know of in dealing with the intelligent."

"That's good."

"No, it isn't. Because I am not ambitious."

"Nor am I," Mark pointed out. "Ambition has nothing to do with it. It is just in order to live on the side of the law."

"You mean," Charles told him, as he went back and sat down, "you mean to *starve safely*. To go on saying *Yes* ever after—unmolested, in a shabby corner. For *without ambition* that is all that you can mean. Well, Mark, that may be a prospect to tempt some people with. You might find that they would come and join you with alacrity. But to employ such arguments with *me* . . . ! I am off to bed and to dream of my own little millennium."

"Pleasant dreams then—full of free enterprise, free speech for the upper classes, and a little freebooting thrown in. Good night, mad rebel!"

_____ 5.

MARK'S dreams that night were coloured by anticipation of the next day's lunch with Ida. Memory led off with an album of dream-pictures of Ida as the most lovely schoolgirl that ever shook a golden curl—seventeen, a year younger that he was then. She poked fun at him, in the dream, and finally gave him a huge pinch, hooting with schoolgirlish mischief. The pain of the pinch woke Mark up. When in a few seconds he was again asleep, it appeared that he was on his way to visit his wealthy aunt who lived at York. Soon he had reached his destination, and as he had been fancying she might be dead he pressed the bell, making ready to say how sad it was and he did hope she had not suffered at the last. However, she was not dead: he saw her crossing the cavernous drawing-room quite skittishly as he entered. "How down-in-the-mouth you look, Mark? Has anything happened!" she was exclaiming, her white teeth flashing in the gloom, holding out briskly a shrivelled hand. And then he perceived it was Ida smiling at him ironically: only an Ida of what would probably be called "a young seventy." The face changed sometimes into that of his aunt Susan (Robins), and then his aunt began to masquerade as Ida, in a really horrible fashion. They were looking into a very large glass bowl containing goldfish when his aunt made a sickly little soft gasping sound. He found himself supporting her in his arms. She was quite heavy, he placed her with difficulty on a sofa, on the way tripping over a rug and almost falling to the floor with her. It was obvious to him that she was dead, and he looked at her face most unwillingly. It was that of Ida, a waxen white deeply lined, the scalp disagreeably grizzled. Turning away violently he cannoned into a parlourmaid who had arrived there behind him without noise. "She passed away quite peacefully," he told her and she smiled. He smiled too. Then he laughed.

When next day at her club Mark found himself in the presence of the real Ida, for a moment he was incredulous. He smiled at her emptily with his teeth, as if to show he was not taken in. But he soon warmed up, for she was no apparition.

Ida looked—oh, around twenty-five. The lazy laughing lips of Rossetti's Jenny ("fond of a kiss and fond of a guinea") were as roseate and indolent as ever: her eyes were steady, an almost imperceptible dance, as well, giving them a remote glitter of gaiety.

As if it were *a top,* humming and spinning on without changing position, perhaps she would go on being like this until suddenly time asserted itself and she stopped dead. Such images of precarious fixity were frankly admitted to his consciousness by the otherwise infatuated Mark: but he was not altogether innocent of cosmetics. He was aware that the illusionist's name might be Rubinstein, but what did that matter? It could not be *all* Rubinstein. A divine mental sloth, it occurred to him, played a major part. She would have agreed actually: she know more about herself than the fish does regarding its marvellous iridescence, or the humming-bird its aerial spinning. Any marvels she could account for.

The quality was still dream-like and introspective, certainly, only Mark felt confident that this time she was not going to turn into a wealthy aunt.

"Your labours at the Ministry have greyed you Mark a little," Ida said at once (no doubt reading his thoughts and diverting attention from her face to his). "Otherwise much the same."

"Yes, I have altered, but *you* my dear Ida are *just* the same— and if there is art, its causes are not found."

She shook her 'twenties curls with a nervous and defensive mirth. "A little vanishing cream, combined with an empty mind, is quite enough," she laughed. So he and the woman he had always been in love with—and had not married any other because she was always there in his imagination—eyed one another benignly. He exposed his haunted vacuum, and she automatically entered and warmed it to the temperature of paradise.

They were a party heated by the suns of the past: they were three people in the nineteen-twenties who entered the Ivy Restaurant. The restaurant personnel, stolidly Italian, were cold and hard in nineteen-forty-nine. Mark, Ida, and Charles talked of old 'twenties books and dishes and jokes, their politics were only those that may be found in a Gilbert and Sullivan Opera where everyone present is a little libe*ral* or a little conserva*tive*—except

for a moment in the small entrance lobby. An authentically proletarian youth, attempting to look dramatic and sinister, was heard
to ask the doorman-vestiaire, "Is Mr. Zilliacus here yet?" Charles
said "I hope not" to the ceiling, but the comment was intercepted
by the doorman-vestiaire, who looked curiously at Charles and
Charles returned his gaze.

Ideology, otherwise, was wiped off this trio who had that *clean*
sensation the non-political have. Mark had actually put the question to himself. Why had he not married Charles's sister? He supposed it was Charles. It would have been too like homosexuality,
which was an absurd sensation. She had not married, herself,
until nearly thirty, and in a couple of years that marriage was
terminated by the death of her husband in the hunting-field. He
had been no horseman, poor chap. She insisted on his learning
to ride in a Bayswater riding-school, however, and she whisked
him off to week-end hunts with a stockbroker outfit in East
Anglia. Since his death she had divided her time between Tadicombe Priory and Withers Norton, the other parklet which had
materialized on her wedding-day and which she had so far been
able to retain.

Three theatre queues outside had an Italian minstrel in at-
tendance; with a most piercing pathos locked up in his sinuses
the high notes of heart-throb of a gutter-Pagliacci penetrated the
lunch-time roar of the ever-full Ivy, and provided a musical sugar-
stick background as the three old friends rolled again in memory
in the Swiss snows at Wengen—or drifted talking very youngly
along "The High" on their way to Blackwell's to buy Lawrence's
Sons and Lovers. And Mark reflected as they talked that one
never knew, one *might* some day (if one did not come to the
point with Ida) get married at this late date and to the wrong
woman. Horrifying thought! He had a premonition of the form
the wrongness would take.

But the cocktails and the Sylvaner were taking effect. What
happened arrived with great suddenness. At one moment they
were blissfully gay as they revisited the landscapes of their youth
—as if by common consent refusing to admit anything to their

consciousness later than 1929 (that as a rather dangerous limit). Next moment almost, it seemed, they were all three glaring at one another. Ida—an Ida at least twenty years older—was denouncing the Socialist Government: she had asked why he, Mark, had not immediately handed in his resignation after the "vermin" speech of "that filthy little man Bevan, who ought to be horse-whipped!" "Ida!" Mark had protested, half-rising. But "why not!" had shouted Charles, half-rising, too, "is he not the lowest and dirtiest . . ." "I am not going to listen to this nonsense!" Mark protested still more strongly. "If Ida is drunk, that is one thing. You, Charles, should have a stronger head! I see you should take water even with your wine!"

The change of climate, however, had been so abrupt and so absolute, and Mark prior to that had been so completely transported into the neutral fairyland of the past, that—though he attempted to silence public abuse of a powerful Minister, and of one personally admired by him as well—he was for a short time dull and bewildered, groping his way about between two worlds.

But the *Navy League* side of Ida, aroused with so alarming a suddenness, tore on into battle, her face distorted with partisan rage. "They have cut down the reserve of officers!" spat those lips so recently models of a charmed aloofness. "The last R.N.V.R. cadets are now in training. There are to be no more. Who are to replace officer casualities? The lower deck I suppose! Only half the Fleet is in commission. Fine fighting units are rotting in port —soon we shall have the navy of a South American republic. We could be defeated in battle by Brazil!"

Her eyes flashed as, in indignant fancy, she saw the flagship of the Home Fleet cock up its stern, explode, and sink, the victim of a Brazilian torpedo.

"Ida, do stop talking such dreadful nonsense," Mark expostulated.

"She is not talking nonsense but very good sense," Charles objected. "Ida has her facts from a pretty reliable source. Admiral Darrell is a neighbour of hers at Withers Norton."

"Wars are decided in the air—surface craft are militarily obsolete," Mark said with cross indifference. "Darrell is gaga anyway."

"Say what you like," Ida broke in again. "England is defenceless. The gang of ex-dock labourers, asiatics, and corporation lawyers who push us around from Whitehall are traitors. They should be hanged from the yard-arm!" She pointed fiercely out of the window at a convenient lamp-post.

At a neighbouring table a man who had been reading put down his paper and signalled angrily the *maître d'hôtel*. He was recognized by Mark as a socialist member of parliament. He was complaining about them to the *maître d'hôtel*, who studied Mark with attention but apparent lack of interest.

Ida by no means desisted—she became personal.

"You, who are of our class, deliberately helping that rabble to enslave England! It does not make sense. Can't you make an equally good living in some more honest way?"

"By engaging in a bit of black-marketing?" he enquired dryly.

"Yes, Mark, yes! That would be a damn sight straighter than what you are doing."

"I'm sorry, Ida, but you see I am a socialist."

"So you say!" Charles smiled with good-natured scepticism.

Mark closed his eyes to shut out Charles's smile. He felt very foolish and his choler was unabated. To the springtime regions where the great sex issues are normally decided he had returned—the greatly retarded mating was in process of consummation when his love transformed herself with nightmare suddenness into a Tory soap-boxer. He had consented to play Romeo, and Juliet, at the critical moment, had acquired the mask of Col. Blimp, haranguing him from the moonlit balcony. An irrational resentment towards the brother and sister he was sitting with possessed him. He was in no mood to see in it an illustration of Time's tigerish leaping. He had been *tricked*, was what he really felt, by Charles and Ida; they had made a regular fool of him. This was a matter of feelings only, though, for he did not suspect a *plot*.

Mark looked across the table coldly at the vindictive female mask. A woman he had a few minutes before theoretically united himself with! He understood that it would be impossible for her to behave otherwise: that even from 1939 to now was a great time-leap for her—from a life of petty pomp to one of straightened anxiety—dismissal of gardener, disposal of a horse or horses, acuteness of the dress problem, and a prospect, as she saw it, should this election go the wrong way, tantamount to *murder*. Murder just as truly by Cripps as would have been murder by Crippen. What was the difference between a man who killed you with taxes or one who killed you with a revolver bullet or a dose of arsenic? None: except that the *taxer* takes longer over it—and is not tried for homicide!

A long silence was broken by Charles's laugh.

"Three old friends," he croaked, "who stopped to look *forward* at the Sodom and Gomorrah of the Future—and they all three are turned to salt!"

Charles was unable, however, to turn them back into flesh and blood; and when not long afterwards these three old friends left the restaurant all three knew that they would never lunch together again, that they were friends no longer. Charles, singly, would have been able to postpone, for some time at least, this break. But Ida had been decisive. The Brazilian Navy had sent to the bottom the good ship Friendship, built in the palmy days of pre-World War I.

Charles had taken his bag away about five—both were a little stiff at the last. That evening a loneliness attacked Mark in quite new places, even interfering, he found, with housework. He had had no time to make any arrangements for the evening, so there he was cleaning up after Charles, and afraid to sit down—for he had already tried to read and found he could not. The expulsion of Ida from her place in his imagination was responsible. These were the final pangs of Mark's rebirth into a novel age, as well as the death-throes of Ida's image. But he did not identify his pangs: he did not analyse. He went to his desk, took out a piece of notepaper and wrote "My dear Wendy." Wendy Richardson was a

good party-woman, with a pretty face. He asked her if she
thought Time was a tiger or a pussy-cat. He had been thinking
a lot about Time lately, he told her. He thought himself it was a
pussy-cat that had grown overnight into a tiger. Anyway, would
she go with him to see the French film "Time the Tiger." "It is,"
he concluded, "a film with a kick in it. Excuse the Americanism."

EPILOGUE

Post-General Election exchange of notes between Mark Robins and Charles Dyat

3 March, 1950.

MY DEAR MARK,

Your "Pick the winning side" argument is only effective if the side you support is at the moment winning. With a majority of merely seven in the House of Commons you have to find a new argument, don't you? What is it?

CHARLES.

DEAR CHARLES,

Like most Tories you seem to forget that the Election was won by the Socialist Party. You will yet be disagreeably surprised by what can be done with a majority of seven. But you seem to mistake me for a recruiting-sergeant. If I were one, however, I should not be interested in you as a recruit. I should tell you to go and join some other army. Meanwhile I suggest you find some other correspondent.

MARK.

THE business of the stories and sketches of which this book is composed is, first, the life of the Hill, of Rotting Hill. You must always supply, in your imagination, the jaded bustle of this key locality, the lumbering torrent of trucks and taxis and buses, the parasites, parade before the bored D.P.s staring out of the café windows of our overcrowded polyglot hill. Next is the big background of the city, which swells around the hill. Beyond that is the island of which the city is the capital: after that the rest of the earth—full of sub-machine-guns and atomic bombs, the grasping Yankee and the treacherous Israelite, the Russian Bear and the French Frog: an earth covered with Iron Curtains and other nightmarish features. To write of the Hill, the city must hang there like a backcloth in a play, with its theatres, cathedrals, palaces and Parliament.

The Hill is covered with houses, as is everything else as far as the pigeon's eye can reach, as it stands in our roof-gutter digesting our bad bread-crumbs, except for Hyde Park and the adjacent Gardens. In a sense there is no hill, for a hill you cannot see is not there. You must not think of it as prominent like the hill of Montmartre. Certainly on the west and south it is a long drop down from it, and you know it is a hill if you approach it from those directions. Even another steep little hill is stuck on top of Rotting Hill, but even that has no vista. For that its height is insufficient. So submerged in bricks and mortar, stucco and stone, is our Hill, that it would be better to say that it was once a hill, where sheep grazed, above the marshes of the Thames.

London is as unplanned as a bush landscape, having multiplied itself like things in nature do. No Baron Haussmann came to its help, or was ever wanted apparently by the English, to arrest the sub-urban and sub-human, welter, to compose a city. The Circus, that is London's Etoile, Piccadilly, is pathetically eloquent of something that just is not there.

It is the social mutations that are my subject; first upon our Hill, but equally as the potent dissolvents affect the ten millions-odd persons in London and the forty millions-odd otherwise on the island—that big coal-mine on which they are marooned, encompassed by the Atlantic and other waters: trading for food, machinery and whisky, tweed suits, and coal when the miners will work: heedless breeders, as the food grows scarcer, as though fifty millions was not thirty too many upon any sort of island.

The shops of Rotting Hill are still well enough stocked, there are provisions for the rentier spending his capital and for persons with good jobs. There is less food than there was two or three years ago, and two years hence there will be much less. The sidewalks are obstructed by hobbling women crippled by living in unheated winter rooms, and perhaps because of draughty undergrounds if they were driven there by the air-war, or surface shelters—war-rot got in their joints. For these the shops have much less food. England is busy (or its old politicians are) killing off its middle-class dowagers and superfluous women—it has doomed them to privation, England that is old itself and a little mad; and it looks with a fish-cold eye upon its pensioned workers, men and women. So to move with reasonable expedition along the narrow pavements of Rotting Hill is impossible, because of the overplus of invalids of both sexes, but mostly women.

Mr. Patricks is a mighty salesman, a pocket-Selfridge. He functions in the busiest part of Rotting Hill, strategically placed close to stations and bus stops, where the over-populated Hill discharges itself and refills itself again daily, rivalling any hectic centre of business in London. Thousands pass his door, buzz round his kiosk, where a member of his staff is always stationed, swarm inside for this and that. He stocks everything from paper-kites to shoe-laces, from "Die Welt" to ice-cream. When sweets came off the ration he ordered tons of cholocate. It was the only instance of defective judgement I know of where this remark-able men is concerned, for chocolates and other sweets went on the ration again almost at once. As his brother-in-law said, with anything so irrational and unpredictable as the Food Ministry one never knows where one is. I still felt that Mr. Patricks ought to have known sweets would not stop off the ration long. But he is excitable. When he smells profit he pounces, with the rashness of a terrier. As the boxes of cholocate were being brought in, two days after the ration had been reimposed, and I watched him eyeing them, I laughed. At once he laughed too.

Physically, Mr. Patricks is quite tireless, as nimble as a mon-key, as merry as a sardonic grig. This little spectacled Yorkshire-man—for he is no Londoner and proud of it—has brought into the relaxed atmosphere of Rotting Hill the exasperated vitality of the great steel city, his place of origin. And his toy, newspaper, sta-tionery, tobacconist trade is terrific.

His toy shop is the youngest child of Mr. Patricks' brain. It is in that he is at his best, though he rushes everywhere and does everything. He sells toys and is himself like a wound-up toy, which works ten hours a day and in fact only stops its mad rush when you lay it down on a bed. That is the sort of toy it is.

In personal appearance he is a small-size Everyman, drab and unnoticeable. When you know him, however, Everyman expands, puts on spiritual weight. In the case of Mr. Patricks he becomes a little well of explosive vitality. You do not have to lower a bucket into it, it bursts and spits gaily up in your face—so do not let us call it a spring but a tiny geyser. And there is no bad tem-per in his face.

His countenance is that of Jean-Paul Sartre without the wall-eye, of a sallow tan: you have have to add horn-rims and a slight scrubby moustache. But with these modifications, he comes very near to Sartre, so much so that I sometimes even have the illusion of a wall-eye (unless one of his eyes does actually shoot off and stare skywards, I couldn't swear that it didn't). There is often, too, an anguished look. It is the existential mask. Lastly the hair is ruffled like a schoolboy's. That is Sartre-like, too.

Of all his Sartrian attributes it is perhaps his corrugated forehead which is the most important. It stamps him more than anything: it is the ruffled surface, ploughed up and graved by the restless contriving beneath, as much as his trousers which are always horizontally creased by his ceaseless violet locomotion. So we have a facial index of the strain involved in conducting a high-pressure petty trade, as much as big business: making good buys from smart Jewish travellers—computing the number of paper-windmills that will sell in a trimester, or toy dartboards in a twelvemonth—working out why the public would buy American Parker pens when you never knew if it was a smuggled article, but now that it is plentiful, oh, what a buyers' market! (the solution, of course, not public perversity, but because everybody stocks them): computing, too, how the baby-slump will affect the purchase of individual articles, knocking some out, bolstering others—guessing right as to the true nature of the slump itself—considering Cripps's health, as that regards a slackening of the pressure on tobacco. But I do not suggest that Mr. Patricks watches bulletins *re* Cripps's condition as would a good stock-jobber: but he is no rabbit darting in and out of its hole. He is an intelligent agent.

This Sartre-faced *petit bourgeois* (as Sartre would call him) rushes into the office with a haggard look, a fountain-pen lying in the palm of his hand: stops in front of his big brother-in-law, and looks up into his eyes. "Her son has sent it back," he says. "Oh!" says Tom Carr. "He has, has he!" "Yep. Says she wants something that will go through a carbon." They both gaze at the pen, and then at one another, emptily. Mr. Patricks asks: "Shall I give her a Blacknose?" Tom is silent. Puzzled, I observe: "But this one would carry perfectly well through a carbon." Tom smiles. "That," he says, "is the point." He shrugs his big Scottish shoulders. "It would be impossible to convince her that it would. Her son is in Wales. He says you can't get a carbon with it. If *you* say you can, she says you're a cheat and a liar." He looks at me for a moment with a blackness charged with meaning. "No other pen sells," he observes pointedly, "for the same price."

Then minutes later I stooped over a copy of *The Leader,* looking at du Maurier's illustrations to "The Moonstone," at the magazine counter. Mr. Patricks held up one of his giddy rushes to squeeze my forearm and to half-whisper "I got another ten bob out of her!" looking down the shop at *her.* The Sartre corrugations are gone—he is the schoolboy who has snatched an apple from a tree under the farmer's nose, or rung a housebell and skipped to the corner to observe the householder poke his head out and look angrily up and down the street. Many business magnates perpetuate I think the sports of childhood, just as general officers do. Mr. Patricks' beer would taste sweeter that night. He played Indians and took the scalps of the stupid. But he was not mercenary.

Now, for London Mr. Patricks feels all the typical contempt of the industrial North: contempt for courtiers and money-jugglers, for Threadneedle Street and Birdcage Walk, for Lombard Street and Mayfair. Cockney humanism he scorns as *soft.* As unclassconsciousness, a bad voter, the creature of another, unregenerate day, of donkey barrows and Pearly Kings—and Pearly Kings of course would be, as he saw it, satellites of the authentic fairy-tale anachronism whose image and superscription adorned the money in his till. He is sarcastic but tolerant of such things. He knows that peers all hired their robes and coronets from Moss Brothers who stocked the required fancy-dress—his brother-in-law had told him: and all that goes on there he regards as typical of London. The arch-spivs in hired regalia at coronations, and the Lord Mayor in his fairy-tale coach, with powdered footmen, completes his picture of this spiv metropolis. His politics are not aggressive, though he does not hide them. When, in a by-election, the socialists gained Hammersmith, his brother-in-law told me they had lost a lot of customers. People came in with long faces exclaiming,

"What do you think about Hammersmith!" To which they would answer, "What have we *got* to think about? Our party has, of course, got in again." After a horrified stare, customers would bolt out of the shop. It did seem to me that for a day or two the shop was a little empty: though some customers, I think, would merely go to the Irish House as the corner, have a stiff whisky, and come back and buy a socialist steam-roller (rolling both ways a dozen times) for little Freddie, or a half-ounce of labourite snuff.

"Spiv" is a sound Mr. Patricks enjoys making. When he is dealing in sociological generalities—which he rarely has time to do—"the spiv" plays an important part. This is, of course, because most of his customers are spivs: and they are the spivs of all nations, what is more. There are female spivs as well as male spivs. There is a shrill old Frenchman, for instance, who Mr. Patricks says is in the black market in quite a big way: he is always accompanied by two dogs, one named Josephine and the other Napoleon (alas, the latter is stonily indifferent to the former). Business acumen is admired by Mr. Patricks, but this old French rascal is an adept at wasting the shopman's time without any adequate financial return. He and his dogs track him down, even if he retires into the office. Napoleon will enter the office and bar his exit to the basement stairs, eyeing his trousers significantly. He once bought a fountain-pen, changed it six times for cheaper and yet cheaper pens every time, and ended up with a ball-pen at seven and sixpence which he always brought in for repairs. Mr. Patricks hates Napoleon and Napoleon hates him— and if the Corsican does not end by taking a piece out of his calf I shall be very surprised.

When he knows you Mr. Patricks will roll a cigarette, and the city in which he has lived and traded for seventeen years is a subject he is by no means indisposed to touch on. He does not speak about the costers or the Crown: that was my gloss, though it is altogether faithful to his thought. What he will tell you is that London is "not creative": his forcible Yorkshire accent caresses the word "cre-a-tive." "What does it *make?*" he will urgently enquire of you. And he answers his own question: *"Nothing!"* (In Sheffield, which the Patricks family have lived in since it was a hamlet, everyone is engaged in "creation," that is understood, or in catering and caring for heroic "creators.") He demands disparagingly, his brow a ploughed field of brown furrows—"But what do they do here after all? They're a lot of *spivs* —well, isn't that what they are?" And I know of course that he looks upon *me* as a spiv of sorts: I have much too much time on my hands, to hang about toy shops and to look at newspapers— though he does catch signs of my name or face, in the latter sometimes—not to merit the epithet. "They're all fiddling, aren't they?" To which one is obliged to assent—to "fiddle" being to break the law. "All are trying to sell to somebody else, something the law says they mustn't sell, or trying to swindle someone out of money *they* did not make. They're parasites on the rest of the country, that's what they are! London is not the *head* of England is it? If it were destroyed the rest of the country would get on better without it!" And he will switch off the diatribe to turn and cry to some hovering customer, so as perhaps to make him jump, "Yes, Madam! What can I do you for?" and to proceed to sell something he has not made at possibly a thoroughly *spiv* price. But he has the wit to recognize the inconsistency and he would laugh with you at himself, if you were to point it out.

Before Mr. Patricks became a shopkeeper he was an engineer. When young he worked with the Yanks in engineering outfits in Caracas and elsewhere in that region: he knows what it is to "create" where nature—the great Spiv—is at its most disordered, violent, and uncreative. As a loyal socialist he is, I think, neutral regarding the "intellectuals," the brain-trusters, ruling us at present: but from his brother-in-law, who is franker, I know that they both would rather have plainer men. They would rather have simple non-intellectual fellows who were not such insanely orthodox taxers, and left cigarettes alone. But Mr. Patricks would not confide in an "educated man." He has a sort of *pudeur* about that side of his politics.

On the way to Mr. Patricks' shop is the chemists, Willoughs Brothers. I am not deserting Mr. Patricks in favour of Willoughs Brothers, I merely stop there to buy a pair of nail-scissors. A conversation I had with Mr. Willoughs indirectly involves the politics of the master shopkeepers I have been writing about, and touches on his birthplace.

If I shall be dwelling for a moment upon quite trivial things, nail-scissors and toilet accessories, let Socrates "great mountain asses," be my precedent. I am often reminded of Cleanthes' complaint, in the Symposium, for men's snobbery with regard to common things is only successfully challenged, at times, by the painter: the writer is seldom allowed to get away with a pedestrian subject-matter (however elevated his motive may be), the equestrian is exacted. The most august problems of politics, however, are implicit in a simple pair of nail-scissors, as I have just discovered, and the housewife's sugar cube leads one irresistibly to the tragedy of the entire Caribbean area, as a loaf of bread of dirty grey—half-way to black—holds the story of a lost or rapidly vanishing civilization within its dry bran-laden crust. Yesterday a whole world of small everyday objects we took for granted. whereas today they have swollen until they have taken on portentous dimensions. A card of safety-pins or a man's utility shirt hardly can be described as pedestrian, and I beg their pardon.

Willoughs Brothers are across the road from the public clock in Rotting High Street: they have been there as long as the clock, which ticked out the landed society at the Repeal of the Corn Laws, and ticked in the Liberal era, which conducted to the Welfare State. I stepped in and crossed the shop to Mr. Willoughs. I asked him if I might see some nail-scissors. Mine have for some time been defective: but as practically everything is that way, I have grown used to the waste of time involved in using them. The nails do not cut, they fold over the blade of the scissors. The blades far from kissing, keep as far apart from one another as possible. I explained the position to Mr. Willoughs.

When I went up to him, that almost ham druggist, a stock white-haired Hollywood feature-player, blanched in the service of Esculapius, bent his eyes upon me gravely: for he saw that service, which he was ever ready to bestow, was about to be solicited. When he had heard my—oh, my *desideratum*, he coughed lightly and said "Well!" As he looked at the ceiling, he expelled in a short quiet bark some tired air from his lungs. Then he eyed me with a scrupulous man's dramatic frustration. "I am waiting, Mr. Lewis, for another consignment of French scissors," he said briefly. "French scissors?" I enquired, genuinely surprised. "Yes," he answered shortly, "I don't know when I shall get them though. Perhaps next week." "Where else round here," I enquired, "do you think I am likely to find some?" "I don't know. But I don't recommend you to buy any scissors in Rotting Hill, Mr. Lewis. They're English. And they're *not good!* All the English scissors I have had have been bad!"

This was a patriot speaking: he resented British manufacturers deteriorating from the once extraordinarily high level to such trashy levels that even the French were to be preferred. He did not desire to conceal and condone it. In this I agreed with him. To hide up defects is destructive. Of course, Mr. Willoughs delighted in ethical melodramatics: he looked pained and resolute. But had practical advice too. "Go to Weiss in Oxford Street. They are surgical instrument makers. They are the only reliable people I know of." "Well!" I said. Said he, "I know."

From nail-scissors we went on to speak of other symptoms. For instance: replacing the metal screw cap on any tube or bottle was invariably difficult. It stuck, it joggled about: those small daily operations were not accomplished smoothly, there was friction and time wasting. The cause? Badly-finished goods was the only answer. The caps of toothpaste tubes never fit neatly. I waste half a minute every morning coaxing the cap on to mine, that is three and a half minutes a week—say fifteen minutes a month, three hours a year. Ink-bottles which I use a lot are nearly as bad. As popular counter-irritants to the bad bread and flour (there are hundreds of new ones on the market) are other examples of time wasting ill-made metal stoppers and caps. But the instances of careless manufacture are legion.

Mr. Willoughs silently went to a drawer beneath the counter from which he produced a tube of "Ipana" toothpaste, an American article. Swiftly and smoothly he unscrewed the cap, and ran it back again upon the tube. "A precision job," he observed, looking up at me. (He did not want to make a sale, on the contrary, this was "under the counter," reserved for Lady Jones. I acquired it. As he had shown it to me it was difficult to refuse it.) Mr. Willoughs takes life seriously: he likes things to fit for ethical reasons.

Returning to the nail-scissors as I was leaving the shop he said solemnly: "And Sheffield goods were once the best in the world!" Whereupon I left, amazed at the situation. A responsible London shopman was dependent upon goods imported from France, such steel goods as scissors, of English make, being worthless. He did not want to jeopardize the reputation of Willoughs Brothers by selling Lady Jones and other valued customers scissors the blades of which would wobble about.

As I entered Mr. Patricks' shop I heard his theme song:

> *In Scarlet Town where I was born*
> *There was a fair maid dwelling.*

As he rushed down behind the counter the whistling of this Border air made his rush more enjoyable. "Young man I think you're dy-ing" was reached as he charged into the kiosk. As his in-laws were Scottish, and he lived with his wife, Tom Carr and his in-laws, "Barbara Allen," I assume, may have been a favourite of the old gentleman's, who came from just north of the border: near "Scarlet Town" perhaps.

I lost no time in repeating what I had heard at the chemists', including his lament as to that once pre-eminent steel centre, Sheffield. Mr. Patricks, licking a cigarette paper, forcibly dismissed these sentimental aspersions upon Sheffield steel—partly because he was a good socialist. "Sheffield goods are still," he insisted, "the best in the world. We know," he argued, "we come from Sheffield. All the people we know work in the factories."

From his lips, this carried conviction. If they were half as active as he was it would bore them to slack.

But the fact remained that English-made scissors were inferior to French products: and the scissors I had bought a year or two ago were rotten scissors. "Most of the top-quality goods are reserved for export," I reminded him. To that he assented: he had never *seen* what was being produced, he agreed. Then his brother-in-law, Tom Carr, threw some light on the subject. Carr is an ex-gunner officer. He is a newspaper-man who threw up his job to come and help his brother-in-law. With the drastically restricted paper ration, on top of the other drawbacks of newspaper-work today, he preferred to make twice the money selling snuff and Christmas cards—and of course newspapers. It is not easy to get the newspapers out of the blood: he passes in review the entire Press at breakfast-time daily. It is with an eye of a Labour man he makes up his headlines.

Carr's information was that since the war, in Sheffield a number of mushroom firms had sprung up. To acquit Sheffield of any complicity he described them as "Jewish"; but we so often describe gentile villainies as "Jewish" that conscience obliges me to insert a caveat. These new spiv companies turned out a shoddy line of goods: of course they would be marked "Made in Sheffield." They were mostly quite small—and of course I was reminded of the Stanley investigation, in which there was mention throughout the proceedings of the construction of factories as if it were a bagatelle. These new shoddy parasite factories would not account for everything: but it was very useful information. It did suggest that a new and spurious England, as it were, was growing up side by side with the traditional England whose "word was as good as its bond" and whose goods were of so lasting a character that a suit of clothes would endure perhaps for twenty years, a penknife or scissors were ground when the knife-grinder came round, but were never re-bought, and a clock, a kettle, or a chopper was an heirloom. I have French nail-clippers I bought in Dunkirk in 1917, when I was a soldier, and they have never been ground. Thirty-two years of clipping: what steel! I remember wondering—after a time—how it came that the French could produce so Britannically solid an article. I shall never be guilty again of that particular naïveté.

That evening I dined at a house where I met a minor member of the Government. The 1949 money crisis had broken the day before. The U.S. annual remittance to Great Britain had, it seemed, with some suddenness, ceased to be enough to keep Britain going. Britain would either have to stop having so high a standard of living (so said the Press, though we all know that the Belgians, French, and even Germans, lived better than we did) *or* our statesmen might advocate that the 25 billions' worth of gold buried at Fort Knox be set rolling again or some part of it. Probably, however, the "crisis" was some bluff: as my fellow guest politician looked as if he couldn't care lest I took it to be some bluff. I asked him if there was a crisis: I hoped he would agreeably dispel my lack of fear. Actually he said something very interesting.

He said matter of factly that there was a crisis. He listed the main causes—such as bad selling methods of England in foreign countries. But his first-named contributory cause was the impossibility of getting people to work. The workers would—not—work. Another of the causes he mentioned for the crisis was that the English were not turning out satisfactory goods for export. Our foreign customers were fighting shy of our goods. So much was this the case that the famous "gap between exports and imports," far from closing, was widening daily. It is obvious how that alone would lead to crisis. This had nothing to do, presumably, with cause No. 1. For this had to do with *quality:* whereas their slowness had to do only with *quantity.*

I could not but think, of course, of nail-scissors. I wondered if our goods for export were as badly finished as those in the home market. I decided it was probably not that but a crisis of stupidity. The manufacturers knew little about foreign countries, rashly dispensed with the help of intelligent advisers, and so produced unsuitable goods. Even the American businessman uses brains, if he can find them, but natural antipathy of the Briton for brains operates in business as it does in politics, art, and in every department of life. It is easy to see how English goods might be to foreign buyers wanting in style and intelligence.

The conversation turned to the home market: whereupon I mentioned what I had heard about the mushroom firms beginning to infest Sheffield. If such a parasite growth had shown itself there, it was doubtless to be found in every great industrial centre. Our politician responded with an emphatic *yes*. When up in Sheffield recently he had heard a lot about the small speculative firms. But then we proceeded to praise the Grand Hotel in Sheffield, with its excellent dining and dancing room and good orchestra: its food and cellar so far superior to anything of the kind in London.

From its roots in everyday life, amid nail-scissors and toothpaste, we have worked upwards, as it were, to a fact of great political significance. The Socialist Government are deeply frustrated by the phenomenon of working-class slackness—of which they are the innocent cause, as representing the working-class Party, and being in Power. Having at length elected a Labour Government (as formerly called) with teeth in it, and willing to bite with them, the working-class lies comfortably back and takes its ease, celebrating the departure of the slave-driving capitalist. Encouraged by its communist shop-stewards, it turns a deaf ear to exhortations to work on the part of their new socialist masters. If bothered too much, they strike, usually under communist leadership. Neither the Trade Unions nor the Administration meanwhile incommodes the communists (the Administration for fear of losing communist support at the election). So, of course, anarchy grows, far more deeply and insidiously than is visible. For habits of indiscipline are being formed in the working-class which one day will bear fruits. The country looked for socialism, and it has found anarchy.

Since coming into office the Government has been engaged in an all-or-nothing gamble. With what they could gouge out of the nation in taxation, direct and indirect, with American subsidies, they have popularized socialism, have produced a socialist elysium. Without a revolution this was the only course. Countless "jobs for the boys," free dental plates for all, canteens and high wages—they created the honeymoon atmosphere of the Welfare State—an atmosphere not conducive to hard work, and its manufacture eating up money at a terrifying rate.

Some Ministers have eyed this carnival askance. To have to pay so heavily for the privilege of bringing social justice to the working-class seemed to them absurd: and the danger of failure, owing to exhaustion of the exchequer as a result of this insensate spending, very great. Mr. Aneurin Bevan, recently discussing a "blood-bath" in the event of a Tory victory, conceded that he personally had never greatly believed in the possibility of ruling without coercion. This meant, of course, that the totalitarian state is perhaps inevitable, to end the welter of indiscipline and insane spending. And we must not say, *"Plus ça change plus c'est la même chose."* It is never—whatever else it may be—*the same thing.*

Meanwhile—to go back to the Toy Shop—I discovered the deft fingers of Mr. Patricks, ex-engineer, busy with a defective toy bus, the smoke from a cigarette curling up against a half-shut eye. The honeymoon atmosphere permeating the factories militates no doubt against the production of flawless toy buses—unless the spiv factories, the small parasite outfits, are to blame. It was plain to me by this time that to identify the culprit in any particular case would be impossible. This socialist shopman, for all his furrowed forehead as resilient as a rubber ball, conducted his business under conditions almost of Keystone slapstick. Sometimes knocked clean off his feet by some particularly austere buffet from the Board of Trade (which Ministry in conjuncture with the Treasury, acted as the official brake upon Honeymoon spending), he came up smiling though dishevelled. The market, again, was a maelstrom of contradictory currents. Shortage would suddenly be replaced by glut—so that, when hemp was scarce, he might lay out some money on a batch of skipping ropes, only to find next minute that skipping ropes became so plentiful that he made a loss on his speculative batch. The disconcerting gluts sometimes might mean that goods unacceptable to the foreigner had been thrown back into the English market. But he has the discipline never to blame his Party, now the Government. Not once have I heard criticism from him: he only allows himself, and that very rarely, an impolite view of Cripps. Seeing that he is a little capitalist himself, engaged in an individualist activity which would earn him a bullet as a kulak if the Left Wing of his Party replaced the Right Wing, his attitude is paradoxical.

The toy bus rushes along the floor, stops, from its abruptly opened door protrudes a tin conductor. Its doors shut abruptly, with a little tin bang, and off it rushes once more. Such in theory is what happens whenever you wind it up. But the door has stuck and will not open. Or once having opened, and thrust out its flat uniformed figure, it will not close its door and resume its mad career. As a rule I find Mr. Patricks seated on his little haunches, demonstrating some such gadget to a watching babe of nine or ten. Or his cheeks are swelled out, inflating a toy balloon. If it bursts because he has emptied his lungs into it, and it is smaller than his lungs, his response is that of a child. He will cut a caper, twirling around and clapping his hands, and then thrusting them between his knees. He looks on such occasions more than ever like Sartre—in bacchanalian mood (perhaps at the moment of delivering a sportive haymaker at Mlle. de Beauclair). The children enjoy it too, but with less *brio*.

Mr. Patricks had a moment of confidential expansion.

"There's no such thing as a good toy today," he grumbled. "None are properly finished." "Don't they work, then?" I enquired. "Oh yes," said he, "they work up to a point: though I often have to fix them, and the damned things come unstuck. But look at this!" He held up three irregular bits of tin attached to each other, hanging down dejectedly, to me incomprehensible symbols.

"What is that?" I asked him. "Is it a plane crash—surely not?" He shook his head.

"That's a lorry," he informed me, as he dropped it with a rattle into a brimming tray. "They make them in bedrooms. Yes, that's right, there're lots of them do that. Foreigners. The best toys come from France. That"—pointing—"is a French toy. But they're not good."—"No?"—"No. The toys today are rot-ten!"

His Yorkshire accent broke rotten most expressively into two autonomous vocables charged with disgust. As he was talking I remembered that we have in a neighbouring flat German-speaking tenants who hammer dully all day. Possibly toy-makers. One of the bedroom industries of Rotting Hill. Another bedroom industry I feel sure is matches: whittling pieces of black-market wood and dipping the tips in some over-inflammable substance. The best brands now are plentiful: but a year ago most Rotting Hill matches exploded in your face. No doubt there are cigarette-makers: and of course there are cabinet-makers. In the distance, perhaps three flats away, we hear some very heavy banging. Mr. Patricks' "French" toy stock might come from Soho, chopped out and painted in a cellar. But Mr. Patricks sells his *"rotten"* toys like hot cakes. Other people's therefore cannot be any better.

The Patricks' toy shop is thronged with the children of prosperous spivs. The stream of showy-looking kids, with the school-caps of local spiv-schools for the sons of black-market gentry, and big fawn-jacketed blondes of eleven, some decked out to look like miniature Gorgeous Gussies, with Corgies or Wolfhounds on a smart leash, never slackens: side by side with these are gangs of shuffling ragamuffins, clutching a copper in their filthy little fists.

All it is my guess like his Yorkshire blarney too. Is there a blarney stone up in Yorkshire I wonder. If so Mr. Patricks has most certainly kissed it—and has skipped away as replete with mischief as a Sartre-faced elf. He treats his customers with the freshness of a high-salaried radio quizzer. But like myself, they seem amused.

CHAPTER 7: The Talking Shop

_____

THE "Talking Shop," as the English call their Parliament, is the only place the public may visit where ruling is going on. Londoners have never been so addicted to sightseeing and peepshows as they are at present. The Zoo is packed, the Tate is packed, and the House of Commons is only a fraction less popular. On a fine summer's day a dense queue of what George Orwell called "proles" stand, loll, sit, and lie for hours to get in and have a look at the M.P.s spouting. There are no doubt a substantial number of provincials, but it is a working-class crowd, and it is as a *sight* that these people regard the Talking Shop. The English are the most unpolitical of any nation. They regard what is going on in such a place as this with a bland detachment, as if it had nothing to do with *them*.

Going there, as I did, to see a Member, with whom you have an appointment, you do not queue. You pass inside; all you have to do is to say to the policeman standing in the doorway that you have an appointment with such and such an M.P. No papers, no passes, are necessary.

It is perfectly easy to get into the House of Commons! If you wanted to blow it up, and were an "educated man," you would walk up to the St. Stephen's entrance, say to the policeman, "I am lunching with Colonel Jones." (Pick a Colonel: policemen always like a Colonel, though Lord Winterton would do just as well, policemen like lords—they respect them.) The constable will pass you in at once and if you have mentioned a lord, he will probably touch his helmet. If a proletarian, you cannot do this, of course. The policeman would not believe you—he would know Colonel Jones would not lunch with you. He would begin bullying you and might end up by arresting you and so discover the infernal machine in your pocket. I am afraid if you are a proletarian and want to blow it up you must take your place in the queue.

But if your accent is good and you are adequately well-heeled, this police constable is the only person to whom you have to address a word. Having negotiated him, the bomb ticking away in your pocket and your heart going pit-a-pat too, you would pass inside the building, enter a long gallery lined with statues—of M.P.s of long ago, in tights (looking like Shakespeare). You march along this in a business-like way and you then emerge in a large and lofty hall, like a railway station, lighted by a circular glass dome. (I think—anyway it is daylight.) Here is where you would have to be careful. A ribboned official, in I suppose police uniform, stands in the centre of the hall. He knows all the Members by sight and by name. He would know you were not a Member, but that would not worry him—there are lots of visitors and other people moving to and fro. Since he is a very busy functionary he would in all likelihood be talking to somebody. He would only notice you if you showed signs of hesitation, and that only if momentarily disengaged.

If embarked on the deadly though ridiculous errand we have supposed, it is necessary to walk straight across this hall, as quickly and unconcernedly as possible. If stopped, say you are a visitor—do not mention Colonel Jones or Lord Winterton—they might be passing across the hall at that moment, which of course would be fatal as you would be led up to them. On the other side of this hall you enter a busy corridor. Almost immediately you will encounter a convenient lavatory, but there is a better, *less frequented,* one a little further on, down one flight of stairs. You go in, deposit your bomb, and leave by the same route. If the policeman at the St. Stephen's entrance should recognize you and say for instance, "Wasn't Colonel Jones there, sir? I saw the

Colonel go in, sir," you just say, "Yes, I saw him, thank you. We are lunching outside." You can then get your taxi, settle comfortably down in it, and, perhaps, a terrific roar apprising you of the success of your mission, out of the rear window observe your time-bomb rock the Talking Shop, blowing all the M.P.s up into the air—just as you are entering Whitehall, or driving into the little park between the Horseguards and the Palace.

But let me give you a piece of advice, should it by any chance occur to you to commit this outrage. Spare yourself the pains. If you regard the Parliament as being not only a Talking Shop but a Power House, you are quite mistaken. Put your bomb away, my dear sir, Parliament has altered a great deal since the days of Guy Fawkes and Catesby. You would not be blowing up what you fondly supposed was there: nothing in fact but what amounts to a large theatrical company. The play is called "Crisis." But there is no crisis. The plot is the conflict in a free democracy between the Lefts and Rights. But there is very little difference in what the Rights want and what the Lefts want—and there is no democracy.

If a bona fide visitor, as I was this lively June afternon, upon reaching the large hall (assuming he is not yet acquainted with the M.P. he has come to see) identifies and addresses himself to the uniformed official who stands in the centre, he must tell him which M.P. he desires to see. Comfortable seats are provided: he is directed to take his place on one of these, and when the Member he is waiting for comes into the hall, the official sees him, shouts his name, and looks at the visitor. I know this part of it because I went there myself; as I failed to contact my man's secretary, I took my place among those awaiting the arrival of some legislator, as friends, relatives, or as clients.

Were it your first visit, as you watched and waited, no doubt you would experience, not necessarily a thrill, but a lively curiosity. You would wonder where the actual Chamber was situated. If you were moderately innocent, it would be the same sort of sensation as being behind the scenes at a Plaza de Toros. *One* of these openings out of the big hall where the official shouts is where the arena is. It would not provide a kick equivalent to being (as a tourist) in a waiting-room at the Lubianka, say, knowing that *somewhere* in the building men were being tortured. But still it would be a kick. Under the same roof with you is the place where life is weighed out daily in little packets for fifty million people. It is not really the place where the weighing is done, you would not know that. As you sat there you would say to yourself that to take a few steps off there to the left, or to the right, would bring you to a *door*. You would push the door, and you would find yourself between two crowds of glaring M.P.s, rushed at by officials, denounced on all hands as an outrageous intruder. At your first visit, *before* you became privy to the reality and were delivered from the grip of the imagination and its intensified dream-imagery, you would be conscious of an electric and oppressive *nearness* to something that was going forward the other side of the wall.

The imaginative excitement of the newcomer to this place is at least one hundred years out of date. The moment the visitor is in the presence of this assembly, as a watcher from the gallery, he must, I think, recognize the fool his imagination has made of him. There is nothing *electric* once he reaches the source of his sensations. The English Parliament is a voting-machine, not a talking-machine. Most of it remains sheepishly silent all the time —except at times when all present are allowed to act as an incoherent chorus. Since in the nature of things at present it always votes the same way, the physical presence of all these people sitting there is quite pointless. They are lectured to, or argued at, by the same handful of people hour after hour and day after day. Even when the two sides are technically evenly matched, there is no necessity for more than a half-dozen *vocal* members on either side. The fact that this voting-machine takes a human form is principally a concession to the anthropomorphic tastes of the crowd. They like to come in and see a lot of people sitting there. A few hundred unemployed men would serve the purpose just as well, i.e. to fill up, and would be far more economical. As to the committees they are not seen. The power has left this assembly completely and is elsewhere. This shadow of a Gemot, like the "constitutional monarchy" and numerous other fossil institutions, deceptively preserved, and painted over to simulate life, cannot be denied a talismanic usefulness. But, at the same time, they act as blinds.

To illustrate the manner in which the voting-machine works, the Lefts very naturally did not like the powers still enjoyed by the Upper House. The House of Lords, as we know, is a non-elective Senate, a thing which at the most should be a phenomenon like the Beefeaters: instead of that it is a fossil institution imperfectly extinct. The Lefts put into the Parliamentary Machine a measure they named "The Parliament Act." It came out, after a brief delay, duly stamped and ready for the Statute Book. The Commons has become a machine-for-stamping-bills. It is a machine that alters the laws of the country at will and with remarkable velocity.

Before continuing, let me answer a criticism which I foresee, namely that I am treating the present socialist monopoly of power as if it were always to be with us. It is true that by the time these words are printed there may be a new parliament, the numbers on Left and Right more evenly matched. But anyone is badly mistaken who believes that the eggs can be unscrambled, or that the so-called Tory Party ever would or can act again as anything but one of those fossil relics of which I have spoken— very useful to the Left since it obstructs the formation of an authentic Opposition. Mr. Churchill, landscape-painter and war-historian, too old for active leadership, is the very perfect symbol of this token-Opposition. And even if the English People returned him to power, he would only take power as a stooge of the Left.

Now to return to the Parliament Act: that measure decrees that after December the eleventh (1949) the Peers can no longer oppose, but must approve, the Steel and Iron Bill—which is the legislative *pièce de résistance* of the Left. Things like the Parliament Act go through as slickly as if the Parliament were made of plastic instead of flesh and blood. The Lords, meanwhile, will not be liquidated. If they *were* it might occur to someone to create a *real* senate, instead of this comic relic. That is the secret of the retention of this medieval waxworks. Also socialists like to end up as a "Lord." (For there are joys as well as jobs for the boys.) It is the one advantage England will always have over Russia—you end "a noble."

I feel sure that if any initiative remained to these latter-day parliament-men their life in this comfortably-appointed club would have the effect of a narcotic. What it was all about would become more and more dreamily uncertain, the facts of life would become more and more remote, everything reduced to a debating point or a wisecrack.

The accommodation in the new Chamber, in comparison with that which was destroyed by a bomb, is very inferior. Let us suppose that the visitor, after witnessing the Speaker's Procession, gazing at the Mace (which, in a light-hearted moment, a former Minister, named Beckett, ran away with) he goes up to a gallery seat, gazing down for the first time at the legislators at work. He will see that nothing is done to impress him. Everything is as undramatic as possible. If you think of a caricatural cricket match, with a run or so every half-hour, bowling unlimited, with only token batting to enable the bowler to perpetuate his gentlemanly bombardment—a match in which the majority of the fielders lie down and watch the batsman and the bowler, with a periodic chorus of "Oh, well played, sir!"—or to show we are socialists now, a massive proletarian bellow: such a game as that would approximate to the parliamentary tempo. Like the Members themselves, the visitor will soon grow fatigued by what, in all likelihood, will be the unrelievedly mercenary subject-matter. And the fact that they call each other "honourable," or "gallant," or, I think, "honourable and learned," will help very little after about twenty minutes.

In my own case I had what I laughingly call business to transact with one of the very many charming gentlemen who have condemned themselves to this waxwork existence. At lunch we discussed the matter which had brought me there, and then went out on to the handsome terrace, the Thames running strong and yellow just beneath its parapet. There is no division, on the terrace, between "the other place," the term used to indicate the House of Lords, and the Commons, only a gap in the line of chairs and tables. A couple of peers sat where the Lords' tables were and among the H. of C. tables, on the other side of the gap, a communist M.P. was drinking orangeade with a man and woman friend.

My host's attitude is, I gather, that a communist provides comic relief. This light-heartedness may be misplaced. It depends how easy you find it to forget how big the Russian Army is, and how near, since President Roosevelt arranged for it to occupy Brandenburg. There are, I believe, no communist peers. Several are as-good-as, and a bishop or two of the same colour as the "Red Dean" of Canterbury. The two peers airing themselves were right-wing, last-ditching lords, who had thrown out the Steel Bill for pecuniary, not for ideological, or for caste, reasons. They were not even Catholics. A seedy pair—right-wingism does not pay. Not content with being symbolic of Rightism by birth these two shortsighted men made things worse by acting Right. As businessmen, had they had better judgement they would have been growing fat on Labour rather than getting skinny defending Capital, in Rome doing as the Romans do.

It was peaceful to sit on this almost deserted terrace, the pink-yellow water swelling nearly on a level with one's feet, the white gulls floating past on it. If the County Council Building across the water conceded nothing to beauty it might, all things considered, be far worse. Meanwhile excursion steamers on their way to Windsor Castle and I dare say Hampton Court, or river buses, barge their way along with full loads of people this sunny afternoon, the fingers of the passengers pointing at us—the three communists, the two peers, three or four other lawgivers and myself.

My M.P. went off to see the Sergeant-at-Arms about a seat for me, for I thought I might as well hear the opening of the Steel Bill business—you could call it a debate if you liked. The peers had sent the Steel Bill back to the Commons with about sixty amendments. All of these, except a few insignificant ones, would be chopped off and thrown away, one by one, then the Bill would be returned to the Lords, who would hug it until December the eleventh, when, as I explained just now, it automatically becomes law. The Rights, or their leader Mr. Churchill, promise to stop it, or wipe it out, if they win the Election. Since the Lefts, were they desirous of doing so, could pass a Bill through to destroy the whole of London, or, for that matter, atomically to blast the whole island (England, Scotland and Wales), there being no one with the power to stop them, there was very little point for me or for anybody else to go up and watch the proceedings, but I thought I would have a look at them all.

I was now sitting at the far end of the Terrace, far from Stalin's boys and the two old lords. I was sitting with a dreamy Celtic Member, to whom I had been made known. He sat perched upon his chair like a bag of discontented bones precariously balanced, with a quizzical, anxious, countenance. He was revolving something dreamily in his mind. He was thinking of Steel.

I knew he was thinking of Steel, because various people came up, sat down, and talked to him about Steel. Question time had started in the House, and very shortly the Steel and Iron question would be outlined by the Minister. The principal Ministers, Leftist and Rightist, had very sensibly gone on holiday. They felt as I did about these proceedings—in fact the Rightist chief, the Leader of the Opposition, seldom comes near the place even when in England. He devotes himself almost exclusively to painting pictures and writing books, which, as I indicated just now, gives the measure of his sentiments about the House of Commons in our time. All the rest of these honourable gentlemen could with advantage follow suit.

The M.P. with whom I sat was, I gathered, against the nationalization of the Steel and Iron Industry, and all that that entailed. This last giant transfer from private owership to state ownership troubled him, one could see. He was a gentle and moderate man, who belonged, I learned, to that gentle and moderate party which had prepared the way over many years for the very immoderate statist-principles which were now approaching realization. It is always doctrinaire libertarianism that ushers in despotism, in classical political theory. For Aristotle this was an automatic matter of cause-and-effect. Even the present government is composed, with few exceptions, of liberals—liberals taking liberalism to its logical conclusion. It would be foolish to think we could escape the periodic despotism to which human society is subject. Despotism is a human norm. So, with the best intentions these good men are preparing an instrument of oppression. This, of course, *may* never be used oppressively (just as the atom bomb may never again be used in war). But there is so slender a chance that some evil man will not be forthcoming to use such an instrument as the total power involved in state-socialism oppressively that we really may dismiss the idea.

It was a melancholy experience to be sitting there with this uneasy, puzzled, liberal-minded man who felt himself drifting out of the liberal Victorian daydream (still potent in the province which always sent him back to parliament, and in which his thinking remained embalmed)—drifting into a hard-boiled world that had none of the familiar features of the libertarian past to which he belonged. He was too gentle to say anything about *that* side of it. He just knit his brows, slightly wrung his rheumatic hands and spun a little theory which disguised the reality. It had something to do with its being impossible to check, once nationalization had been pushed through the voting-machine upstairs, the success or unsuccess of the stewardship of the Steel Board. The fundamental question he would never face of course: namely, would it be a good thing or a bad thing to consummate the absolutism of a state-system. Perhaps it would be too boringly obvious.

However, when I said unexpectedly, "Would not the concentration of *all* power in the hands of the State be a bad thing?" he turned round towards me immediately with a charming twisted smile and brilliant eyes and answered, "Oh, that is of course the basic issue."

I was amazed at this readiness. But next moment a man sat

down at the table with a sheaf of papers and my liberal friend began to expound his cherished theory. His gentle face was anguished, his eyes glittering and remote, as he argued his case with much dexterity (and this may, for all I know, have been at this great turning point the strategy to be used by his party). As the man with the sheaf of papers went away I should have liked to have asked him: "Why put up an argument that is certain to draw you deeper and deeper into a dialectical bog. Why not say all the time that what is proposed—what is decreed—will result in state-absolutism, which is at least as obnoxious, as the liberal sees it, as royal prerogative or caesarian power? It would involve the extinction of what is left to us of our democratic liberties. Why not say that? What is the use of saying anything else? Bear witness, brother, and, as a party, die!" But if I had expressed myself in this way he would only have smiled charmingly and half-deprecatingly, as if I had made a rather feeble attempt at a joke. For you do not remain a Member of Parliament if you allow anything too real to establish itself in your consciousness, and all Members of Parliament only wish for one thing—to remain Members of Parliament.

After a time my kind host returned, having arranged for a seat. He accompanied me upstairs, and then he left me, for he himself was speaking a little later: and I may add, without flattery, that he spoke with remarkable skill and vigour. I looked down upon him, a stockily foreshortened figure, holding his paper, and in the voice-transmitting agency above my head his voice rattled in my ear pugnaciously and is now embalmed in Hansard. He at least had some fun. He was a *speaking* M.P. A young Leftist of great ability, in better times he would have made an outstanding parliamentarian. He may yet be a Minister.

It was Question Time when I took my seat, and the official answers were being rattled off, followed by the lame protests or reiterated enquiries: usually almost before the last word is out of the mouth of the questioner the next answer comes rattling out, and one's mind takes a hairpin bend and spins off in the opposite direction. Mine bounced from Seaside Boarding Houses to the

Daily Worker. Then the Steel Bill business started. The Minister, moderate and reasonable—even detached and most accommodating—proposed turning everything over to his Party (for steel, as everyone knows, means, directly or indirectly, everything). When the Steel and Iron Bill becomes law, it will transform England forever into one vast Concern in the hands of a political oligarchy. There will be no appeal against these overlords, for no new *checks* are contemplated, and such checks as exist will be swept away. The very Trades Unions as an effective instrument will go. Such are the fruits of permanent Crisis.

At this opening stage the Opposition took the line that Steel experts should be appointed to the Steel Board, when nationalization came—accepting nationalization as a *fait accompli.* The mind of the Opposition appeared to be full of the question of how many posts it could secure. That was all. From time to time Mr. Churchill bursts out in his old-fashioned way about freedom and so on, words which for him have long since lost their meaning. But his party does not indulge in rhetoric: it confines itself to securing a share of the control. And only his party was present on this occasion.

There will be no word breathed by His Majesty's Opposition about the undesirability of *too much power.* Rightists as much as Leftists would acquire as much power as Stalin tomorrow if that were feasible—all were absolutists under their skins—and the Opposition apparently assumes that everybody knows this, so it never mentions *power.*

In the last analysis, Opposition as much as Government seem to argue that a new absolutist world is imposed on them anyway, which is of course quite correct. My host, for instance, had asked me if I had considered the philosophy of the Atomic Bomb—and from the dramatic way he peered at me over the luncheon table I could see he regarded it as a pretty difficult philosophy to refute. (I was, as a matter of fact, in complete agreement with him, and had no desire to confute him.) From the "pike and gun" and "infallible artillery" of the seventeenth century we had moved onwards, in the twentieth century, to what might be called

Atomic Absolutism. What this young politician described as "the philosophy of the Atomic Bomb" is the philosophy, in one degree or another, of every person in that House, whatever his party. It is the fatalism ensuing upon consciousness of a Power so overwhelming that it makes nonsense of the old humanist values.

The main impression I took away from that curious place was the oppression of almost a doctrinaire fatalism—or if you like, the determination *not* to be oppressed, but to construct a new scale of values within this framework. With the release of such powers as *those* among men, where was the use in talking of *les nuances?* All must be Black, or White—power or no power: all-power or slavery. The philosophy of Atomic Fission is not, I am afraid, worked out to its logical conclusion by these people, nor made explicit as I have done here. None are frank, it would be far better if they were. The trouble about the English methods of make-believe and the employment of the fossil-structure is that when suddenly they emerge into the glare of reality they are quite unprepared and deeply astonished; though in the artificial twilight in which they prefer to live they have been moving steadily (and one would think deliberately, if one did not know them) towards some frightful climax.

LETTERS that I receive from unknown correspondents requesting an interview (mostly to do with other peoples lives, not mine) I drop automatically in the waste-paper basket. Such letters are often those of a person who rates flattery very high among the stock baits—a person who fancies himself as a trapper. (An "eminent" man must be a vain man, otherwise—so obviously the unknown argues—he would never have sweated his way up to eminence.)

I have experience of what happens if one does *not* treat these letters as waste-paper. It does the correspondent no good to see him—it is just as humane therefore not do so. Besides, I do not happen to be vain.

Mr. Walter Gartsides' communication lay before me, I looked down at it as I lighted a cigarette: and it was not a half-dozen lines before I reached "I have haunted the cocktail parties in the hope of meeting you." Of course at this point I prepared to get rid of it. As I gripped it to tear it in half I saw the word *Rochdale*. Mr. Gartsides (the sweet euphonious name—I could see it was hideous though the signature was only partly legible) was "taking up an appointment," I read, "as art-director." It was in connection with this that Rochdale came to be mentioned; that was where he was going.

Rochdale I had seen ten days before. In a railway train after puffing your way through the Pennines, gazing with indolent sadness at those hill-villages of chilly charm—for they force you to think of England before it began to dig in its black entrails and cover its pretty little face with soot—after the Pennine interlude you re-enter the bleak huddle of this mass-day, the factories of Rochdale. Would Mr. Gartsides' job take him up where it is still beautiful in the hills, or on towards the metropolis of soot, mighty Manchester? "A few miles from Rochdale," could mean either: but there can be no "colleges" in the Pennines. . . .

To discuss with me the policy he proposed to pursue at this college, such was Mr. Gartsides' wish. At present he taught in Bermondsey: he picked ugly neighbourhoods, did this man with the ugly name. I pictured him as a big seedy earnest man. The letter was not badly written, was not embarrassing as some are, was unsmiling, was just cordial enough to be agreeable.

An aversion to humanity is not what makes me difficult of access, only an aversion to painters or poets. There are so many thousands of individuals wasting their time at the game of "self-expression"; brooding over some midget talent in some dirty little room, with some dirty little woman. After a great war they are found to have alarmingly multiplied. Were it the tinker or the tailor who wanted a conferecene, or the local builder, tobacconist, or publican, that would be different. I am uncommonly sociable. It was undoubtedly the fact that Mr. Gartsides lived in so underprivileged a neighbourhood as Bermondsey that decided me to write and ask him to come to tea the following week. Owing to great pressure of work I regretted that about an hour was all I should be able to spare. There is no pretentiousness, I may add here, in being particular about time, I am short of time. It is the government makes me short of time, or the penury of the country.

On the appointed day, and, with great precision, at the appointed hour, his knock was heard: loud—firm—short. Upon opening the door I had a surprise, which was apparently reciprocated. In such cases embarrassment is usual on the visitor's part, whereas the rules prescribe that the grantor of the interview should be bursting with self-importance—or if he is not bursting with it, is weary with the weight of it, or most "graciously" waives it—or perhaps moves circumspectly like a man with something sensational on his person—say a bomb. Mr. Gartsides, though for some reason surprised, was in no way embarrassed.

My visitor was a raw-boned man of thirty-nine, not to say forty, an age to which I do not think he had in fact attained. He carried a khaki raincoat over his arm, wore no hat, his reddish hair was rough but thinning; he was short, brisk, poker-faced, a man who had never been a great many feet above the gutter. I should expect to see him in a strike-picket, and his hard voice was like one coming out of a picket too.

Whatever it was had halted my visitor was effective for perhaps the one tick-tock of a clock: then his underdone pink face, rationed as regards expression, admitted what I assume was his party-look, and his harsh voice rasped quietly out my name. He marched straight in without much invitation. "Be seated, Mr. Gartsides," I said, and was glad the letter had been answered, and I had got something more primitive than I had asked for, and he sat down at once in my best and largest armchair, and gave my room and belongings a resolute look or two. It was not a *stare* for his aggressiveness was quiet and reserved. He sat up red and alert and silent. But his redness was not that he coloured, it was always there, and no one who lives in a class-room keeps such a face.

"I was not able to read your signature," I told him.

"No? I am sorry."

"But I am glad my letter reached you. In addressing the envelope as I could not make out the name I imitated the shapes, and put Esquire after them."

He smiled—probably he thought I was being superior about his handwriting.

"What *is* your name however!" I politely laughed. "Your handwriting is beautifully clear, but, like many people, when you write your *name* you become illegible!"

"Gartsides," he barked back, making the name sound even harsher than it is.

"An uncommon name," I said.

"Not in Durham where I come from."

"Indeed."

"Yes, Gartsides is a name you often hear."

"I can see how that might be, is sounds as if it could have belonged to a collector of the Danegelt."

To put an end to these trivialities Mr. Gartsides announced, "I have read your books, Mr. Lewis, at least some books. I am very glad we could meet. I have haunted parties and shows in the hope of meeting you."

I gave him a reproachful look and hastily changed the subject.

"How do you come to live," I enquired, "in Bermondsey Mr. Gartsides. You teach, you said in your letter."

"Yes, that's right, in an Elementary School."

"You dispense elementary education to those whose parents were insufficiently acquisitive and so had not the cash to send their kids to more classy places."

"Yes. I went to one like that myself too. Elementary—that's all I got."

This was given out coldly, as an indifferent fact, but he was laying bare an injury that society had inflicted upon him. It had given him a clown's equipment, and a clown's tongue.

"Token instruction. It's disgusting!" I protested. "Does it not worry you; to help perpetuate this system?"

Mr. Gartsides looked politely blank. Sympathy, or "understanding," was a commodity the bona fides of which he doubted, and for which he had no use anyway.

"But it is art I teach," he explained. "Sometimes in *art* the elementary is the best."

"*Sometimes!*" I conceded with extreme dryness.

Tea arrived, and some of the lardless, sugarless, eggless cakes of Great Britain 1949. The tea had suddenly improved about Christmastime, before which it had no taste whatever, having deteriorated during months in the warehouse. As he drank he remarked. "Good tea. Darjeeling and China. I always bought that": he laughed—"when I could get it."

His laughter was the public enjoyment of a private joke, and I was impelled to ask him:

"Have you always taught art in elementary schools?"

He gave a short laugh at that. "Oh, no," he answered. "Only for a year. I was a soldier."

"During the war—but before that——"

"No, I was a regular. I was seventeen years in India."

India, with its mosques and temples, its solar topees, polo-ponies—seventeen years of it violently expelled the image of Bermondsey as the background for this little figure. It was with a new eye that I focused him. It was literally as if he had confessed to a prison sentence.

"What was your rank?" I asked.

"Sergeant."

"Quarter-bloke?" I suggested.

"No, just sergeant. I trained the boys for jungle-warfare. Blackett's boys."

I digested this.

"I'm an old man," he said harshly. "I know I have not much time. I have to be quick."

He spoke as a man with a mission. But I had not been prepared for a long-service sergeant—that was one of the half-dozen things for which I was totally unprepared.

It was not the ranker—my class-bar works in reverse: but this is a Briton who comes out of a mould manufactured at the same period as the footman. On retirement, if personable, old soldiers became Commissionaires, or such up to now has been the case: prison warders, police constables or what not. With domestics they traditionally have shared a necessary obliquity, unshakeable appetite for tips, a philosophy of sloth. Following the mass-training of citizens for the first world-war the type has suffered a change—but in such cases a type is apt to keep the worst of the old while incorporating the worst of the new. Finally, it is not a creative occupation, and cannot but be a servile one, so long as the old disciplines hold.

In "total war" the first regular sergeants had left no over-all pleasant impression upon me. On the other hand, there was this: I could not imagine any of them, by any stretch of the imagination, becoming art-teachers. So we stared at one another, at this point, blankly and bleakly—for no more than the interval decreed by punctuation by its colon sign—he, reddened by the sun that "never set" on the Empire that is no more, I paled by electricity, under which I labour nightly to distinguish myself and attract ex-sergeants: he who—in his sergeants' mess in Hindustan —so he was to tell me, would listen to some ex-service minstrel who, for a drink or two, would give the sergeants "The Road to Mandalay" (where the old flotilla lay)—a year or two before the English "hurled themselves"—to use an American columnist's phrase—"out of" Kipling's India—and *I* who—(to find a minstrel for myself) once listened to an American minstrel who read a lay of his own, which he had called "The Waste Land," while the ink was scarcely dry on it. That was after Western civilization had committed suicide in a blood bath. The second decade of this ill-starred century had just banged its way off the stage.

The sergeant revealed a brand-new set of state teeth—first fruits of the famous Health Act, falsely white and symbolically of a deadly uniformity. His smile advertised polite satisfaction at the effect produced by his words.

"Well all right, so you're a soldier," I began, with ostentatious finality.

"I *was* a soldier," he mildly corrected.

"How does it come about though that you teach art?"

He seemed surprised at the question. It appeared the most natural thing in the world that he should teach art.

"Oh, I see," I said.

But he proceeded to open my eyes still further—he relished the operation, it was quite plain. Upon leaving the army he had at first no idea what to do with himself. As regards the length of this blank interlude I know nothing, but it cannot have been long. Mentioning the problem one day to a chance-met man, he heard how soldiers were being turned into teachers (not of art—that came later). The idea appealed: he fancied himself as a teacher. Sergeants develop an appetite for the imparting of knowledge.

Of course in fact he had had a wide choice of callings. Upon demobilization he could have become almost anything from a Harley Street consultant to an Anglican clergyman, by means of a Government grant: to the mind of the politician, who is anti-craft, the notion that it takes a long time to become anything worth the being is repugnant. The politician, like the journalist, is a professional amateur. The only thing there was no grant for was to learn how to be a politician. The laziest of the ex-service-men naturally chose the fine arts. The nation's money was drained off on oil-paints, palettes, mahlsticks, six-foot lay-figures, poppy-oil and sable-brushes—and of course studio rents. Sculpture was not so popular, it sounded too much like work.

Gartsides was sent to an emergency training centre. In one year he would have qualified as a teacher in an elementary school. Shortly, however, he discovered that there was no obstacle to his transferring, if he so desired, and training to be an art teacher. So he changed over (he probably found arithmetic a bit of a sweat): whether remaining in the same training centre or not I forget. On the completion of a brief period of art-training, he blossomed forth as art-teacher, was appointed to a slum-school. The other teachers there, of whatever kind, were "certificated"—which meant they had matriculated and spent some years in procuring their licence to teach. It seems he was not a popular figure, even before he showed what stuff he was made of. But it was no time at all before he did that. He quite literally painted the school red.

A thigh thrown over a desk, an arm akimbo, his utility shoe dangling, the children were addressed by Gartsides; and their fidgety little eyes popped out of their curly little heads. They were told that what was *spontaneous* was best. Spontaneous meaning what *spurts* up, free and uncontrolled, not fed out by a nasty *tap*. The freest expression—the most *innocent* release—of their personalities was what *he* was there to teach. They would get no *direction* from him, his role was that of a helpful looker-on. Ready to give a hand, that was all. (He conveyed a very vivid imper-sonation of these transactions I am obliged naturally to abridge). Art was *doing what they liked*. It was not doing what *he* liked. They must pay no attention to him or to anyone else—it did not matter a hoot what *anyone* thought. He waved a rebellious eye over towards the office of the superintendent. He could teach them nothing. What can one person teach another except to be himself, as if he lived on a little island all by himself? They all lived on little islands all by themselves. No, he was simply there in the capacity of a wet-nurse, to assist them to be their little selves, and to bring forth—to create—whatever was inside them!

The children—typical Giles-like gnomes from the neighbour-ing sooty alleys and crapulous crescents—were of course alarmed and excited. Then he appeared one morning with a number of tins of house-painters' colours and a couple of dozen suitable brushes (and he was very proud of introducing house-painters' colours into the teaching of art). He pointed dramatically to the walls of the class-room crying: "Here's paints and brushes and there's the old wall! Atta boy! Paint me some pitchers on it!"

His petrified class suddenly saw the light. With squeaks of rapture they went to work. Soon the walls, part of the ceiling, as well as the cupboards and doors and even some areas of the floor of the class-room were as rich with crude imagery as the walls of a public lavatory. Some of the children were smeared from head to foot with paint.

After this his popularity suffered a further decline among the teaching staff. Next the school-inspectors arrived one morning and "nearly threw a fit" when they saw his class-room. He played the simpleton. He grimaced with a wooden jaw, hanging open an idiot lip and goggled with his eyes, to show me how smart he could be. It seems that the inspectors were satisfied that he was practically imbecilic. Of course they recognised that this was the type of man called for to teach art. They bullied the children, however, a little, for obviously *they* should have had more sense.

After the paint he obtained some plasticine.

"What do you think they did with it?" he asked me.

I shook my head, to indicate my inability to guess what might supervene if their personalities were left alone with so malleable a substance as plasticine.

"Well, they all made the same sort of thing," he told me.

"Indeed. How curious."

"Yes," he agreed. "They stood their piece of plasticine up on end like this." And he stood a safety-match upright on the table. He smiled at me. "I asked them what it was," he said. "They told me a lighthouse."

"Ah, yes. That lighthouse rescue probably. It was in all the papers: I suppose it was that."   . .

"No," he said, obviously disappointed in me. "It was—well a phallus. Phallic."

"I beg your pardon," I said. "I see, of course. How amusing. Their personalities vanished momentarily. They became one—the primeval child."

He looked at me with surprise.

"No," he objected. "Each did a different lighthouse."

I laughed at that. "I wonder," I asked him, "if you have read Herbert Read's *Education of the Child?*" For his goofy goings on, without looking any further, might be the response to some such stimulus.

"Oh, yes." In a slightly drawling tone of voice which dismissed my suggestion as irrelevant. "The book that has had most influence on me, Mr. Lewis"—and he bent his gaze upon me as if I were showing a little ingratitude—"is your *Caliphs Design.* I have got more fun from that book than any other and I was meaning to speak to you about it."

My consternation may easily be imagined. My *amour propre* reeled at the impact of such approbation. *The Caliphs Design,* with for sub-title *Architects Where is Your Vortex?* was my earliest pamphlet. It is to do with the fine arts, with especial reference to the case of the architect. The human shell, dwelling or public building, should be demolished, I protested, no city should be spared or time wasted, and our architects should construct upon the *tabula rasa* thus created, a novel, a brilliant city.

The teaching of this book is violently opposed, surely, to the emotional "personality"-world of Mr. Gartsides and his true master Mr. Read. I put pressure upon my memory to produce some passage, or perhaps chapter, which would give aid and comfort to my "admirer." But my memory of my own work is imperfect and I abandoned the attempt.

"*The Caliphs Design?*" I asked coldly.

"Yes. It's a book that ought to be reissued."

I blinked.

"Do you still think the same as you did when you wrote it?" he asked me.

"Just the same." But I began to understand. "That the outdated dingy shells in which we live—indeed everything, you mean, should be razed to the ground and a national city replace it? Dazzlingly white in place of blackened brick and dirty stucco? That the sordid antiquated apology for a city in which we dwell disappear as if by sorcery, and a new city stand there suddenly where it was—of hard white logic?"

He nodded.

"Well, I want that now as I did then. The only difference is I know I shall not get it!"

"Why not?" he retorted, with a touch of what was for him almost heat. He became guarded at once. "It's worth trying for, anyway."

"Oh, yes. However, since you have expressed such interest in that. . . . When writing *The Caliphs Design* I was superbly ignorant of the difficulties."

"Of course there are difficulties," he agreed airily.

"Firstly, the obstacles which stand in the way of pulling down, or of building, a single house, let alone a street—or a city."

"Property rights."

"That is so. But there are factors more fundamental." I got up and passed him to fetch a box of matches. Back again I said. "I was not a social-revolutionary."

"I know you were not." He was prompt and businesslike. "You had the vision though. You saw what should be done to the *outside*—to house the new society."

"Very well—I had a vision, like my Caliph—but suppose for a moment that I had found a social-revolutionary, Mr. Gartsides, to act upon my vision. What would he have done with my vision?

Naturally what Hollywood does with a literary masterpiece. He would have diluted, vulgarized, and betrayed it. It is no use going into partnership with a violent reformist philistine. Yet to realize your 'vision' you require capital: and in this case the capital required is *action.*"

Gartsides jerked himself over from the right arm of the chair to the left. He stroked his raw face as if it hurt. "The man of action," he murmured lazily, "is not always a philistine though."

"Well, we won't have to parade of Men-of-Action! How I see it, and you came to me as to an oracle, is this. All the dilemmas of the creative mind seeking to function socially centre upon the nature of action; upon the necessity of crude action, of calling in the barbarian to build a civilization. The result is as disconcerting as what is unmasked at the basis of the structure of the human reason—I mean the antinomies."

That was my longest speech, in this access of volubility. I lay back and smoked. Then I said: "A penny for your thoughts, Mr. Gartsides!"

"My mind is a perfect blank!" He smiled the smile of the smart.

As a result of our conversation so far I understood, of course, that art was the last, not the first thing that weighed with Mr. Gartsides, whose interests were political or sociological. Like most astute men of this type he had no time for private feelings, he did not take too seriously the non-political character of my mind —especially as I was not hostile but only had not trained myself to think of the human being as a power-unit.

But I think he felt this was becoming a stalemate, or we had drifted away from the fiery purpose that had brought him to see me. Sitting up, he again mounted his savage hobby-horse.

"So you still think like that—that's good, Mr. Lewis. I'm glad. That's how I think. It is why I came to see you. I can make people enthusiastic," he assured me brightly, "I can make them see what I see." This he repeated later several times. He regarded it as his *raison d'être*—to be an intoxicator of innocents, with big brash phoney phrases. "You remember what you said in your book about the artist and the engineer?"

"That they should co-operate?" I looked at the clock.

"That's right. That's what I am going to do up in the college—make the engineers art-conscious. They never think about art. I want to make them see they can use art in their work."

"I see." I looked at the clock: but I was unable to make him time-conscious. I had not his power to make people see what I saw—at least not when it was a timepiece.

"Why don't you go out, Mr. Lewis, and make people enthusiastic, make people see what you see?"

"My way of doing that is to paint pictures," I told him. "I paint pictures of a world that will never be seen anywhere except in pictures."

"You don't think so? But the day of the easel-picture is over."

"Then there will not even be that pale reflection of something more intelligent."

"No one sees what the artist does in his studio."

"You mean that like the Borough Group he should take his canvases into the Public Gardens so that the dormant responses of the common man may be stimulated? Or the way artists stick their things up in an alley near Washington Square, New York?"

"Why not?" he said. "The artist is wasting his time doing easel-pictures. What he puts into the easel-picture he should put into the world outside. Spread his vision around—in things that people can touch—eat out of —*live* in! Their houses, their clothes."

He was all-set evidently to intoxicate *me*. I resorted to the grin, which is all that it is necessary to do when people like Mr. Gartsides who cannot paint easel-pictures, and understand nothing about the art of painting, condemn the easel-picture: or the novel or indeed any of the other so-called individualist art-forms the destruction of which they are apt to predict if not to urge, basing the abolition upon some utilitarian moral.

"You could make people enthusiastic!" How right was the eighteenth century, I reflected as I listened, in its deep distaste for "enthusiasm."

But he proceeded to enlarge upon the novel functions involved in his job of "art-director," and explained the purpose of the new colleges invented by the socialist administration. (In the field of Education they are not seen a their best.) He had gone up to Rochdale and was accepted on the spot. The director had said: "You're the only one who took the trouble to come up and have a look. You shall have the job." What would his "art-direction" consist of, I wanted to know. Would he sit down the engineers-in-the-making this college had been created to train and make them copy plaster-casts? He laughed away all plaster-casts. Or the nude model? I enquired. He smiled away the nude.

He was not evasive. He made no difficulty about explaining that what he would do was just to *inspire* and *enthuse*.

"How do you mean," I persisted. "You will in the morning leave your quarters charged with enthusiasm. You will walk around the work benches or rooms where young men are bent over blue-prints, and spout art as one would spray some intoxicant into the air? Will you get these young men to paint the college walls and ceilings?"

"Certainly that is the form their enthusiasm might take," he answered. "I don't know what form it will take however. I am here to discuss that with you."

"There would be no work on pieces of paper or canvas—which might lead eventually to . . . the easel-picture?"

"No, of course not that. What's the use of that?"

"What indeed. Do you paint yourself, Mr. Gartsides?"

At this he was convulsed a little.

"Oh, I shouldn't like you to see any of my pictures"—he gulped down a self-deriding laugh at the mere thought of the feebleness of his own "creative" efforts.

"Are they not good?" I asked.

"No, they're rotten," he assured me.

"Your activities are mainly destructive"—I assumed the air of one musing.

"No, I am creative. I can fill people with enthusiasm."

"For what?"

"For art."

It was six o'clock and I stood up. He had had his sixty minutes —and so had I.

But I rather liked Mr. Gartsides. I even secretly wished him luck. This remarkable sergeant naturally regarded art as an uproarious racket. In that, however, he was by no means alone. Many dignified gentlemen, who draw fat salaries as—*directors* just like Gartsides only on a far bigger scale, regard art in precisely the same way. The parasites that art attracts are legion. What I liked about Gartsides was the way he had jumped into it with military alacrity, out of the farmyard or the Barrack Square. He had taken Time by the forelock. He had swung himself up on to the tremendous bandwaggon. If we were going to live with nonsense, rather Gartsides and his "enthusiasm" than the higher-up impostors—the "stripe-pants" of the art-racket.

I took a fancy to Gartsides. From that day to this I have breathlessly followed his career. He has grown to be a somewhat different person: but he retains, to the full, his fine rough artlessness. If only he could learn to paint, he might do for the Army what Rousseau did for the Douane.

Most of the country near London may be classed as Greater London. One is still among the factories or in a suburb. But the county of Ladbrokeshire is rural, remarkably intact, and only a county or two away from the capital. If I feel I have rotted long enough in Rotting Hill, if I want to be where the Machine Age has not dirtied the buttercups or choked the throat of a cow with soot, I go up into Ladbrokeshire.

Last summer I found myself in the ancient township of Blatch-over, and at the top of the hill got out and entered Blatchover Church. I know nothing of the history of Ladbrokeshire and imagine that it must have had a period of great prosperity judg-ing from its churches. The wool trade probably would be respon-sible for this, around the time England was freeing itself from exploitation by the Hanseatic League and ceasing to be just a "wool-farm" for the Germans. Cloth merchants were responsible for the building of fine churches in other parts of England; their presence in Ladbrokeshire, in their burgess "halls," was doubtless the reason for this crop of rectories and vicarages. Blatchover was, seemingly, a skinners' town, and I suppose the church is the work of the Skinners' Guild.

Inside it is one of the most beautiful churches I know. Gilded banners of the apostles, showing their bearded figures in blues and blacks, with patches and strips of icy white, depend the entire length of the chancel, which has two ornate chapels on either side of it. Such embellishments, for there are many others, including a large and beautifully carved Pietà, and a Bavarian Madonna, bequeathed by a refugee, furnish it handsomely as well as visibly sanctify it. But without the hanging banners and carved pillars it would be a rich and splendid interior. In this church Robert Blaise, the former vicar, who was a peculiarly liberal cleric, at a certain moment installed the Red Flag—perhaps among these saintly banners, I do not know. On the South Wall is the chapel of John Ball, one of the inspirers of the Peasants' Revolt in 1381. History is full of rhymes, and one of the first to be impressed upon our infant memory is one that this aggressive priest borrowed from the German.

> When Adam delved and Eve span,
> Who was then the gentleman?

Dick Bartleton, the present incumbent, is almost as liberal as his predecessor. He follows Ball in believing that "Things will never go well in England so long as goods be not in common." Upon a table, not far from the Chapel of John Ball, is a great deal of inexpensive literature reflecting the same priestly abhorrence of property shown by Ball. You may buy, for a penny or two, little pamphelts explaining that socialism is identical with the teaching of Christ. (With this, I may say, I am in complete agreement.) Dick Bartleton, in a little brochure of his own, describes how a believer in Christ ought to vote. "Jesus was a partisan: he did not hesitate to take his stand with the weaker side. He ranged himself fearlessly upon the side of the oppressed and the exploited, and condemned the exploiter and the master-class. We, as Christians, must follow the example of Jesus Christ." As I have always hated *any* government, and despised any employer, and have always been exploited, I was of course glad to see Dick ranging Jesus on our side. I hoped he was not making any exceptions in favour of some governments.

Straight-from-the-shoulder Dick Bartleton preaches a grand sermon, they say. He has one of the saints of revolution in his South Wall and he, too, teaches that nothing will ever go well in

England until goods are held a great deal more in common than is the case at present. In the social history of England in these years it is worthy of note how many clergy—both clergymen and ministers—are at least as economically "advanced" as is the present Government. Some even are open and declared members of the communist party. (How they reconcile Marxist materialism with the Christian idealism I cannot guess.) A socialist society exists of Anglican clergymen, whose delegate at a recent Paris conference was a Sheffield clergyman married to a Bishop's daughter. This phenomenon should be compared with the attitude of the French priesthood before the French Revolution.

I left Blatchover's beautiful church with regret. That night I passed at Meldrum not far away, and from that place drove over next morning to visit a clergyman of a very different type from the Vicar of Blatchover, yet equally, if not more, unconventional. It is this clergyman, the Reverend Matthew Laming, and the story of his rebellion, which are the subject of the present chapter. It is far more usual to find a contemporary clergyman agreeing with the powers that be, than to find one in active opposition. Matthew Laming is not unique, but he is one of a small number of country clergy attempting to stem the socialist tide. It is only worth while putting this episode on record because it demonstrates how futile any such resistance has become. It seems to me I am ideally suited to report objectively this conflict between a centralizing Government and a dissident country clergyman. For my part the English village is only a pathetic relic; it depresses me rather, so there is no sentiment to bias me *there*. Then centralization is not a thing to which I personally am averse. Further, I regard centralization as quite inevitable—which is of some importance. On the other hand I admire this resister: and many of his beliefs I share—his attitude to war, for instance, is almost identical with my own. I meet very few people in England who think intelligently about war. Most stick their chests out. Perhaps the best way to give an idea of Laming's quality would be to quote from the editorial of the Meldrum Deanery Magazine, which is from his pen. We have Dick Bartleton with his primitive interpretation of Christianity, and then Rymer elsewhere, with his highly personal version of the same religion; Laming is quite distinct from either of these—not primitive at all, holding more to the traditional substance of the Catholic Church: but in Laming's case, a minority economics of a most violent kind complicates his traditionalism, and, at the moment, causes him to occupy a far more revolutionary position than the popular leftism of Dick Bartleton. Yet in both his case and Dick's the aggravating cause and prime incentive is Christianity.

Here then are the passages from the editorial, headlined "Remembrance," for it is a short sermon for Flanders Poppy day.

"We misuse this solemn season unless we make the effort to reflect on some of the causes that produce the catastrophes. 'What is the use of experience if you do not reflect?' Anatole France's *L'Ile des Pinguins* had a great sale in France about 1908, but the lesson of the following extract was not understood: 'These are doubtless,' replied the interpreter, 'industrial wars. People without commerce and industry are not obliged to make war, but business people must perforce have a policy of conquest. Our wars increase in number, necessarily, along with our productive activity. When one of our industries cannot dispose of its product you have to make a war to open new markets. Thus, this year, we have had a coal war, a copper war, and a cotton war. In Third-Zealand we have killed off two-thirds of the natives in order to force the remainder to buy umbrellas and braces.' The endeavour was made between two wars to explain why industries are unable to dispose of their products in the home market, but counter-efforts were made to suppress rather than to spread the truth that the chief reason was the restriction of buying-power.

"Murder, after all, is repellent to the Christian conscience, but through some natural or injected perversity it is too readily assumed that mass murder is justifiable and that any analysis of the causes of mass murder deeper than those of a hysterical press is indecent and irrelevant to the Church's work. Yet Christian ethics are no more *confined* to the Seventh Commandment (against adultery) than the American Constitution is *confined* to the Eighteenth Amendment (against alcohol).

"Here are some lines written in 1938 on 'The Silence in Britain.' The author believed it would be the last Silence:

> 'A million of our dead to make us free,
> Whose dying marked the path of usury.
> Eight thousand million pounds they cost to kill
> Eight thousand pounds per man each grave to fill . . .
> And on that scale full interest we've paid:
> Six thousand million pounds in twenty years,
> Cash value of the Nation's blood and tears.
> As tribute from war's wild and bloody reek
> Each corpse still yields them seven pounds a week.'

"As the old fallacies are readily embraced by almost every politician, as the effort to stamp out small villages goes almost unchecked, as the 'first fruit and flower' who might put things right have been destroyed, the commonwealth defence system is liquidated from within and from without." He concludes as follows:

"The issue is put candidly by a well-known critic and reformer: 'It is clear beyond question that the gates of hell are wide open, and the torrent of evil will sweep away anything not *intrinsically* stronger than evil.' We need to search our own consciences to decide whether we are intrinsically stronger than evil and to turn our backs on tainted public 'servants' and tarnished principles that have bedevilled our land for so many, many years —the architects of ruin." The passage continues: "You know that long-distance air-pilots mark on their course-charts the 'point of non-return'—where you must go on, because you can't return to your base. The devil has passed the point of non-return and we had better recognize it."

Now of course this extract consists mainly of quotations. It is perhaps a vocational trick, but it is a method to which the Reverend Matthew Laming, Vicar of Ketwood, frequently has recourse. He will conceal himself in a cloud of quotations, in the way a clergyman's admonitions reach us in the form of a hail of judgements picked out of sacred texts. It is *his* voice, but the words are those of the saints and prophets, and of God Himself.

But there is another thing. Laming has no desire to say, "This is what I think, this is what I say." It is what IS that interests him, not what is Laming's, what a multitude of elect witnesses from the past and in the present day recognized as real. Such is the nature of his speech, for he is quite a modest man, and not interested to set up a personal mind: he prefers a common currency. He is a priest, that is enough for him. And in his principal work so far (unpublished, for it is one of those books which publishers recoil from at the impact of the first sentence and upon first sighting the subject-matter in the Contents page), *The English Church and Usury*, it is as a priest he writes. He is sometimes an almost embarrassingly unassuming man. He is no Prince Hamlet, to use a phrase of a contemporary poet, just a quiet background gentleman, coming on the scene with a deeply courteous aloofness. Then from this secondary figure, destined for silence it would seem, proceed to issue words—many words. These words lay bare the roguery of practically all the leading characters. This is not a Thersites act at all: this anomalous background gentleman in a quiet undertone carries on a shocked soliloquy. None of the other characters pay any attention to him. So in his writing he most exactly talks to himself—and perhaps to posterity. For one day I expect, his history of Usury may be unearthed, in a world grown liberal once more; a faded text, in the by then almost invisible typescript. I am supposing that it will come into the possession of a historian. "History" will not, of course, to the men of that time signify a fairy-tale of the past, composed as a department of propaganda, but be a matter of impartial factual research, as disinterested and unbiased as an ethnological treatise. Let us go a step farther with this imaginary historian of the future, and say that he has just completed a massive work, the title of which is to be *Causes for the Eclipse of the Christian Nations of the West*. It might well be that after persuing Laming's typewritten analytical account of the origin and development of

Usury, this poor man would consign to the dustbin what he had written.

Here we have been assuming among many other things that to our historian of a distant future none of the Social Credit material of the past forty years is available. I hope I shall not be seeming to tone down my estimate of Laming's book if I say I am not claiming that it is a master-work. After all it is but an enlargement of a university "thesis." It is the subject-matter which is of such overwhelming significance, that alone is what would attract the historian, more especially when, as in this case, it is handled with exceptional skill. Finally, this is not to be understood as saying that I subscribe to the social theories of the "Creditors," or regard the solution they favour as valid, only that the *condition* to which they persistently call attention appears at least as blood-curdling to me as it does to them.

The word "usury," it must be realized, does not refer to that minor nuisance, the trade done beneath the familiar sign of a trinity of brass balls. The Banks and Insurance Companies, the coiners of false credit, the whole of the iniquitous Credit system, is what is involved—the chairman of your bank is an arch-usurer. And somewhere stands the Minotaur at the heart of the labyrinth. Obviously what Debt has done to ruin our civilization cannot possibly be exaggerated. A great War means a great Debt. And there is now so vast a mountain of Debt that we merely exist in order to pay it off, which, slave as we may, day and night, we can never do.

In the editorial I have quoted we saw the gates of Hell wide open, and out of them streaming the legions of the Fiend. "We need to search our conscience," he says, "to decide whether we are intrinsically stronger than evil." Evil is admittedly strong: have we in our moral nature enough of evil's opposite to overcome this enormous onslaught rushing at us out of the gates of Hell? That is the question. Up to a point, only, is "evil" for Laming what it is for Dick Bartleton. And I am sure the latter would be apt to welcome as a Saviour what in Laming's eyes would be the Fiend. Their resemblances and differences are equally strik-

ing, the simple—not to say *simpliste*—contrast of the rich man and
the poor man—the Haves and the Have-nots would hardly suffice
as a complete picture of the ills of the world for Laming: though
(in the above quotation) the instigators of the coal wars, the
copper wars, and the umbrella wars are the same as they would
be for Bartleton. There, their villains would be the same villains.
Laming is interested in many more things than the other and he
worries about many more things. In the end, his economics do
become hostile to any cut-and-dried "working-class-in-power"
theorists. That is not because the working-class is not in his heart:
but talking about that *exclusively* is a way of banishing so many
other questions.

I stayed at "The Maid's Head" at Meldrum that night, having
arranged for a car to call at ten, for the five- or six-mile drive to
Ketwood. During breakfast a man at a neighbouring table addressed some remarks to me, and after a little he said he was a
farmer. His farm was in Northampton. He had just returned from
a holiday at Bournemouth. And now he had somehow got to
Meldrum—perhaps sight-seeing, hoping to see the famous Caves.
It transpired that he was fond of music. We are all of course de-
voted to it—except when someone in the next flat turns on a radio
—which is mostly off and on all day—and music is certainly the
noisiest of the arts. But this man played himself.

His instrument was the violin which he practised from two to
six hours daily. I asked him if he had any stock. No, he had no
stock. "Not a horse?" At the word horse this musical farmer's big
red shiny face (oval in shape with a small dark moustache)
acquired an expression at once surprised and disgusted. "No, I
would not have a horse on the place," he told me. When I asked
why, the main reason seemed to be because it was an animal.
Horses had to be fed and cleaned, at awkward hours—in the early
morning for instance. A hired man had to get to the farm before
anyone else was up if one had a horse (while one was still dreaming in a Heal bed of Beethoven Quartets) and the hired man
didn't like it either.

It was a new experience for me encountering prosperous middle-aged farmers, with oiled hair but tight and ungainly clothes —far from their farms, drifting around the countryside *en touriste* with a favourite pet hound and (doubtless) a violin-case.

As to the driver of the car who took me to Ketwood after breakfast—a man of robust intelligence—his views on the modern farmer were extreme in character and communicated with great readiness. There was nothing he could find too bad to say about the modern farmer. When I enquired if there was much *stock* in these parts he exclaimed derisively: "Stock?" No, he said, no young farmer would have anything to do with stock. They did everything, the farmers of to-day, on their backsides on a machine. Sowing, reaping, hoeing, harrowing, ploughing, was all done with a machine. As to the combine harvester, there is no more criticised implement, and he had plenty to say about that. Only signing a cheque couldn't be done with a machine—and that was all the work a young farmer ever did, and it was as much as he could manage.

Rymer had insisted that *the farms must be run as factories.* Since the poetry of farming has vanished, or is vanishing, anyway, it does not seem to matter very much if collective farming is introduced at once. It would, of course, be more economic. I would never sacrifice poetry to economics. But since there is no poetry! To this, however, Laming would not agree, though he confirmed that the young farmers were very averse to having stock. Those large work-making quadrupeds, horses and cattle, were universally unpopular in this neighbourhood. But my driver was an almost Ruskinian "reactionary": of the new-fangled schools the Government were introducing he disapproved as much as did Laming, though no doubt for different reasons.

Ketwood Vicarage is not screened from the road. The front door was open and the sound of the car's arrival brought to the door a small shirt-sleeved reddish man—with the general working-class appearance imposed on a class whose stipend amounts to the earnings of a not very lucky railway porter. How much better, this, than the well-heeled patronising cleric of the past, who treated his villagers as if they were villeins and he a medieval abbot.

This shirt-sleeved man, standing just inside his door, looked at me as I came up with some severity, indeed with suspicion and animosity. (I had not announced my arrival.) He stood there, his small head thrust forward in displeased enquiry. "Yes?" he said. "Mr. Laming?" said I. "That is my name," said he, and stood frowning at me. And this is where I reach the part this young clergyman was playing in the civil war between the old order and the new order. He was in the midst of an encounter with the Socialist Government: the issue that of the continued existence of the Village School. In respect to that he stood for the old order: for the Family against the State, and he mistook me, at first, for an emissary of the Socialist. Such persons were often despatched from the offices of the local education Czar, and even from London itself, to harry, to intimidate or to cajole. How he received these officers might be judged from his bellicose attitude as in the present instance he stood on guard just inside his front door.

It is amusing to compare the *weight* of the respective parties to this battle. On the one side is the terrible colossus of socialism: on the other this frail, impecunious, *clerc*. It is extraordinary how this small animal, without I expect any serious backing, can defy the omnipotent State—even if it is only as yet omnipotent-in-the-making. But he is possessed of a great deal of will and his entire being has been hardened into a resistant human particle in the social body by the agency of an economic creed both aggressive and unorthodox. It is, of course, the Christian ethic, as interpreted by this professional of religion, which has produced an unbreakable belief, at once mystical and practical. He *believes*—in as radical a sense as that of physical apprehension—that it is an evil impulse on the part of the Government to break up the villages and to turn *all* of England into a factory—to break up the home of the peasant—to work for the destruction of the Family. Two creeds combine to assure him of the malignity of this action.

Laming is much younger than the other clergyman of whom

I have written, much more the modern intellectual. His wife is a very handsome young woman, with the brave and simple carriage of the head, the fresh fair skin, of a pre-Raphaelite creation. So he is not, after all, alone in his village-school battle. And he has a perfect army of chickens, geese, ducks, and goats. This host is visible the moment you step out of the road into the Vicarage precinct. A background as reassuring as a private army. His wife rather weakened this impression for me, however, by complaining that he would never allow any of the birds to be killed!

The London papers had most of them carried accounts of the struggle going on in the villages—for the vicar of Ketwood was not the only resister—against the closing of the village schools and setting up in their place of the "Central Rural Primary Schools." Press photographs had made me familiar with the "dauntless breast" of this village champion. I had read how when the village school had been closed in accordance with the decree of the central authorities, the vicar, acting for the parents of the children, had set up a village school of his own in the Church House. That was about all I knew concerning my host (for as soon as we had reached his living-room he asked me if I would have lunch, and I most gratefully agreed to do so). My sociological curiosity had been aroused by this showdown between Family and State, one of the major issues in the present collectivization of our society, if it is not the greatest of all. Laming's own words may be quoted in this connection. "In this small matter of the Parents' School," he writes, "we can see huge issues at stake." And this is certainly no exaggeration.

Later I shall be making use of his circumstantial report more fully, but at this point I will quote from the opening pages. It will provide what is needed by way of background to this storm in a tea-cup. Here are his words:

"During the war, the village schoolmistress and her assistant were reinforced by a third teacher to deal with the evacuees. They had a hard struggle with the uncultivated city children. There is no one rich in the place, and the local people had known many years of acutest depression, but they retained a culture of the fields which had no trace of servility, or of city slickness. After the war, the headmistress was specially commended for her notable work. When we came to the village, the evacuees were leaving and the third teacher soon took another post. A scullery had been added and a sand-pit.

"It would have been in 1946 that the children over eleven were suddenly told that they were to attend a central school, at Blatchover, to which they would be driven by car. This event caused little stir in the village, and mothers felt that their children would have better opportunities at a larger school. As it turned out, we should probably have been wise to have made a strong protest at the time: this would have been, I suppose, good politics.

"This left about thirty children at the village school, and they were divided into two classes, the upper of which held children between seven and ten. The children left when they reached eleven. Several of the older children have told me, without being asked, that they would much rather have continued their education at Ketwood. I believe the headmaster of Blatchover at the time, a man of great experience and ability, thought that they would have been as well in their own village. But working teachers have little say in educational policy. Some of the parents complained about their children having to wait for the car in bad weather. But parents have even less say in their children's education than the teachers. The whole organization is in the hands of a few experts, assisted by an army of clerks. We were to learn what 'Stateism' could mean, and to hear a great deal about the 'expert' whose word was law.

"But on the whole no one was very worried about the more distant education of the children over eleven. We still had our headmistress and her assistant, and the school was in excellent repair. When school time was over, the children had the freedom of many acres for their playground, and rarely abused it.

"Early in 1947 we read in a local newspaper that Ketwood Council School was scheduled for closure in the Ladbrokeshire

Educational Committee's Development plan. This was the first warning, and the village reacted sharply.

"It might make matters clearer to explain briefly the educational set-up of this county. The County Council has many committees, and one of the most important is the Education Committee. The Education Committee has power to co-opt, and divides the county into three for educational administration. The committee appoints an Education Officer for the County, whom we will call Mr. Ladbrokeshire, and officers in charge of each division. Ketwood falls into the mid-Ladbrokeshire division, and the immediate supervisor for education is the Mid-Ladbrokeshire Education Officer. These officers, needless to say, have a tidy salary, and the mid-Ladbrokeshire officer alone—Mr. Mid, we can call him—has thirty-two secretaries, housed in a Georgian mansion.

"The teachers have no effective organization that deals with educational policy, nor do the parents. In other words, the children's education is in the hands of a few 'experts' with a nominal check that the committee can apply. Committees usually back their paid officials, we found. The teachers have, if not a fear, at least a great respect for these officials, in whose appointment they have no voice and over whose policy they have no control. This, of course, robs the teaching profession of its integrity, and the officials doubtless know how to indicate the big stick of finance in their cupboard. All of the committee might be, or have been, practising teachers, but this does not prevent the profoundest cleavage between 'expert-teacher' and 'working-teacher.' The expert is, in fact, master of the situation instead of servant, while the parents who might be allowed some 'representation' have no voice whatsoever.

"The announcement about Ketwood brought a crowd to the Parish Meeting in March. Ketwood was then considered too small to have a Parish Council, so an elected chairman presided over our civil affairs assisted by a clerk. The previous year the parish meeting had been drowsy and poorly attended: a few desultory remarks about drains, an unhopeful question about electricity, and the re-election of the chairman had practically completed the business. It was the shadow of a lost autonomy. But in 1947 we had a topic, and all agreed that the school ought not to be closed. The Welsh fire of the schoolmistress's husband had its rousing effect. He and I were selected to go into the matter. The meeting decided to send a protest to the Ladbrokeshire Education Authority, and to hold a parents' meeting."

For the documenting of this account of mine I have happily been able to avail myself of the log of the dissident young person. And wherever I can with advantage use the authentic delivery of the central figure in this little drama I shall do so. The above extract shows us exactly how the storm broke. We see the official army of secretaries, in their Georgian mansion, on the one side, and the handful of villagers, and the ill-paid clergyman upon the other. For we cannot suppose that Matthew Laming received any very substantial support from his diocesan superiors, since his bishop advised the diocese in a speech that "the lion's tail must not be twisted too hard." The lion, of course, in this case, was Britannic socialism.

Let us now go back to the living-room of the embattled Vicar, where he sat curled up in a monstrous chair, like a squirrel in the bole of a tree, but unlike a squirrel surrounded frame to frame, by a gallery of dismal Victorian portraits; there was not much in this poor Vicar's living-room, except for the panelling of the portraits. Outside the windows swarmed all the cook-pot animals he has collected but refuses to kill—which is why there are so many. He will devour their eggs, but declines to murder them, which relates this Ladbrokeshire divine to St. Francis and I suppose the "Sons of Freedom" (Canadian Doukobors). Alas he is thin, very much too thin. As I gazed at this aesthetic, under-nourished figure I hope that Providence would strike down a goose with lightning and his wife, pouncing on it with alacrity, carry it in triumph to the kitchen. In a lengthy circumstantial report of his struggle with the Government over the village school, he writes that he was "cleaning out the chickens" when I arrived. He was taken off guard, looking as present-day clergymen must always do except when wearing their Sunday suit. At first he was shy. When a little later he learned from me that I knew other clergymen he was more at ease, and ceased endeavouring to conceal a hole in the elbow of his shirt. He actually smiled with a flicker of mischief while I was narrating the sartorial plight of Rymer—not of course revealing my friend's name nor the part of England where he has his vicarage.

"Are you proposing to go through with this?" I enjuired.

He started as if I had awoken him by sticking a pin into his leg.

"With . . . ? Yes. At—at least I hope I can, you know."

Under similar circumstances what would be the attitude of a minister in the United States? It is, of course, not difficult to imagine the pugnacious poses, the jutting chin, the eyes narrowed to slits, the boastful words. He would "lick the pants off" the administration. This little Ladbrokeshire vicar had with great determination and considerable skill disputed the right of a well-nigh totalitarian government to start the work of liquidating the family in his village. But he allowed no trace of aggressiveness to appear in the depreciating angle of his head and the quietist, almost apologetic expression of his personality.

His wife came in to say that lunch was ready. Her beauty looks as if it had been rarefied in the atmosphere of some mountain valley. We (which includes one of their two delightful children) ate our spam, an egg, an apple, very simple fare, though I was ashamed of eating it as I was well aware how limited was the larder of a poor clergyman in the Crippsian Ice Age. Battalions of geese waddled around outside, while fat hens pecked around the kitchen door, and the cocks crowed at the tops of their voices. Food on two legs was triumphantly vocal. It was like a meal with St. Francis in a time of dearth, but haunted by edible birds, which one knew to be a mischievous device of Satan.

"So Cotton is your M.P.?"

We were on our way back to the sitting-room, and I remembered I had intended to ask him about this.

"Unfortunately, yes," he said in a voice of resigned regret.

"Cotton had a lot to do with framing the bill, in a pre-socialist administration, and with seeing that eventually it found its way into the statute book," he told me mildly, and a little sadly.

"However, there are just as many socialists all of whose instincts are Tory, as there are conservatives who would change England into a quite different country."

"I suppose so."

"Have you seen this mis-cast King's Man, this conservative with socialist leanings?" I asked.

"He came over here," he told me.

Apparently as a member for the Halchester division he thought he would come over and find out exactly what was happening in Ketwood. One day Laming found him on his doorstep. The politician asked the vicar to step outside and have a talk. Laming answered no—you come inside if you wish to speak to me. The politician preferred outside. He beckoned the frowning clergyman (for the Laming that is shown to me is not what a man whose foolishness had opened the gates to Abstraction would see). For some moments this "you-come-out—no-you-come-in" continued and then the "great man" became a little less great and went inside. There Laming reminded him of the part he had played in the passing of the Bill which decreed the centralizing of the rural schools. But here Mr. Cotton protested that he had not intended schools for the younger children to be interfered with. Subsequently in all Ladbrokeshire papers Cotton published the following statement: "In my view it is most undesirable that children of ten years old and under should be removed from their villages for instruction in regional Schools. It is most important that in those earliest years they should remain in the neighbourhood of their families, and not be taken away to an abstract centre where they become alienated from parental disciplines. This has always been my view: and it was the intention of those of us who were responsible for the act decreeing the new organization of rural education that the village schools where children of ten years and under receive their instruction should remain intact. It is for me a matter of great regret to see these original plans overridden."

Such was the defence of Mr. Cotton, and he repudiated any responsibility for the recent high-handed actions of the socialist government. This is what Mr. Cotton explained to the indignant young clergyman, standing outside the improvised class-room in the latter's house—headquarters of the revolt against socialism —with which revolt, of course, this politician wished to have no contacts, though he *did* wish (on the time-honoured English principle of running with the hare and hunting with the hounds) to disinculpate himself of so socialist an intention as nationalizing small children.

"Hell is paved with good intentions," I commented, and the Vicar of Ketwod agreed that the hell of totalitarian socialism must always be paved with Liberal altruism and Conservative attempts to steal the thunders of the Labour Opposition, or shall we say, as it is a question of a pavement, by planks stolen out of the socialists' platform.

"Autocratic state-socialism, a monster with great ugly teeth in it you say, is undeniably one of the most repulsive forms of government! Is any sort of socialism acceptable?" I enquired. Laming digests leading questions—from a friend—uneasily. I have a parson friend who is painfully reminiscent of a Gilbert and Sullivan or a Du Maurier curate who would cry if a friend seemed displeased with him, but with non-friends, if need be, is as tough as a Hemingway hero (if you cut out the bloody climax). Laming is an intellectual: and the answer was obvious. He only looked surprised.

"Religious communities are instances of a type of socialism of a very good kind. Christian society in the Middle Ages offers many examples of . . . yes, communism."

"All true communisms are of a religious character. You come to a full stop when you try to think of any others. The communism existing in primitive societies is conditioned by supernatural pressures. I am aware that it might be said: 'What is the difference between pressure by supernatural agency and compulsion by terrorist police methods? Do they not boil down to the same thing? The compulsion, however, is of an entirely different nature. Religion is as the communists say a drug. Men to whom this drug has been skilfully administered exist in a dream. They will live on bread and water gladly, anaesthetized by incantations and prayers. There is no substitute for some such drug. The artist, especially the musician would understand immediately what I mean. They administer drugs. Men die quite easily to the sound of the pipes. There are no spells and drugs in socialism of the same potency as a Bach Mass."

My young host was naturally shy of this talk of drugs. He nodded politely and said:

"No communism works."

His voice was full of decision. But we were approaching this question differently, it was plain.

"Only within the framework of a religion?" I sought his confirmation.

"That is so, I think. Yes."

"Without the appropriate drug the rational faculty breaks down the solidarity in a very short time."

"Not the reason, surely you do not mean that," he protested politely.

"You must not scorn stupefying agents. The human reason is merely a nuisance without—without——"

"I think I see what you *mean.*"

I examined the massed portraits on the walls of nineteenth-century statesmen and soldiers. All of them might have been portraits of the same man—say a quick-change artist who disguised himself successively as some prominent general or politician. I rose and studied one carefully.

"My father painted all of them. When his army life was over—he was a soldier—he copied portraits as a hobby."

This of course accounted for the curious likeness. They served rather to empty the room than to fill it. This vacant look suited the vicar. He is a man who is quite indifferent to his personal surroundings, and the dark anonymous portrait gallery, for heaven knows who these soldiers and politicians were, was an ideal setting for him. To have a parent weave a pattern of anonymity in his ruminative old age of decorated nobodies, was for Laming a good arrangement. He is unquestionably somebody. He sits symbolically ringed with painted mediocrity. Lightly he rests there, a squirrel that plans. His worried head propped upon his hand, he spoke of the duplicity of the state.

"All administrations," I pointed out, "of Rights as much as Left, lie deliberately, without stopping, in a democratic state. When Cripps solemnly announced that the pound would never be devalued, I knew that it must have been arranged to devalue it. And in a surprisingly short time devaluation occurred. In a similar way President Roosevelt in an election address solemnly declared American boys would never again be asked to fight on foreign soil. He was elected, and soon afterwards American boys were fighting on foreign soil. How else can you rule a modern democracy? The newspapers in a two or more Party state make any other course impossible. No one is shocked that the diplomat practices every duplicity (and the skilfuller the liar the better the diplomat). The limitation imposed upon the democratic politician's power-impulses is responsible for an ugly mood, and he would actually come to relish deceiving this ignorant multitude which possessed the right to strip him of power at the ballot-boxes."

"I suppose so," said Laming.

"Democracy confers much power but stops short at the real thing. It is like a woman who is a sexual tease. It wears out a man very greedy of power. He gets to hate in the end this jade democracy, who says, 'Rule me—but I shall dismiss you at once if you take too many liberties.' As you know all our Ministers are wrecks. The cause is the strain imposed on their temperament because of all the things they are not allowed to do."

Laming laughed discreetly.

"Slyness develops to a terrible extent. For instance, nurses. Everyone hates nurses, and the Administration is no exception to the rule. But it was common knowledge that the payment nurses received was archaic: a quarter of a century ago it might have sufficed, but for some time it has been recognized to be scandalously small. In these circumstances it was suddenly announced in the Press that a New Deal for Nurses had been decreed by a benevolent Government."

Laming nodded. "Yes. I read about that. I suppose they had to do something."

"Well, listen. A shopkeeper in Rotting Hill with whom I gossip, and actually a socialist, has a sister who is a nurse at a large London hospital. This sister spent a week-end with him a fortnight ago. What she imparted on the subject of the New Deal for Nurses filled him with indignant astonishment. When the New Deal came into force, she was owed eighty pounds, of this she received only five or six. The new scheme was retroactive as much as twelve months. Another nurse who was owed forty or fifty pounds received nothing, but actually had to pay six pounds."

"How extraordinary."

"Yes. The explanation is that under the new ruling nurses have to pay for their own keep, there is an increase in income-tax payments, and so on. Consequently these nurses, earning four pounds instead of three a week are much worse off instead of better off, but the Government has had all the benefit of the ballyhoo."

"Ho, ho, ho," cheerlessly but expressively hooted Laming.

"That is, of course, frightfully sly," I continued.

"I should think it is."

"Do not let us blame Ministers for this, it must be the work of some malignant underling. I cannot see Bevin or Cripps or Attlee —much as they must dislike nurses, having spent considerable periods in their company—I cannot see any of them playing so scurvy a trick."

"Oh!"

"No. I am not interested in Party. Only in a Party spirit could one suppose that a Minister could think up so vindictive a trick. And the same applies to many other disgraceful tricks, yes and major acts of legislation."

"They are responsible, aren't they?"

"But they are grey and old and full of sleep."

"Oh, I see. I must remember that in future."

"Whether it is the collective policy of the Cabinet or not, there are steps taken under their aegis leading in a direction I regard as humanly bad. Here is an example. What a National Health Act dentist receives for an entire dental plate, top and bottom, is nine pounds. He and his mechanic cannot be expected to turn out a very good plate for that money, and they in effect do not turn out an awfully good plate. But it is now planned to supersede the present old-world picture of thousands of little free-enterprise outfits, each making its own little dental plates and the same man doing a stopping as extracts a tooth. 'Clinics' are to be set up, where the little client of the Welfare State can have the mass extraction in one department and get his plate in another: a building where thousands of dental artisans will be emptying the gums of teeth and clapping little plastic plates into rows of little open mouths in assembly-line fashion. In the United States I have seen establishments given up to mass extraction of teeth. My own reaction to such methods is to find them degrading. If more and more of that is socialism I don't like socialism. The men now in power seem to regard it as part of their sacred mission to create an assembly-line world and to reproduce the atmosphere of the factory in every part of human life, from the dentist's chair to the marriage bed. This I am sure is nothing specifically to do with socialism. But it is inseparable from socialism as it is served up today."

"To make everything in the image of a machine is an idiosyncrasy, yes, it is." Laming nodded.

"Not only an idiosyncrasy of British socialism. But the trouble is that our socialists are inclined to think the more mechanistic a thing is the more socialist. This is referred to as planning. There was too little planning formerly: our chaotic cities bear witness to that. But an over-planned life is at least as bad as no plan at all. It is their rigour that is the worst thing about our new masters—not their socialism."

"Socialism is always rigid," Laming objected, "that is what is bad about Socialism, it is not something peculiar to these socialists. The collectivizing of society involves the tightening up of every control. No, I do not see how it can be otherwise than rigid."

"Whether that be so or not, the intoxication of industrial techniques seems to impel men everywhere to transform any human process into a mechanical process. This is described by Toynbee as the Apathetic Fallacy. The sense of power obtained from the control of a machine must not be forgotten. Finally, infection from Russia is a big factor. Industry was made into a power-god there."

"In a society predominantly agricultural socialism would be inhuman just the same," Laming politely but firmly insisted. Socialism for him could only signify a reformatory for anti-social humanity, or a puritan AUSTERITY parching up the human world.

I lit a cigarette, and he courteously watched me.

"I might become a socialist," I announced.

"Oh yes? Oh."

"As an obscure member in that racket I should be scrupulous about several things. For instance, I should make no objection to the closing of the village schools!"

"Oh yes?"

"No. That would be ridiculous. But I should set a limit, in my mind, beyond which mechanization should not go. Also I should propose, for those taking office, a thorough overhaul; with a view to checking up on power-complexes, latent as well as in flower."

"Oh, really. I see."

As we sat silent Laming gazed at the floor. And then we began talking about the Parents' School, as he called it. He did not appear embarrassed as a result of my thoughtless confession that I would regard it as ridiculous to oppose the closure of Village Schools. He may have assumed that I was joking, and he regards himself as somewhat slow in recognizing the absurd. At lunch he had given me an outline of what had occurred. Since we had been back in the sitting-room I had been going into the political back-grounds of the dispute about the village school. I wished to acquaint myself with his attitude towards Welfare State politics in general, for at that time I had not of course read anything he had written. I enjoyed his youthful firmness, but he could not be acquitted of rigidity himself. His politics, I felt, were two-dimensional.

This young clergyman belonged to the type of Englishmen of which the most perfect specimens are Edmund Burke, Henry Maine, and a half-dozen others. Those who experience the violent "rebound of a powerful mind from . . . philosophical Radicalism," to use Maine's words, are described today as "reactionaries." More clumsily they might be termed "rebounders." Reactionary is of course a term originated by the radicals, as a way of describing a man who shies away or violently "bounds" or bounces off, radical dogmas. In this sense Laming is undoubtedly reactionary.

I must here interpolate a reminder. There are of course other types of mind equally powerful, which rebound with equal violence: but in this case it is from the spectacle of the abuses flourishing in the systems to which Maine and Burke gave their support. And I must add that there is, in my opinion, an even powerfuller type of mind which does not rebound in this manner at all. I refer to that order of mind which prefers not to see things in such stark black and white.

Laming's recoil from the radical is extremely severe, but his disinclination to appear in a passionate role leads to a deceptive assumption of philosophical composure. But beneath perhaps not a saintly but a properly priestly aversion from passion, could be found enough fighting spirit to equip a wild cat. Sublimated as it is, it enables him to appear hardly interested at times.

It was a Saturday so, if I was to see the improvised village school in full swing, it would be necessary to come over again on Monday. This I decided to do. Accordingly at eleven o'clock on that day I found myself once more at Ketwood Vicarage, a very different place to what it had been two days earlier. It was now a school.

Let me quote from the typed report of the Parents' School a short passage explaining how the school had taken shape.

"Everyone wanted a school to be opened in Ketwood. We could use the Church Room, which had been a Church School before the Council School was built. One man and three ladies offered to help with the teaching. We enrolled cleaning and catering committees. Several people offered to give one child his midday meal with their own children, and the residue fell to my wife to feed in the Vicarage. Numerous offers of equipment were made, of potatoes, and of labour and materials to make a boys' lavatory. We also enrolled an entertainments committee to provide funds. And we chose a treasurer. We decided to follow the times and terms of the Council School. . . ."

There were between twenty and thirty children all told. "A Mr. Adams of East Gidding, the next village, had offered to help me with the juniors, and two ladies were going to alternate with the infants, one of these, Mrs. Tracey, was a parent herself, and the other, Miss Puscy, was a farmer's daughter. We also had voluntary needlework and music teachers."

The Church Room was divided by a screen; the upper end was reserved for the juniors, the lower end for the infants. Sufficient small chairs and tables were somehow collected, and so the school could begin. Where Laming is describing the opening day he writes: "After religious instruction I gave the boys writing, composition, and sums. At dinner-time my wife found a large party to feed. But farmers had provided the potatoes, and as long as rabbits were seasonable we had plenty of them. A farmer's wife gave a pudding for almost every day of the year."

The day I visited the school, classes were proceeding both in the Church House and at the Vicarage, and I suppose this was always the case. In the room lying between the sitting-room and the front door a drawing lesson was in progress, and these village children had filled this largish nursery, the use to which it normally is put, with barbaric and sometimes arresting images.

A farmer's daughter presided over these creative enterprises. A short way down the road is the Church House. There we found engaged in strenuous pedagogy, a highly-competent volunteer, Mr. Dunns.

Here is what Laming writes about this colleague.

"I was pleased to receive the following from a Mr. Dunns who was then living in a London hotel. '. . . My last permanent job as a teacher ended in 1925 when I resigned from the Hong Kong Government Schools to enter business. During the last war, however, I assisted the Rev. —— in running a school in an internment camp in China.' (All these names are fictitious, lest their presence in this context should lead to victimization)." Such caution I feel is excessive. At least I think I may say that the East Gidding helper is not Adams but Carson and the author of those excellent verses I quoted, used by Laming in his Church magazine editorial.

Laming is a Robinson Crusoe, a castaway in a hostile social element. Carson and the ex-schoolmaster are fellow castaways: though I am not aware what Mr. Dunns' views are, he knows communist China and has certainly thought his thoughts. These men of bad will, each one a misfit or displaced, had put much enthusiastic ill-will into the creation of this academy for infants outside the law. For although the local educational authorities had informed Laming that they would not prosecute immediately, it was quite certain that prosecution would ensue before long.

In Laming's detailed account of the Parents' School many facts connected with the methods of the bureaucracy, and even more to the point, the state of mind of the socialist officials, are brought to our notice. I have here before me the young Vicar's Notes, in which he parades his authorities, all affirming the inviolability of the Family. His authorities did not, to my surprise, seem very good ones. That, however, is immaterial: the main thing was that this clergyman, like all good clergymen, was holding fast to the past, to the tradition, and standing in the way of innovation. Religion is an immovable block of dogmas, anchored in the past; it belongs to the past, in order to survive, it must prevent people, at all costs, from getting too far away from the past. Obstruction, and again obstruction, is its watchword. Laming should have had more impressive a battalion of authorities, for it is also the priest's business to persuade and to overawe with Authority. But the main thing is that he should stand in the way of Progress, that he should point back to the Past, and the Family stands for all that is stable, and is essentially a thing of the sacred Past, and if for no other reason its integrity must be defended with heroic desperation. I hesitated about his authorities, but it is better for me not to quote such stuff as this: "John Stuart Mill . . . quotes Lord Atkin as saying, 'Each house is a domain into which the King's writ does not seem to run, and to which his officers do not seek to be admitted,' and he adds, 'In Seymayne's Case (1604) it laid down: "the house of Everyman is to him as his castle and fortress."'" Who is this likely to edify or to convince? I will not burden you with such musty testimony, if only to protect in this instance the heroic little clergyman from himself. It is enough to stand witness, as I am doing, that Laming is one of the most retrograde individuals in England; through and through "antimoderne," authentically contemporary in all his tissues with Aquinas.

So it is for what he stands, in line with the natural law, that is interesting and respectable (I say respectable because I am not myself an advocate for the Past—though I should not be writing this were I an advocate for Progress either). Where he sees so well the futility of "gaining debating points" when describing the course taken by his enemies, he fails to recognize, it seems to me, this futility of debating points in the service of religion. But let me quote him where he is describing an interview with the enemy, to make clearer what I mean. "The mistake of the officials was to treat this expression of natural feeling of natural law as a subject off which to score debating points. This was a stupid and untimely attitude. We stood for the family unit and the Village, while they stood for what appeared to us an abstraction, 'the Children.'"

This is actually very well expressed, and *abstraction* is precisely the word demanded. Laming says that he and his Village are for the *concrete* ("the family unit and the Village"), whereas his enemies are for something theoretic and abstract. The concreteness which Laming has acquired from his scholastic reading and his sympathy for the roman communion is possibly the main attribute of this frail but resolute priest.

Not only did the action of the State in closing down the Village schools seem to Laming to be putting an axe to the roots of a civilization which had endured for nearly two thousand years, but he feels that the utterances as well as the actions of the officials concerned first and last, revealed a considerable degree of consciousness of what they were doing. Some of the most instructive passages in his Notes are those dealing with the contacts of the officials with himself and the spokesmen of the Village. The outfit which the Village of Ketwood had to deal with was the Mid. Ladbrokeshire. You will recall that Laming refers to the official in command of this region as "Mr. Mid." Here is a note describing a meeting at Ketwood between "Mr. Mid," the Villagers and Laming with his associates in the Parents' School Scheme.

"Mr. Adams of East Gidding made elaborate imputations against Mr. Mid's strict veracity—he would not venture on anything more explicit, certainly not a word of four letters. Mr. Mid replied hotly that he thought an attempt was being made to insult him! This passage incited Mr. Mid to a rash frankness. When a resident said that the closure of the school would kill the village, Mr. Mid said that the small village would dwindle away in the next twenty years: agriculture was all right, it only needed a man and machines; industry was what needed attention. He would prefer to cart labourers from towns than children to centres for education. I wondered, afterwards, what Cobbett would have said to this thesis; the Ladbrokeshire villages, in his time, had about double their present inhabitants, and Cobbett constantly complained of the flow of people away from fertile parts to barren areas.

"Then a calm and rational parent suggested that it was inhuman for young children to wait about for the proposed transport in bad weather, and asked Mr. Mid to consider a concession on the grounds of humanity. 'I cannot afford to be human,' was Mr. Mid's answer.

"Several ex-service men were parents, and they raised a clamour about 'freedom.' Mr. Mid rounded on them. 'You are not free,' he said. Only people who had as high a salary as Mr. Mid were free and he could afford to send his daughter a considerable distance from Halchester. The others had, in reality, no choice or freedom."

The following is one of the most instructive passages of all.

"But the most important remarks of Mr. Frost were those that described conversations he had had with other members of these committees, in to which he had introduced himself in our interests. Alderman G., an educationalist of high position who has been mentioned several times, told Mr. Frost that he 'had no time for parents.' Alderman B., who also had more than a finger in the educational pie, declared to Mr. Frost that 'parents were the greatest obstacle to their children's education.' These phrases need underlining. They need contrasting with the American view, expressed in the *House Committee's Report on unAmerican Activities,* which combats the Marxian view that: 'Women should have children for the state to educate, train and use, but parents should not have any say in training according to their own ideas.' Then it follows that these remarks attributed to Aldermen G. and B., although they would be considered un-American and Marxian, are not un-British. The inferences are that the family as a unit has been irreparably destroyed in England, the educational authorities taking good care that it should not crop up again, and that a Marxian form of education *has been* substituted in its place."

These words, "Parents are the greatest enemies of their children," is the key to the official attitude. In the official world of Education they occupy much the same position as horses in the official world of agriculture.

I have here a cutting from the *Sunday Express* which spotlights the Horse as a bugbear of the mechanizing innovator, symbolic of another day as is the Parent. "Lord Leigh, Midlangs agriculturist, said at a ploughing competition at Warwick yesterday that the best ploughing was done by horses—not traction. Then he challenged a reported statement by Mr. Harry Ferguson, the tractor manufacturer, that the 'horse is the real enemy of agriculture.'"

Next are a few lines from the Laming Report about Blatchover's vicar, which serve to bring into sharp relief the conflicting views of the traditional clergy and the Socialist clergy.

"My surprise was, I suppose, due to a report that Mr. Blatchover had called the Ketwood parents selfish. But anyone quotes Robespierre now and then. And the Christian Crusade, which originated at Blatchover under Mr. Blatchover's predecessor, claimed to have reconciled Christianity and Marxism. Marx, of course, had a poor opinion of the family and family life."

With considerable good sense, however, Laming points out that, whatever one may think of his position, Dick Bartleton is an honest man.

"At the same time Mr. Blatchover's position as a Christian-communist (and the Archbishop of York said that this was a valid position, whatever the reader considers!) is more honest than that of 'conservatives,' etc., who introduce communism by stealth. I dare say that my guess about Russia is as worthless as is Mr. Blatchover's."

There are many things in this fascinating report I should have liked to have quoted, but I must turn to the last pages where we come to the dénouement, which, as could be foreseen from the start, was dismal and disheartening. The village as well as the improvised personnel, at a meeting full of sadness for Laming, voted that the Parents' School dissolve, and that the children, after all, obey the dictates of the centralizing State. Let me give you this in the language of the defeated Vicar.

"Then the ladies began their movement. How far it was concocted of influences from without, it was not possible to guess. But one of the ladies said that if the school continued the children would probably be victimized in the matter of scholarships, and would at any rate be deprived of free medical treatment, etc. Other mothers followed. A secret ballot was suggested. Then a father interjected that if anyone could not state their opinion openly, it was not worth much. So each parent was asked whether he or she wished (*a*) the School to be continued at Ketwood; (*b*) their child to attend Melton or (*c*) Blatchover. The voting fell into three nearly equal groups. A third did not mind whether their children attended Melton or Blatchover: a third desired Blatchover; and a third—predominantly men—wanted Ketwood private school to continue. Mr. Adams used all his eloquence in vain. Mr. Dunns supported him. A lame resolution was carried that those who wanted to should continue Ketwood school. But the firm opposition of the ladies (my wife is excepted from all this) was evident enough.

"Partly, of course, the split was due to weariness. The women had carried most of the burden of teaching (the infants), of cleaning and of catering. The housewife's lot is 'not a happy one.' Then fear of victimization and of missing something for the children was at work. Few families these days are solid enough to educate or provide for the education of their young beyond a very tender age.

"But there is another factor, which I will barely indicate, that was added to the monotonous economic motive. It may be that men are less completely suburbanized, in this land, than their women. And the suburban dweller, who supplies neither food nor thought, is less free and more infantile than members of real towns or real countrysides."

I suppose that our quixotic vicar left that meeting with some comprehension at last of the reality of village life in England in mid-twentieth century and some recognition not only of the power of the Welfare State, but of the absurdity of expecting anyone to back you up, except for an excited moment or two, in your defiance of authority.

The quotations will not, I hope, have been found too fatiguing. All this minutiæ, if it can be tolerated, provides one with a close-up as it were, which is invaluable for the student but rather irksome to the general reader I have taken this risk because of the necessity in such a case to provide convincingly factual data. Should we, or can we, in the twentieth century, have a religion? Can the amateurish, infinitely latitudinarian English Church— allowing, as it does, every idiosyncrasy in its priesthood, so that we find in its ranks everything from a Marxist to a papist—can so doctrinally flaccid and obligingly adulterated a faith—can so go-as-you-please and teach-as-you-like unmilitant an institution as the Church of England, do anything but read the burial service over religion, and keep its grave in a decent condition? It is the Church of England itself that has emptied its churches.

In Laming and Dick Bartleton we have a vigorous type of priest. The first stands for institutional Christianity: the second for the Christianity of the early Church. The second would echo the injunction of St. Augustine to purge your heart of all human affection, love of mother or father, love of family, love of your friends. These emotions must be eradicated: in their place will be abstract Man. And here is the difference between St. Augustine and the Vicar of Blatchover. The former would install God in the place vacated by Mother, by Family, by Friend. The latter would install Man, as symbolized by the State. The Vicar of Blatchover is, I should say, a very honest and good-hearted man, and there is no reason not to add a devout man. The only thing at issue, in the present context, is whether he is an efficient priest. His kind of mind, or rather his type of faith, may not furnish the best material (I suggest with due humility) for the priestly calling.

There is institutional religion, of course, and there is religious experience and religious feeling. Institutional religion is a technique for enabling a certain teaching to survive, that is all. The Catholics have been the great masters of that technique. When I read the other day how the Pope had dealt with the question of whether the Holy Mother of God ascended to Heaven as flesh and blood or not, I reflected how excellent the Catholic judgment is. For, of course, he answered, "Yes, as flesh and blood, dressed in the costume of a carpenter's wife of the period." In a similar case an Anglican Divine would have reflected how absurd the carnal account would sound to the average bank clerk or stock-jobber and would have answered, "No, of course not. She left her mortal envelope on earth." Yet it seems obvious if you star the Resurrection of the Dead as a major article of faith there must be no obliging modifications to satisfy protests on the score of "unlikelihood." All effective institutions, determined to *endure* at all cost—like Russian Communism, for instance—do not *debate*. No arguments could make them alter a syllable of their doctrine. If you worship a Blue Cow you disregard the standard criticism, to the effect that in the natural order there are no cows of that colour. What is more, it makes it easier for the believer, the colour being an improbable blue. This is not a paradox. The *blueness* gives the imagination something to bite on, as it were, and with religion the imagination is the high faculty involved.

The "truth" of the imagination is, of course, quite different from the "truth" of physical science. A Church attempting to assimilate its truth to the truth of the slide-rule is what we have witnessed in England.

To summarize what I have wished to say: that to endure, an institution cannot be too rigid. The inviolability of the Family is a major doctrine of Catholicism: there any concession would be impossible. The Family is, or was, a microcosm where age, not youth, rules; it was from that fact that it derived its great importance for the Church. Now my point is that the Vicar of Ketwood is the type of *institutional* clergyman able to appreciate the only terms on which a creed can survive, or rather the only technique that insures endurance. But although his action at Ketwood was a model for what a village priest should do faced with the closing of the village school, there were several small matters he had lost sight of, or had never seen. One was that the village is now, in England, only a name. Then the Family he so rightly set himself to defend, no longer exists—or at least not in the way that in the first instance made it an object of such interest to the Church. I think the fact is that Laming had taken action to protect something which his grandfather or great-grandfather had sold, or had been too sleepy to notice was being removed piecemeal.

For anyone who has lived in America, where on Sunday the churches are crowded to capacity, England is now almost a country without a religion: I cannot accept Rymer's theory that in a village where the only people ever present at divine service on Sunday are the Vicar and his family, the rest of the inhabitants being good-Christians-who-do-not-go-to-Church the Christian religion flourishes. I cannot believe in good Christians who never visit the church at the end of the village street. Although it does not follow that the people who fill the local church in the U.S. are all good Christians, the efficacy of liturgical disciplines appears to me obvious.

Two world-wars in rapid succession have hurried the end of Christianity in England. Socialism, as time passes, melting into communism, will take religion's place in the form of a brotherly millennium—a heaven on earth for good socialist boys and girls, and a hell-on-earth for the wicked (*vide* slave-camps, salt-mines, etc.). In place of Christ there will be men-gods like Stalin or Hitler, a High God being dispensed with. But that is taking the long view: it may be a decade before matters go as far as that. Meanwhile, it is difficult to see how Christianity can live, if only for a moment, except by some heroic measure. One that recommends itself to me, is that all the churches, vicarages, bishops' palaces, etc., be closed.

The clergy would then become a missionary army, as friars, I suppose: poor but impassioned men, tramping from village to village, and filling the cities with their prayers and curses. I have mentioned above how the Bishop of Halchester recommended his clergy to refrain from any serious twisting of the Lion's tail. But having turned its back upon its empty churches and worldly possessions, the Church could if it wanted to nearly twist the old Lion's tail off its rump. The prisons would be so full of obstreperous friars that there would be no room for the normal delinquents.

For it is quite certain that if any sincere Christian expressed his views at the street corner and at the market place concerning *any* government he would find his way into the lock-up. But probably as the time is so short now before the extinction of all religion has been consummated, it would be better to continue to pretend that there is a religion. So long as men can be found to live a retired country life at about five pounds a week, or for the same sum lead a far less secluded one in a populous suburb, to keep the churches there, since the money involved in the servicing of a national Church would be put to some unchristian use by whatever government received it!

A final word regarding the Reverend Matthew Laming. The last I heard of him, he was to interview the Principal of the London College of Divinity. That signifies, I think, that his pastorate at Ketwood is coming to an end, and he will temporarily, at least, find himself in a more theoretic field. The *Meldrum Deanery Magazine* will have less unconventional editorials, the village of Ketwood will prepare to fade away, according to the wishes of the new urban-minded rulers of England, the parents following their children to some approved centre, but repudiating the functions of "The Parent." The probably ill-made village houses will quickly drop to pieces, and the vicarage become the week-end residence of some suburban spiv.

Meanwhile, wherever Laming goes, it will seem that the clock has been put back and Anglican Christianity will be seen displaying a Roman energy; and if ever he should come to wear the mitre and leggings of a bishop, an entire diocese would be mobilized on Ketwood lines. A head-on collision with the State would immediately ensue. The Church would be disestablished, its funds sequestrated.

But the time required to realize this glorious climax, Laming's career having but just begun, will no doubt be denied him by some Apocalypse.

I WENT up the hill, up Rotting Hill, to the rot camp, near the top. One needs some exercise, and this is where I prefer to take it. It is not that they have a monopoly of the rot in the camp, but it is where the rot flowers, the rot of Rotting Hill.

This is in a manner of speaking the Fun Fair of the Hill. I met Blossom on her way from market who gave me a brilliant decent smile. She is a plump flower of the Cornish Riviera, a walking Matthew Smith. I loathe thin flowers and her luxurious bulk breasts the waves of Rottinghillers, flowing around the fish shop and the butcher's counter. Seen in the shops, she is like a figure-head of a gallant ship, a Saxon Queen perhaps, moving irresistibly, gently cleaving the surging mass. She is my toast in her sky-blue mackintosh.

I approached Colquhoun. He was stooping over a book in an untidy book-tray. I said "Hallo, what book?" He turned with some shyness towards me. "I was looking at a guide book. It is out of date." Colquhoun is not at all himself: I feel that he stagnates, there is something the matter. I know him very slightly and can only guess at what is adversely affecting him. He has been excluded from the Festival of Britain, he has not been invited to send a picture and he feels very bitterly this strange slight. Of the Hillworthies who are creative I place him first. I passed on and saw a kilt. This was MacBride, wittiest of Hillmen, swinging his kilt along without consciousness of the anomaly. He had an apprehensive eye upon Colquhoun whom he had seen handling a book. A few nights before MacBride and his inseparable companion had been sitting at a table in a public house. The kilt was not visible so I gathered, and his rich Scottish idiom was to be heard as he told Colquhoun a story of a trip to Wigtown. "The marn went aroond the heel, and then came back wuth eet," is the kind of way he talks. Several men at the bar hearing this strange music cocked a Britannic ear, one more especially. This latter eyed MacBride with undisguised xenophobia. "The bloody Irish are bloody well everywhere." But the man he was addressing had caught sight of the kilt beneath the table. "They're Jocks, Harry, they're no bloody Irish." "So they are. Good old Jocks," he vociferated, the minstrelsy of Harry Lauder warming his Brixton heart. But the popularity of this kilt had little effect upon MacBride, who said to the first man: "If you have anything you wish to say why do you say it to heem, why not to me!" What happened afterwards I was not told: but I reflected that a kilt might be a safeguard, among people whose dislike of all foreigners grows, though the kilt seems to dispel their mistrust.

Roy Campbell passed and he raised his large coffee-coloured hat. He walked as if the camp were paved with eggs, treading slowly, putting his feet down with measured care. 'Tis his warwound imposes this gait on him of a legendary hidalgo. He was followed by a nondescript group, some say his audience. I noted a poetaster, a photographer, a rentier, and a B.B.C. actor. He is the best poet for six miles or more around. But he suffers from loneliness I believe. He is like a man who rushes out into the street when the lonely fit is on him and invites the first dozen people he meets to come up and have a drink. He led his band into "The Catherine Wheel."

As he was about to enter there was an incident. A small old lady in a bonnet appeared suddenly, shooting out of the Jugs and Bottles, seemed to get her ankles entangled, and fell. She was clutching something bright, I believe a new half-crown. Campbell stooped with the grandiose stiffness of a lay-figure, and lifted the disreputable old marionette to her feet. Saluting her majestically with lifted headpiece, he proceeded on his way into the tavern.

I had not gone far before I was met by the stupidest man on the Hill. He intercepted me near a rifle range, with targets representing Hitler, Hirohito, and Mussolini. I picked up a rifle and killed the Führer several times. Ironically observing my marksmanship, Mr. Stupid said, "Poor Hitler!" I put down the rifle. "I take a pot at all mass-murderers, whether sanctimoniously democratic, 'heroically' military, or bloodthirstily proletarian." "Oh, you do, Lewis. Very comprehensive. Why aren't you more up to date!" he asked the man. "You should have Uncle Joe, you know." The man said in a hoarse undertone, "Ah, Uncle Joe and ole MacArthur too. I don't make them, guv'nor." The stupidist man on the Hill looked at me slyly, as though to say, "I know how hard it is for you to bear me!" It is a kind of joke between us. He knows his power and knows how I fear him. He released me with a playful tap.

Having left the stupidest man I proceeded to the Borough Reading Room, where my playmate Arthur was in dark communion with the scribbling war-hounds of the United States, in the pages of an expensive monthly. As I passed he nodded gloomily, I nodded brightly back. After examining the advertisement columns of a half-dozen newspapers with a view to finding a second-hand dictaphone I left, discovering Arthur outside the swing-doors grimly replacing his spectacle-case in his overcoat pocket, as if displeased with the optician who had provided him with these aids to seeing, as he was with the printed page which they had enabled him to read. He blew his nose with a purgative blast.

"Arthur," I said, "you need a gin-and-tonic."

"That is so," said he and we directed our steps to "The Flying Horse," not far from "The Catherine Wheel." We seated ourselves at a round table and I went to the bar and fetched the drinks.

" 'Tis a rotting world," said Arthur, picking up his drink which I had placed before him.

"It is rotten," said I. "It stinks, Arthur."

"I feel I am buzzing through space inside a rotten egg."

Arthur was in bad spirits. His periodic glance at the World Press, always makes him like this. The expensive U.S. monthly I had seen him reading had informed him that Russia already had enough hydrogen bombs to blow the British Isles out of the water, but that the United States had ten times as many, twice the size, and could sink half of Russia in the Polar Seas. There seemed little doubt that both these countries would soon be at war. Arthur was one of those men who was forever nittering about in the future.

"I cannot see, Arthur, what you expect of this earth-ball. You know it is composed of dung. You talk as if we were flying around upon one of space's fairest mud-drops played to by the music of the spheres. This is a nasty place, Arthur. Millions of little organisms compete, only the police make them keep their hands off one another. I could name at least a hundred citizens who would kill me if it were not for the C.I.D. But with nations it is a different matter. There is no police force to restrain them from exterminating their neighbours. I cannot see why you should expect a nation to behave itself better than a man, Arthur."

"All right," he said. "But must we have this rotten government?"

"You think it would be better to conserve than to socialize?" I asked him.

"Yes, it would," grumpily muttered Arthur.

"But can you not see that they are the same? The conservers flung all our money away in mad wars. Now, disguised as an honest working man, they are engaged in a huge confidence trick. The stars have been changed, but the play is the same. Cannot you feel the state's great greedy hand in your pocket? It is robbing you to pay its gambling debts. Its war debts. It is the *same* hand. These names, Arthur, 'conservative,' 'socialist,' 'communist,' mean very little. They're just like the fancy-names of medicines. You should keep your eye fixed upon *the State*. Stalin is a Czar in a cloth cap. Mr. Attlee . . ."

"Yes, yes, all right. But these gamblers, these states, that gamble with our money, get progressively poorer. What will they be like after another fling?"

"Millions of Englishmen will be cancered or starved. The states, all earth's states, dazed and imbecilic will be squatting in the gutter. But my God, Arthur, how did fifty million people get on to this island. It is a rabbit warren, on a coal mine. You can't feed that number. Quite impossible. But there is no decent excuse for keeping our numbers down with rat poison or something, so what does a poor state do? It gets another state to come and kill us off. Russia is the Ratin man, of the 'fifties of the twentieth century."

"All right."

"You always say all right, Arthur.

"What do you expect me to say?"

"Well, something different to that, Arthur. It is not in harmony with your customary attitude of unrelieved gloom, where *nothing* is right."

"Is it? But I agree with what you say about the state. It is rotten luck having these beastly things fixed on our backs. I wish we could get rid of these infernal states of ours, don't you?"

"Of course I do. We *are* out of luck and *that's* a fact. But you speak of the state, Arthur, as if it were a parasite. Really it is the other way round. The state to which we belong is a truer image of the universe than we are, just as our private minds depart from the norm. The 'mob-mind' is the more central, the nearer to nature."

"All right," howled Arthur, "I agree. And where do we go after that?"

"Nowhere, Arthur. We are always at the same spot. We go nowhere, Arthur."

"All right," muttered Arthur. "All right."

I was obliged to say good-bye to him at this point. He remained in the public house brooding upon the socialist administration, for I had not succeeded in convincing him that socialism was the same thing as conservatism or as communism. I delivered a parting shot before I left however: "If your lovely conservers were here, Arthur, they would have to pawn you for what you are worth just as much as the present lot. Debts have to be paid. No government would have any choice but to sell you up."

"Rot," shouted Arthur. "The socialisms use me as a golden brick to build their New Jerusalem."

"That's politics, Arthur, not economics."

Near "The Flying Horse" was the booth of the sorceress Betty, who looked the beautiful witch that she was, just nut-crackery enough to qualify and no more. She crouched over her crystal, her black eyes riveted upon the future. I went up and crossed her palm with silver. "What do you see in your crystal, Betty, as that affects myself!" Drawling a little, "I see a tall, dark man," she said. "How original, Betty."—"I see a small woman with red-dish hair."—"Has she got bad teeth."—"No, she gives a dazzling smile as she picks your pocket." I laughed, saying "Good morn-ing," and headed north. Betty always tells your fortune that way if you venture to be ironical.

As I was nearing "The Catherine Wheel," Roy Campbell at the head of his group, responding to the mirth of his followers with a series of spasmish nods of the torso of jovial assent, emerged from the famous public house. From the expressions of those about him I could see that he had been telling them how the bull tossed the matador the full length of the arena, how Campbell caught him and laid him gently down, executed a tourniquet before the bull could reach them, but when he did, head down, and kicking up the dust, Campbell killed him with the fallen matador's espada. He was now obviously walking out of the bull-ring, stepping gingerly to the deafening applause of the officionados.

Ours is a great hill. Almost at its gates I encountered Augustus John, his blue headlights blazing on either side of his bronzed beak. He had heard there were some mumpers encamped not far from the Borough Reading Room. There was an anticipatory glare of fraternity in the old Romany Rye's gaze.

Lastly, standing by one of the gate-posts, was Britannia. She wore what Yankees call a "liberty-cap" (hired from Moss Bros.).

Once so robust, she was terribly shrunken: some wasting disease, doubtless malignant. The trident now employed as a crutch, she held out a mug for alms. I saw in the mug what looked like a phoney dollar bill, and dropped myself a lucky threepenny bit. I would give my last threepenny bit to poor old silly Britannia. In a cracked wheeze she sang "Land of Hope and Glory." I must confess that this last apparition, and its vulgar little song, rather depressed me.